PERFORMANCE

New York City—First Edition

STANDARDS

Science

NEW **STANDARDS**™

This first New York City edition of the *New Standards™ Performance Standards* for Science was developed under the leadership of Judith A. Rizzo, Ed.D., Deputy Chancellor for Instruction. The project was completed through the joint efforts of the Office of School Programs and Support Services, Margaret R. Harrington, Ed.D., Chief Executive, and the Office of Program Development and Dissemination, William P. Casey, Chief Executive. Elsie Chan, Administrative Assistant Superintendent/Director, New York City Urban Systemic Initiative, (NYC USI), a National Science Foundation Funded Project, supervised the production of this edition in collaboration with the NYC USI Team: Robert J. Kane, Ed.D., Deputy Director, Betty D. Burrell, Stephanie Caporale, Arlene Francis, Jonathan Molofsky, Lawrence Pero, Carl Raab, Myrna Rodriguez, and Anne Judy Walsh, and Laura Rodriguez, Administrative Assistant Superintendent, Office of School Programs and Support Services, Russell Hotzler, Ph.D., University Dean of Academic Affairs, The City University of New York, the New York City Urban Systemic Initiative Advisory Council, Judith Chin, Executive Director, Division of Instructional Support, Robert Tobias, Executive Director, Division of Assessment and Accountability, Lillian Hernandez, Ed.D., Executive Director, Office of Bilingual Education, Evelyn B. Kalibala, Director, Office of Multicultural Education, and Gerald Haber, Assessment Specialist, Office of Performance Standards, Division of Instructional Support.

TABLE OF CONTENTS

BOARD OF EDUCATION OF THE CITY OF NEW YORK
RUDOLPH F. CREW, ED.D., *CHANCELLOR*

OFFICE OF THE CHANCELLOR
110 LIVINGSTON STREET - BROOKLYN, NY 11201

May 17,1999

Dear Colleague:

During the past couple of years, you have been hearing and reading about the adoption of *New Standards™ Performance Standards* by the Board of Education of the City of New York. The rationale for this decision is clear: New Standards has developed the best national standards because teachers can use them. The *New Standards™ Performance Standards* are based on common sense as well as academic excellence; and they are ready now.

Two years ago, the first New York City edition of *New Standards™ Performance Standards* for English Language Arts, English as a Second Language, and Spanish Language Arts was published. Last fall, the first New York City edition of *New Standards™ Performance Standards* for Mathematics was published. These important pedagogical books were distributed to all teachers, supervisors and administrators in the system. I am delighted to present to you the first New York City edition of *New Standards™ Performance Standards* for Science.

Teachers, science supervisors, and administrators representing the 40 school districts and superintendencies, and representatives from colleges, universities, and informal science-rich institutions met regularly during the past two school years to conceptually plan and to calibrate the collection of student work samples contained in this New York City edition of *New Standards™ Performance Standards*. This calibration reflects the New York State Learning Standards for Mathematics, Science, and Technology, the New York State Commencement Standards and their assessments, as well as the diversity of our students. The work samples selected for inclusion in this edition show work that illustrates standards-setting performances. They demonstrate that all students can meet high expectations in science. Selections were made as the result of an in-depth examination of the standards and extensive discussion among the members of the group.

The New York City edition enhances the original New Standards work in science. It demonstrates vertical (K-12) and lateral (life science, earth science and physical science) conceptual development, task related student work and correlation of *New Standards™ Performance Standards* Science with New York State *Mathematics, Science, and Technology Learning Standards*, the National Research Council's *Science Education Standards*, and the American Association for the Advancement of Science's *Benchmarks for Science Literacy*.

I expect the New Standards to be used by everyone involved in teaching and learning in our system. At the school level, teachers and administrators should use these standards to set goals, plan for effective instruction, and monitor and assess student performance. Districts and superintendencies should use the standards in all curriculum initiatives and as one way of planning professional development activities. Central staff will work closely with the districts and superintendencies on behalf of their local efforts. Central will also take action to integrate the New Standards throughout the school system.

We all agree that having the highest expectations for our students is a just goal. The Science standards are clear, direct and attainable. Your discussions must now turn to "how good is good enough" and to making the goal a reality. Together we can and will make a positive difference in the lives of our students.

Sincerely,

Rudolph F. Crew
Chancellor

PREFACE

This volume contains the first New York City edition of the *New Standards™ Performance Standards* for Science. The standards set out in this volume establish the same high expectations for student performance as those published by New Standards—the standards are unchanged from those published by New Standards. What distinguishes this edition is the collection of student work samples included to illustrate the meaning of standard-setting work. The collection has been revised extensively to reflect work produced by students studying in New York City's public schools.

This volume of the New York City edition of the standards focuses exclusively upon Science. The first New York City editions of the *New Standards™ Performance Standards* for Language Arts and Mathematics were published in 1997 and 1998 respectively. A volume focusing upon Applied Learning is in preparation.

ABOUT NEW STANDARDS

New Standards was established in 1991 as a collaboration of the Learning Research and Development Center at the University of Pittsburgh and the National Center on Education and the Economy, in partnership with states and urban school districts. The Board of Education of the City of New York was a member of the New Standards partnership from its inception. The New Standards partners set out to build an assessment system to measure student progress toward meeting national standards at levels that are internationally benchmarked. The performance standards are one of the major products of the New Standards partnership. Support for the development of the performance standards was provided by the Pew Charitable Trusts, the John D. and Catherine T. MacArthur Foundation, the William T. Grant Foundation, and the New Standards partners.

The New Standards Governing Board included chief state school officers, governors and their representatives, and others representing the diversity of the partnership, whose jurisdictions enroll nearly half of the Nation's students. These performance standards were endorsed unanimously by the New Standards Governing Board in June 1996.

The New Standards partnership formally ended in June 1997. Continuing research and development, and technical assistance to support implementation of the products of New Standards, are managed by the National Center on Education and the Economy on behalf of the National Center and the University of Pittsburgh.

ABOUT THE PERFORMANCE STANDARDS

New Standards adopted the distinction between content standards and performance standards that is articulated in *Promises to Keep: Creating High Standards for American Students* (1993), a report commissioned by the National Education Goals Panel. Content standards specify "what students should know and be able to do"; performance standards go the next step to specify "how good is good enough."

These standards are designed to make content standards operational by answering the question: how good is good enough?

The performance standards for Science were based directly on the content standards produced by the National Research Council (1996) and the American Association for the Advancement of Science (1993).

STANDARDS FOR STANDARDS

In **recent years** several reports on standards development have established "standards for standards," that is, guidelines for developing standards and criteria for judging their quality. These include the review criteria identified in *Promises to Keep*, the American Federation of Teachers' "Criteria for High Quality Standards," published in *Making Standards Matter* (1995), and the "Principles for Education Standards" developed by the Business Task Force on Student Standards and published in *The Challenge of Change* (1995). New Standards drew from the criteria and principles advocated in these documents in establishing the "standards" we have tried to achieve in these performance standards.

Standards should establish high standards for all students.

The New Standards partnership resolved to abolish the practice of expecting less from poor and minority children and children whose first language is not English. These performance standards are intended to help bring all students to high levels of performance.

Much of the onus for making this goal a reality rests on the ways the standards are implemented. The New Standards partners adopted a Social Compact, which says in part, "Specifically, we pledge to do everything in our power to ensure all students a fair shot at reaching the new performance standards…This means they will be taught a curriculum that will prepare them for the assessments, that their teachers will have the preparation to enable them to teach it well, and there will be…the resources the students and their teachers need to succeed." These performance standards are built upon the assumptions expressed in that pledge.

There are ways in which the design of the standards themselves can also contribute to the goal of bringing all students to high levels of performance, especially by being clear about what is expected. We have worked to make the expectations included in these performance standards as clear as possible. For some standards it has been possible to do this in the performance descriptions. For example, in Science, we have gone beyond simply listing scientific thinking among our expectations for students. We set out just what we mean by scientific thinking and what things we expect students to be able to do with their scientific thinking. In addition, by providing numerous examples we have indicated the level of complexity of the situations in which students should be able to exercise that scientific thinking.

The inclusion of work samples and commentaries to illustrate the meaning of the standards is intended to help make the standards clearer. Most of the standards are hard to define precisely in words alone. In the conceptual understanding standards (**S1**-**S4**), for example, the work samples show what it means to use, represent in multiple ways, and explain the important scientific concepts. The commentaries describe how these aspects of conceptual understanding are evidenced in the student work samples. The work samples and commentaries are an integral part of the performance standards. They give concrete meaning to the words in the performance descriptions and show the level of performance expected by the standards.

The work samples will help teachers, students, and parents to picture work that meets standards and to establish goals to reach for. Students need to know what work that meets standards looks like if they are to strive to produce work of the same quality. Students also need to see themselves reflected in the work samples if they are to believe that they, too, are capable of producing such work. The work samples included in this volume not only illustrate the meaning of the standards but also reflect the diverse backgrounds and experiences of the students studying in New York City's public schools.

Standards should be rigorous and world class.

Is what we expect of our students as rigorous and demanding as what is expected of young people in other countries—especially those countries whose young people consistently perform as well as or better than ours?

That is the question we are trying to answer when we talk about developing world class standards.

Through successive drafts of these performance standards, New Standards compared our work with the national and local curricula of other countries, with textbooks, assessments, and examinations from other countries and, where possible, with work produced by students in other countries. Ultimately, it is the work students produce that will show us whether claims for world class standards can be supported.

New Standards produced a *Consultation Draft* which was shared with researchers in other countries. They were asked to review the *Consultation Draft* in terms of their own country's standards and in light of what is considered world class in their field. Included among these countries were Australia, Belgium, Canada, the Czech Republic, Denmark, England and Wales, Finland, France, Germany, Japan, the Netherlands, New Zealand, Norway, Poland, Scotland, Singapore, Sweden, and Switzerland. These reviewers were asked whether each standard is at least as demanding as its counterparts abroad and whether the set of standards represents an appropriately thorough coverage of the subject areas. The *Consultation Draft* was also shared with recognized experts in the field of international comparisons of education, each of whom is familiar with the education systems of several countries.

The reviewers provided a wealth of constructive responses to the *Consultation Draft*. Most confined their responses to the Language Arts, Mathematics, and Science standards, though several commended the inclusion of standards for Applied Learning. The reviewers supported the approach of "concretizing" the performance standards through the inclusion of work samples. Similar approaches are being used in some other countries, notably England and Wales and Australia. Some of the reviewers were tentative in their response to the question of whether these performance standards are at least as demanding as their counterparts, noting the difficulty of drawing comparisons in the absence of assessment information, but did offer comparative comments in terms of the areas covered by the standards. Some reviewers provided a detailed analysis of the performance descriptions together with the work samples and commentaries in terms of the expectations of students at comparable grade levels in other countries.

The reviews confirmed the conclusion New Standards had drawn from its earlier analyses of the curricula, textbooks, and examinations of other countries: while the structure of curricula differs from country to country, the expectations contained in these performance standards represent a thorough coverage of the subject areas. No reviewer identified a case of significant omission. In some cases, reviewers noted that the range of expectations may be greater in the *New Standards™ Performance Standards* than in other countries; for example, few countries expect young people to integrate their learning to the extent required by the standards for investigation in New Standards Mathematics. At the same time, a recent study prepared for the Organisation for Economic Co-operation and Development reports that many countries are moving towards expecting students to engage in practical work of the kind required by the New Standards Science standards (Black and Atkin, 1996). The reviews also suggest that these performance standards contain expectations that are at least as rigorous as, and are in some cases more rigorous than, the demands made of students in other countries.

None of the reviewers identified standards for which the expectations expressed in the standards were less demanding than those for students in other countries.

New Standards will continue to monitor the rigor and coverage of the *New Standards™ Performance Standards* and assessments in relation to the expectations of students in other countries. In addition to the continued collection and review of materials from other countries, our efforts will include a review of the *New Standards™ Performance Standards* by the Third International Mathematics and Science Study, collaboration with the Council for Basic Education's plan to collect samples of student work from around the world, continued review of the American Federation of Teachers' series, *Defining World Class Standards*, and collaborative efforts with visiting scholars at the Learning Research and Development Center.

Standards should be useful, developing what is needed for citizenship, employment, and life-long learning.

We believe that the core disciplines provide the strongest foundation for learning what is needed for citizenship, employment, and life-long learning. Thus, we have established explicit standards in the core areas of Language Arts, Mathematics, and Science. But there is more. In particular, it is critical for young people to achieve high standards in Applied Learning—the fourth area we are working on.

Applied Learning focuses on the capabilities people need to be productive members of society, as individuals who apply the knowledge gained in school and elsewhere to analyze problems and propose solutions, to communicate effectively and coordinate action with others, and to use the tools of the information age workplace. These are capabilities that were highlighted in *Learning A Living*, a report of the Secretary's Commission on Achieving Necessary Skills (SCANS, 1992).

Applied Learning is not about "job skills" for students who are judged incapable of or indifferent to the challenges and opportunities of academic learning. Applied Learning refers to the abilities all young people will need, both in the workplace and in their role as citizens. They are the thinking and reasoning abilities demanded by colleges and by the growing number of high performance workplaces, those that expect people at every level of the organization to take responsibility for the quality of products and services. Some of these abilities are familiar; they have long been recognized goals of schooling, though they have not necessarily been translated clearly into expectations for student performance. Others break new ground; they are the kinds of abilities we now understand will be needed by everyone in the near future. All are skills attuned to the real world of responsible citizenship and of dignified work that values and cultivates mind and spirit.

Many reviewers of drafts of these performance standards noted the absence of standards for the core area of social studies, including history, geography, and civics. At the time we began our work, national content standards for those areas were only in the early stages of development; we resolved to focus our resources on the four areas we have worked on. As consensus builds around content standards in this additional area, we will examine the possibilities for expanding the New Standards system to include it.

Standards should be important and focused, parsimonious while including those elements that represent the most important knowledge and skills within the discipline.

As anyone who has been involved in a standards development effort knows, it is easier to add to standards than it is to limit what they cover. It is especially easier to resolve disagreements about the most important things to cover by including everything than it is to resolve the disagreements themselves. We have tried not to take the easier route. We adopted the principle of parsimony as a goal and have tried to practice it. At the same time, we have been concerned not to confuse parsimony with brevity. The performance descriptions are intended to make explicit what it is that students should know and the ways they should demonstrate the knowledge and skills they have acquired. For example, the standards relating to conceptual understanding in Science spell out the expectations of students in some detail.

The approach we adopted distinguishes between standards as a means of organizing the knowledge and skills of a subject area and as a reference point for assessment, on the one hand, and the curriculum designed to enable students to achieve the standards, on the other. The standards are intended to focus attention on what is important but not to imply that the standards themselves should provide the organizing structure for the curriculum. In Science, for example, we have established a separate standard for tools and technologies. This does not imply that tools and technologies should be taught in isolation from other elements of Science. Our intention in defining a separate standard for tools and technologies is to make it clear that the work students do should be designed to help them achieve the Tools and Technologies. Skills and tools should not only be among the things assessed but should also be a focus for explicit reporting of student achievement.

Standards should be manageable given the constraints of time.

This criterion follows very closely on the last one, but focuses particularly on making sure that standards are "doable." One of the important features of our standards development effort is the high level of interaction among the people working on the different subject areas. We view the standards for the four areas as a set at each grade level. This orientation has allowed us to limit the incidence of duplication across subject areas and to recognize and use opportunities for forging stronger connections among subject areas through the work that students do. A key to ensuring the standards are manageable is making the most of opportunities for student work to do "double" and even "triple duty" in relation to the standards. Most of the work samples included in this volume demonstrate the way a single activity can generate work that allows students to demonstrate their achievement in relation to several standards within a subject area.

Standards should be adaptable, permitting flexibility in implementation needed for local control, state and regional variation, and differing individual interests and cultural traditions.

These standards are intended for use in widely differing settings. One approach to tackling the need for flexibility to accommodate local control and differing individual interests and cultural traditions is to make the standards general and to leave the job of translating the standards into more specific statements to the people who will use them. We have not adopted that approach. Performance standards need to be specific enough to guide the assessment of students' achievement of the expectations established by the standards; we have tried to make them specific enough to do so. We have also tried to achieve the degree of specificity necessary to do this without unduly limiting the kinds of flexibility outlined above. Most of the standards are expressed in a way that leaves plenty of room for local decisions about the actual tasks and activities through which the standards may be achieved.

However, the specificity needed for standards intended to guide an assessment system does place some limits on flexibility. To tackle these apparently contradictory demands on the standards, we have adopted the notion of "substitution." This means that when users of these standards identify elements in the standards that are inconsistent with decisions made at the local level, they can substitute their own. There is, however, one important provision: substitution only works when what is substituted is comparable with the material it replaces in terms of both the quality and the quantity of expectation.

Standards should be clear and usable.

Making standards sufficiently clear so that parents, teachers, and students can understand what they mean and what the standards require of them is essential to the purpose for establishing standards in the first place. It is also a challenge because, while all of these groups need to understand what the standards are, the kinds of information they need are different. The most obvious difference is between the way in which the standards need to be presented to elementary school students so that they know what they should be striving to achieve and the way in which those same standards need to be presented to teachers so that they can help their students get there. If the standards were written only in a form that elementary school students could access, we would have to leave out information teachers need to do their job.

This version of the standards is written primarily for teachers. It includes technical language about the subject matter of the standards and terms that educators use to describe differences in the quality of work students produce. It could be described as a technical document. That does not mean that parents and students should not have access to it. We have tried to make the standards clear and to avoid jargon, but they do include language that may be difficult for students to comprehend and more detail than some parents may want to deal with. Efforts to make the standards more accessible to audiences other than teachers need to take these differences into account.

Standards should be reflective of broad consensus, resulting from an iterative process of comment, feedback, and revision including educators and the general public.

These performance standards were the result of progressive revisions to drafts over a period of eighteen months. Early drafts were revised in response to comment and feedback from reviewers nominated by the New Standards partners and the New Standards advisory committees for each of the subject areas, as well as other educators.

The *Consultation Draft*, published in November 1995, was circulated widely for comment. Some 1,500 individuals and organizations were invited to review the draft. The reviewers included nominees of professional associations representing a wide range of interests in education, subject experts in the relevant fields, experienced teachers, business and industry groups, and community organizations. In addition, we held a series of face-to-face consultations to obtain responses and suggestions. These included detailed discussions with members of key groups and organizations and a series of meetings at which we invited people with relevant experience and expertise to provide detailed critique of the *Consultation Draft*. We also received numerous responses from people who purchased the *Consultation Draft* and who took the trouble to complete and return the response form that was included with each copy.

The revision of the performance standards was further informed by a series of independently-conducted focus group meetings with parents and other members of the community in several regions of the country, and with teachers who were using the *Consultation Draft*.

The reviewers provided very supportive and constructive commentary on the *Consultation Draft*, both at the broad level of presentation and formatting of the performance standards, and at the detailed level of suggestions for refinements to the performance descriptions for some of the standards. These comments significantly influenced the revisions made to the standards in the preparation of the publication in finished form.

CREATING THE NEW YORK CITY EDITION

Work on "calibrating" the performance standards for use in New York City's public schools began in February 1998 and continued through to the end of May 1999.

The work samples and commentaries form an essential element of the performance standards because they give concrete meaning to the words in the performance descriptions and show the level of performance expected by the standards. While the principal goal of the calibration process was to supplement the collection of student work samples used to illustrate standard-setting performances in the *New Standards™ Performance Standards* with work produced by students in New York City's public schools, a group of New York City educators met with staff of the National Center on Education and the Economy and devised a plan to make the New York City Science Standards more valuable to educators in New York City by showing the relationships among science content standards and by showing conceptual development over the grade spans. To achieve these goals, a group of approximately sixty educators gathered for five days in the Spring of 1998 to serve as a Conceptual Planning Task Force.

Showing the relationships among science content standards

There are two widely used and respected national documents in science which provided the foundation for the work of New Standards: the National Research Council (NRC) *National Science Education Standards* (1996) and the American Association for the Advancement of Science (AAAS) Project 2061 *Benchmarks for Science Literacy* (1993). The AAAS analysis of the Benchmarks and the NRC Draft was helpful in seeing the substantial degree of agreement between the two documents. New Standards partner statements about standards and international documents, including the work of the Third International Mathematics and Science Study and the Organisation for Economic Co-operation and Development, were also used. Many of these sources, like the *Benchmarks*, give greater emphasis to technology and the applications of science than does the NRC.

The framework for the Science performance standards reflects New Standards partner representatives' distillation of these several sources of guidance:

S1 **Physical Sciences Concepts;**

S2 **Life Sciences Concepts;**

S3 **Earth and Space Sciences Concepts;**

S4 **Scientific Connections and Applications;**

S5 **Scientific Thinking;**

S6 **Scientific Tools and Technologies;**

S7 **Scientific Communication;**

S8 **Scientific Investigation.**

As the amount of scientific knowledge explodes, the need for students to have deep understanding of fundamental concepts and ideas upon which to build increases; as technology makes information readily available, the need to memorize vocabulary and formulas decreases. There is general agreement among the science education community, in principle, that studying fewer things more deeply is the direction we would like to go. The choices about what to leave out and what to keep are hotly debated. There are 855 benchmarks and the content standards section of the NRC standards runs nearly 200 pages, so there are still choices to be made in crafting a reasonable set of performance standards.

The New Standards Science Standards carried the statement, "The Science standards are founded upon both the *National Research Council's National Science Education Standards* and the American Association for the Advancement of Science's Project 2061 *Benchmarks for Science Literacy*. These documents, each of which runs several hundred pages, contain detail that amplifies the meaning of the terms used in the performance descriptions." The New York City Conceptual Planners said that the document would be much more useful if it showed, explicitly, the statements from these two documents and from New York State's *Learning Standards for Mathematics, Science, and Technology*.

There were three reasons for making the correlations evident:

1. The New York City Science Standards should be self-sufficient; additional standards documents should not be necessary to understand what New York City students are expected to know and be able to do.
2. There is a tremendous degree of agreement among the content statements; teachers and others should be reassured that there are not divergent instructional demands.
3. In a small number of cases, the New York State Learning Standards are slightly different from the New York City Standards; since the State's tests will be based on the State's standards, these differences should be noted.

Thus, the set of related standards are presented so that educators can ascertain the extent of agreement for themselves.

Showing conceptual development over the grade spans

When the goal is deep understanding, it is necessary to revisit concepts over time. Students show progressively deeper understanding as they use the concept in a range of familiar situations to explain observations and make predictions, then use the concept in unfamiliar situations; as they represent the concept in multiple ways (through words, diagrams, graphs, or charts), and explain the concept to another person. The conceptual understanding standards make explicit that students should be able to demonstrate understanding of a scientific concept "by using a concept accurately to explain observations and make predictions and by representing the concept in multiple ways (through words, diagrams, graphs, or charts, as appropriate)." Both aspects of understanding—explaining and representing—are required to meet these standards.

For most people and most concepts, there is a progression from phenomenological to empirical to theoretical, or from a qualitative to a quantitative understanding. New Standards illustrated the progression using one important concept, density, and these student work samples: "Flinkers" at the elementary school level (see page 42), "Discovering Density" at the middle school level (see page 93), and "Density of Sand" at the high school level (see page 169). The New York City Conceptual Planners said that it would be worthwhile to illustrate conceptual development for additional concepts. For each of the major areas of science, they selected five topics or concepts in which they would focus the collection of student work. They also drafted tasks that teachers could use to elicit student work so that they could illustrate the variety of curricula that are used in New York City. In addition to density, the Physical Sciences concepts are acids and bases, heat and temperature, energy, force and motion, and chemical reactions. The Life Sciences concepts are interdependence, structure and function, change over time, responding to stimuli, and reproduction and heredity. The Earth and Space Sciences concepts are surface features, weather, rocks and soils, water cycle, and space.

While it was a challenge to find standards-setting work for every concept in the list at every grade level, it was possible to find eight sets of examples that illustrate conceptual development over time—from simple to complex, from descriptive to analytical, from familiar to unfamiliar. Eight such "storylines" are described below. Each storyline demonstrates a progressive level of understanding of a particular concept. As you review the work samples in each storyline, you'll note that some tasks show particular success at moving students into deeper levels of understanding.

Work produced by students in New York City's public schools

The Conceptual Planners thus provided a framework for the work of the Calibration Task Force. All districts and high school superintendencies nominated representatives to complete the correlations and to collect work samples and meet regularly throughout the process to select the work to be included in this New York City edition.

Deciding what constitutes a standard-setting performance

The benchmarks against which these work samples were judged are the work samples that were selected for publication in the *New Standards™ Performance Standards* to illustrate standard-setting performances in relation to various parts of the standards. Those work samples were selected through a variety of strategies designed to tap the judgment of teachers and subject experts around the country about the "level of performance" at which the standards should be set at each of the grade levels: elementary, middle, and high school.

We define the elementary school level as being the expectations for student performance at approximately the end of fourth grade; middle school level

Work That Illustrates Conceptual Development Over Time

"STORYLINE"	ELEMENTARY SCHOOL	MIDDLE SCHOOL	HIGH SCHOOL
1. Force and Motion: Simple to Complex Quantification.	Students measure changes in direction of motion. "Come Back Can," p. 36.	Students investigate more than one variable influencing motion. "Mechanical Nut," p. 86.	Students investigate more than one variable influencing motion. "The Challenger Disaster," p. 153.
2. Acids and Bases: Phenomenological to Application.	Students identify acids and bases using an indicator. "Acid/Base," p. 40.	Students do a quantifiable analysis of pH. "Acid Rain," p. 89.	Students work with the molecular structure of acids and bases and apply their analyses to real-life situations. "Buffer Lab," p. 156.
3. Density: Phenomenological to Quantitative.	Students identify the phenomenon of density. "Flinkers," p. 42.	Students quantify density. "Discovering Density," p. 93.	Students do error analysis in measurements of density. "Density of Sand," p. 169; "Density," p. 173.
4. Response to Environment: Simple to Complex Organisms.	Students identify plant responses to environmental factors. "Bean Farmers," p. 44; "Water Tolerance," p. 50; "Toasted Bread vs. Non-Toasted Bread," p. 54.	Students identify animal responses to environmental factors. "Snails," p. 104.	Students study hormone regulation in humans. "Endocrine Feedback Exercise," p. 183.
5. Interdependence: Organism to System.	Students identify what lives where. "Biomes," p. 52.	Students analyze the nutritional flow within a specific food web. "Bio Box," p. 98; "Owl Pellets," p. 101.	Students analyze the ecological impact of predator/prey relationships and other environmental factors. "Eagles," p. 186; "The Invincible Cockroach," p. 188.
6. Reproduction: Whole Organism to Molecular Structure.	Students discover a life cycle. "Butterflies," p. 47.	Students identify genes as the basis of heredity. "It's All in the Genes," p. 106.	Students work with the molecular structure of DNA. "DNA Models," p. 176; "DNA Concept Map," p. 179.
7. Erosion: Phenomenological to Quantitative.	Students identify the effects of water on soil. "Erosion," p. 62.	Students quantify the effects of erosion over time. "River Cutters", p. 112.	—
8. Pendula.	Students quantify the motion of a pendulum and the effects of changing different variables. "Pendulum," p. 38.	—	Students quantify the effects of changing different variables and perform multiple trials with sophisticated apparatus. "Pendulum Experiment," p. 144.

as the expectations at approximately the end of eighth grade; and high school level as the expectations at approximately the end of tenth grade. We used the concept of grade level as our reference point because it is in common use and most people understand it. However, "at approximately the end of fourth grade," for example, begs some questions. Do we mean the level at which our fourth graders currently perform? Or, do we mean the level at which our fourth graders might perform if expectations for their performance were higher and the programs through which they learn were designed to help them meet those higher expectations? And, do we mean the level at which the highest-achieving fourth graders perform or the level at which most fourth graders should perform?

We set the expectations for level of performance in terms of what we should expect of students who work hard in a good program; that is, our expectations assume that students will have tried hard to achieve the standards and they will have studied in a program designed to help them to do so. These performance standards are founded on a firm belief that the great majority of students can achieve them, providing they work hard, they study a curriculum designed to help them achieve the standards that is taught by teachers who are prepared to teach it well, and they have access to the resources they need to succeed. These conditions form an essential part of the New Standards Social Compact which underpins our belief that all students can and should be expected to meet high standards.

Some of the work samples included in the *New Standards™ Performance Standards* were also included in the *Consultation Draft*; some appeared in earlier drafts as well. The appropriateness of these work samples as illustrating standard-setting performances was the subject of extensive review, through discussions among the New Standards advisory committee for Science and through round-table discussions among experienced teachers and experts in Science. Some of the work samples included in earlier drafts did not pass the scrutiny of these reviews and were not included in the eventual publication. Many additional work samples were identified in the process of consultation and then subjected to the iterative process of review that was used to establish the level at which the standards should be set and the selection of work samples to be used to illustrate the meaning of the standards.

Selecting the work samples included in this New York City edition

The calibration group for the New York City edition of the performance standards followed a similar iterative process of review of collections of work samples to arrive at the selection that is included in this volume. Our goal was to identify candidate work samples for each part of the performance standards as the basis for selecting samples that would reflect the diversity of the communities that make up New York City and to demonstrate different approaches to producing standard-setting work, for example, student work that demonstrates conceptual understanding using the familiar format of expository writing as well as more innovative methods such as creating murals, models, and concept maps. (See "Biomes" on page 52, "DNA Models" on page 176, and "DNA Concept Map" on page 179.)

Districts supported the process by encouraging schools to provide samples of student work for review through their representatives on the group. We organized ourselves according to our expertise and experience at each of the grade spans and in each of the major areas of science and divided responsibility across the various parts of the standards. In this way, sub-groups developed expertise in relation to specific parts of the standards through the experience of reviewing work samples with reference to the relevant performance descriptions and to the work samples and commentaries published in the *New Standards™ Performance Standards*.

When the calibration working group met, we discussed the characteristics of the work samples collected. In some cases, work that was judged as nearly meeting the expectations for standard-setting work was returned to the students who had produced it with an invitation for revision and suggestions about the aspects of the work that would benefit from revision. These students returned revised work for further review.

At each stage of the process, review of the work collected to date helped sharpen our focus on the characteristics we needed to look for in the work we collected. Among the by-products of this process was our growing appreciation of the significance of the tasks or assignments that generate student work in influencing the quality of the product. Put simply, the work students produce generally reflects the assignment they have been given and the instruction on which the assignment is based. We are resolved to make this direct connection between standards and instruction the focus of our continuing efforts to assist all students to meet the expectations illustrated in the work samples in this volume.

Throughout the process, we had to remind ourselves continually that work that illustrates standard-setting performances is not the same as "best" work or "most exceptional" work. Some of the work samples we reviewed exceeded the expectations of the standards. Those work samples do not appear in this collection. We also had to remind ourselves that we were not trying to put together an anthology to celebrate the work students produce, valuable as such anthologies can be. Rather, our purpose was to identify samples of work that would help to give concrete meaning to the qualities described in the performance descriptions and establish the level of performance we should expect of work that is "good enough" to meet the standards. This meant that we chose some work samples over others because they provided clearer exemplification of the "bullet points" in the performance descriptions, even though some of the work we passed over unquestionably counted as "good" work.

We also learned that practice in making judgments about work in relation to the standards pays off. As the number of pieces of student work we had read and reviewed closely grew larger, we became clearer about the meaning of the bullet points in the performance descriptions and more confident of our judgment about the features that need to be demonstrated in work if it is to be considered standard setting. Some pieces of work that we judged to be candidates for inclusion in the collection early in the process did not rate among our judgments later on. Equally, there were some pieces of work that we rejected early in the process and later brought back to the table for further consideration.

Work produced by a diverse range of students

The work samples in this book reflect the diversity of backgrounds and experiences of the students studying in New York City's public schools and the communities of which they are a part. The student work illustrating standard-setting performances in science comes from schools throughout the city. The work comes from students with a wide range of cultural backgrounds, some of whom have a first language other than English or are studying in ESL or bilingual education programs.

In some cases, the diverse backgrounds and experiences of the students are evident in the work samples. In other cases, the students' work reveals little about who they are. While we worked to ensure that the collection reflected the diversity of our students, we have not made specific reference to these characteristics in the commentaries that accompany the work samples. Work that illustrates a standard-setting performance is standard setting no matter who produced it. What unites the work samples is that they all help to illustrate the performance standards by demonstrating standard-setting performances for parts of one or more of the standards and demonstrate that all students can produce work that meets high expectations.

Genuine student work

In all cases, the work samples are genuine student work. While they illustrate standard-setting performances for parts of the science standards, many samples are not "perfect" in every respect. Some, for example, include imprecise language or graphic representations. Others have some spelling errors or awkward grammatical constructions. We think it is important that the standards are illustrated by means of authentic work samples and accordingly have made no attempt to "doctor" the work in order to correct these imperfections: the work has been included "warts and all." Where errors occur, we have included a note drawing attention to the nature of the mistakes and commenting on their significance in the context of the work.

Resources

Reviewers of the New Standards edition have pointed out that our expectations are more demanding, both in terms of student time and access to resources, than they consider reasonable for all students. We acknowledge the distance between our goals and the status quo, and the fact that there is a tremendous disparity in opportunities between the most and least advantaged students. Indeed, the National Research Council included a program standard that delineates all of the resources–professional development, time, materials, adequate and safe space, and access to the world beyond the classroom–needed to achieve the *National Science Education Standards*. This program standard is reprinted in its entirety in the appendix.

In addition to taking advantage of existing school, district, and board resources, we think that there are two additional strategies that must be pursued to achieve our goals—making better use of existing, out-of-school resources and making explicit the connection between particular resources and particular standards.

Best practice in science has always included extensive inquiry and investigation, but it is frequently given less emphasis in the face of competing demands for student time and teacher resources. An elementary teacher faced with the unfamiliar territory of project work in science or a secondary teacher faced with the prospect of guiding 180 projects and investigations can legitimately throw up his or her hands and say, "Help!" There are many science-related organizations in New York City, such as the American Museum of Natural History, the Bronx Zoo, and the City Parks Foundation, that have science education on their agenda. Thus, we invited representatives of those organizations to participate in the calibration process and have incorporated examples of projects and investigations that are done outside of school to make clear that help is available. There is an extensive list of science-rich organizations, professional organizations for science teaching, and other resources to support teachers and students in the appendix.

All of the district, state, and national documents in science make explicit the need for hands-on experiences and using information tools. Thus, for example, Standard **S6**, Scientific Tools and Technologies, makes consistent reference to using telecommunications to acquire and share information. We know that more students have access to the Internet at home than at school, so this raises an equity issue. We feel that the best way to encourage schools to make sure that students' access to information and ideas does not depend on what they get at home is to show several examples of work that was enhanced by use of the Internet and other technologies.

ASSESSMENT BASED ON STANDARDS

Performance standards define a student's academic responsibilities and, by implication, the teaching responsibilities of the school. How do we determine whether students have lived up to their academic responsibilities? We assess their work—is it "good enough" by comparison with the standards.

Assessment is an integral component of the educational process. If properly designed and administered, assessments can provide important information to help guide and inform instruction. In order to perform these functions, there must be a strict alignment among standards, educational strategies and resources, and assessments. That is, what we assess must be what we teach, and both must focus on what we want students to know and be able to do—the performance standards.

Assessment takes place in a variety of formats and situations, but a convenient distinction separates informal, ongoing classroom assessment from formal, standardized assessment. The former consists of the evidence teachers collect in class on a continuous basis to track the progress of their students in mastering the skills and material that are taught. The latter are the tests and on-demand assessments administered to all students in specific grades as part of the city- and state-wide assessment programs. Both types of assessment are essential to effective instruction. Ongoing classroom assessment provides continuous feedback on student progress to students, teachers, and parents; standardized assessment measures the mastery of critical skills and concepts at key developmental milestones. Regardless of their differing perspectives, both classroom and standardized assessment must be fully aligned with the performance standards.

The state is redesigning its standardized assessment program in Science based on performance standards that are aligned with the New York State Standards. Fourth grade students currently take the Elementary Science Program Evaluation Test (ESPET) to assess science programs in Grades K-4. ESPET includes an objective test as well as a test of manipulative skills. The state is designing a new science test at Grade 8 to be implemented for the first time in the spring of 2001. This test is designed to show whether students are meeting the higher academic standards that are being required and whether they are on track to passing the new, more rigorous Regents Science examinations in high school. The new science test at Grade 8 will include multiple-choice questions, open-ended questions, and a laboratory project.

Beyond standardized assessment, it is equally important to ensure that the performance standards provide the focus for ongoing classroom assessment. In the absence of standards, teachers are left without a common frame of reference to determine whether the work of their students is good enough. Standards could vary widely from classroom to classroom resulting in wide variation in instruction and achievement. The work samples that form an essential part of the performance standards provide graphic guidance to all teachers in assessing the level and quality of their students' work.

How the assessments are connected to the performance standards

The performance standards define a domain of expected student performances. Take the science standard **S1** at the elementary school level as an example (see page 18). This standard begins with a definition of science concepts that describes what we expect students to be able to do at approximately the end of fourth grade. The performance descriptions go on to spell out expectations for what students will accomplish in terms of demonstrating conceptual understanding, explaining observations and making predictions, and by representing concepts in multiple ways. Furthermore, students are expected to put their reading to work and the standards say so; students have to produce work based on their understanding of particular concepts.

We assess the different elements of the domain defined by a standard by using assessment methods appropriate to the expected performances. Although the assessment system that will fully align with the performance standards is currently under development, some of the components are already in place. The assessment methods comprise a variety of on-demand standardized and ongoing classroom assessments.

The standardized assessments are of two types that differ in format, method of scoring, and the information they provide. One type of assessment serves the purpose of telling us how well students are performing in comparison with standards (standards-referenced assessment); the other compares student performance to that of representative samples of other students (norm-referenced assessment). Typically, the former are performance-based assessments that require students to produce work that is rated by teachers or other professionals using a rubric, or scoring criteria, based on the standards. The latter are usually multiple-choice in format and are machine scored.

In the new state assessment system, these two different types of assessment are used to complement one another. Performance-based assessments are combined with multiple-choice tests in ways that measure both the depth and breadth of student achievement. Moreover, beginning in 2000, the state will revise its Elementary Science Program Evaluation Test (ESPET), add a test at Grade 8, and revise the high school Regents examinations in Science.

Classroom assessment

The last part of science standard ▓S8▓a requires that students communicate results to audiences and defend conclusions from peer review. The appropriate assessor for these requirements is the teacher or another adult close to the student who can verify the student's claims for meeting this requirement. This component of the system for assessing achievement of the Science standard is designed to work like a merit badge in the style of the awards developed by the Girl Scouts of the U.S.A. and the Boy Scouts of America.

Raising standards for all students has important implications for the quality of curriculum and instruction. Indeed, one of the most important reasons for setting high standards is to challenge the system to perform for the students. Appropriate assessments based on these high standards can give the system feedback on how well it is doing and what it has to do next.

HOW TO READ THESE PERFORMANCE STANDARDS

This volume is organized into three main sections: Elementary School (beginning on page 16), Middle School (beginning on page 66), and High School (beginning on page 120). Each section follows the same format.

Each standard is identified by a symbol.

Turn to the performance descriptions for the standards for elementary school on pages 18-32. There are eight standards for Science at each of the three levels, each identified by a symbol. The symbol for the Physical Sciences Concepts standard is **S1**. This symbol appears wherever there is a reference to this standard.

1 Most standards are made up of several parts.

All of the standards are made up of several parts, for example, the Physical Sciences Concepts standard has three parts at the elementary school level. Each part is identified by a lower case letter; for example, the part of the Physical Sciences Concepts standard that refers to properties of objects and materials is **S1a**. These symbols are used wherever there is a reference to the relevant part of a standard.

Performance descriptions tell what students are expected to know and be able to do.

Each part of a standard has a performance description. The performance description is a narrative description of what students are expected to know and be able to do. It is shown in bold type.

2 Examples are the kinds of work students might do to demonstrate their achievement of the standards.

Immediately following the bold-typed performance descriptions for the standard are examples of the kinds of work students might do to demonstrate their achievement. The examples also indicate the nature and complexity of activities that are appropriate to expect of students at the grade level. However, we use the word "example" deliberately. The examples are intended only to show the kinds of work that students might do and to stimulate ideas for further kinds of work. None of the activities shown in the examples is necessarily required to meet the standard.

3 Cross-references highlight the links between the examples and the performance descriptions.

The symbols that follow each example show the part or parts of the standard to which the example relates.

4 Cross-references also highlight links among the standards.

Often the examples that go with the performance descriptions include cross-references to other parts of the standard and parts of other standards.

5 Excerpts from other standards highlight the many similarities and few differences.

Quotations from the *New York State Learning Standards*, the *National Science Education Standards*, and the *Benchmarks for Science Literacy* show the many similarities and few differences among these state and national documents and the *New York City Performance Standards*.

6 Margin notes draw attention to particular aspects of the standards.

The notes in the margin draw attention to particular aspects of the standards, such as the resources to which students need access in order to meet the requirements of the standards.

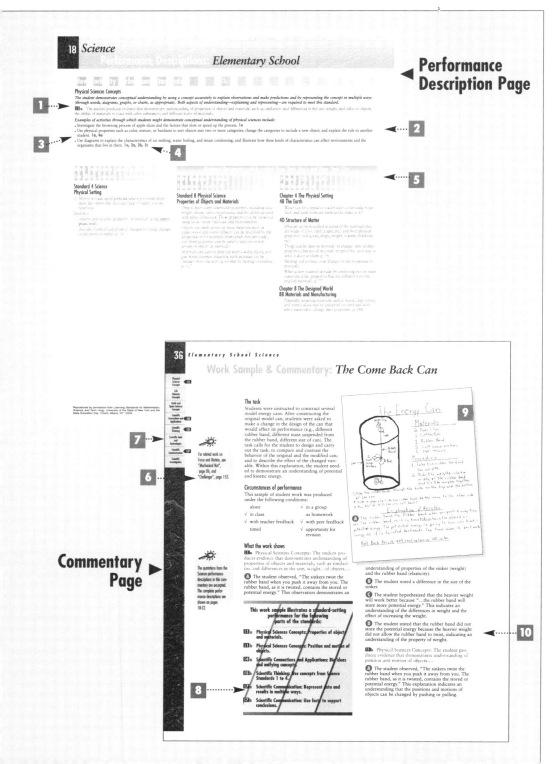

Performance Description Page

Commentary Page

Comparing the grade levels.

The Appendix (see page 199) shows the performance descriptions at each of the three grade levels: Elementary, Middle, and High School.

Work samples and commentaries.

Work samples and commentaries appear on the pages immediately following the performance descriptions.

7 Standards are highlighted in the bar at the side of the page.

The bar along the side of the pages showing student work highlights the standards that are illustrated by each work sample.

8 The box at the bottom of the page shows what is illustrated in the work sample.

The shaded box at the bottom of the page lists the parts of the standards that are illustrated in the work sample.

9 Work samples illustrate standard-setting performances.

Each work sample is a genuine piece of student work. We have selected it because it illustrates a standard-setting performance for one or more parts of the standards.

10 The commentary explains why the work illustrates a standard-setting performance.

The commentary that goes with each work sample identifies the features of the work sample that illustrate the relevant parts of the standards. The commentary explains the task on which the student worked and the circumstances under which the work was completed. It draws attention to the qualities of the work with direct reference to the performance descriptions for the relevant standards.

The commentary also notes our reservations about the work.

The commentary also draws attention to any reservations we have about the student work. (See "Genuine student work," page 11.)

Performance Standards = performance descriptions + work samples + commentaries on the work samples.

Performance standards are, thus, made up of a combination of performance descriptions, work samples, and commentaries on the work samples:

- The performance descriptions tell what students should know and the ways they should demonstrate the knowledge and skills they have acquired.
- The work samples show work that illustrates standard-setting performances in relation to parts of the standards.
- The commentaries explain why the work is standard-setting with reference to the relevant performance description or descriptions.

Each of these is an essential component of a performance standard.

Most work samples illustrate a standard-setting performance for parts of more than one standard.

Most work samples illustrate the quality of work expected for parts of more than one standard. For example, some of the work samples selected to illustrate parts of **S1**, Physical Sciences Concepts, also illustrate a standard-setting performance for part of **S5**, Scientific Thinking, or for part of **S7**, Scientific Communication, or, possibly, all of these.

"The Come Back Can" (see page 36) is an example of a work sample that illustrates parts of more than one standard.

Physical Sciences Concepts

Life Sciences Concepts

Earth and Space Sciences Concepts

Scientific Connections and Applications

Scientific Thinking

Scientific Tools and Technologies

Scientific Communication

Scientific Investigation

OVERVIEW OF THE PERFORMANCE STANDARDS

The elementary school standards are set at a level of performance approximately equivalent to the end of fourth grade. It is expected that some students might achieve this level earlier and others later than this grade. (See "Deciding what constitutes a standard-setting performance," page 9.)

S Science

S1 Physical Sciences Concepts

S1a Demonstrates understanding of properties of objects and materials.

S1b Demonstrates understanding of position and motion of objects.

S1c Demonstrates understanding of light, heat, electricity, and magnetism.

S2 Life Sciences Concepts

S2a Demonstrates understanding of characteristics of organisms.

S2b Demonstrates understanding of life cycles of organisms.

S2c Demonstrates understanding of organisms and environments.

S2d Demonstrates understanding of change over time.

S3 Earth and Space Sciences Concepts

S3a Demonstrates understanding of properties of Earth materials.

S3b Demonstrates understanding of objects in the sky.

S3c Demonstrates understanding of changes in Earth and sky.

S4 Scientific Connections and Applications

S4a Demonstrates understanding of big ideas and unifying concepts.

S4b Demonstrates understanding of the designed world.

S4c Demonstrates understanding of personal health.

S4d Demonstrates understanding of science as a human endeavor.

OVERVIEW OF THE PERFORMANCE STANDARDS

S Science

S5 Scientific Thinking

S5a Asks questions about natural phenomena; objects and organisms; and events and discoveries.

S5b Uses concepts from Science Standards 1 to 4 to explain a variety of observations and phenomena.

S5c Uses evidence from reliable sources to construct explanations.

S5d Evaluates different points of view using relevant experiences, observations, and knowledge; and distinguishes between fact and opinion.

S5e Identifies problems; proposes and implements solutions; and evaluates the accuracy, design, and outcomes of investigations.

S5f Works individually and in teams to collect and share information and ideas.

S6 Scientific Tools and Technologies

S6a Uses technology and tools to gather data and extend the senses.

S6b Collects and analyzes data using concepts and techniques in Mathematics Standard 4.

S6c Acquires information from multiple sources, such as experimentation and print and non-print sources.

S7 Scientific Communication

S7a Represents data and results in multiple ways.

S7b Uses facts to support conclusions.

S7c Communicates in a form suited to the purpose and the audience.

S7d Critiques written and oral explanations, and uses data to resolve disagreements.

S8 Scientific Investigation

S8a Demonstrates scientific competence by completing an experiment.

S8b Demonstrates scientific competence by completing a systematic observation.

S8c Demonstrates scientific competence by completing a design.

S8d Demonstrates scientific competence by completing non-experimental research using print and electronic information.

New York City Performance Standards

S1 Physical Sciences Concepts

The student demonstrates conceptual understanding by using a concept accurately to explain observations and make predictions and by representing the concept in multiple ways (through words, diagrams, graphs, or charts, as appropriate). Both aspects of understanding—explaining and representing—are required to meet this standard.

S1a The student produces evidence that demonstrates understanding of properties of objects and materials, such as similarities and differences in the size, weight, and color of objects; the ability of materials to react with other substances; and different states of materials.

Examples of activities through which students might demonstrate conceptual understanding of physical sciences include:

▲ Investigate the browning process of apple slices and the factors that slow or speed up the process. **1a**

▲ Use physical properties such as color, texture, or hardness to sort objects into two or more categories; change the categories to include a new object; and explain the rule to another student. **1a, 4a**

▲ Use diagrams to explain the characteristics of ice melting, water boiling, and steam condensing; and illustrate how these kinds of characteristics can affect environments and the organisms that live in them. **1a, 2a, 2b, 2c**

New York State Learning Standards for Math, Science, & Technology

Standard 4 Science
Physical Setting

3. Matter is made up of **particles** whose properties determine the observable characteristics of matter and its reactivity.

Students:

observe and describe properties of materials using **appropriate tools.**

describe chemical and physical changes including changes in the states of matter. p. 30

National Documents which guided New York State and New York City

NRC National Science Education Standards

Standard B Physical Science
Properties of Objects and Materials

Objects have many observable properties, including size, weight, shape, color, temperature, and the ability to react with other substances. Those properties can be measured using tools such as rulers, balances, and thermometers.

Objects are made of one or more materials, such as paper, wood and metal. Objects can be described by the properties of the materials from which they are made, and those properties can be used to separate or sort a group of objects or materials.

Materials can exist in different states—solid, liquid, and gas. Some common materials, such as water, can be changed from one state to another by heating or cooling. p. 127

Project 2061, AAAS
Benchmarks for Science Literacy

Chapter 4 The Physical Setting
4B The Earth

Water can be a liquid or a solid and can be made to go back and forth from one form to the other. p. 67

4D Structure of Matter

Objects can be described in terms of the materials they are made of (clay, cloth, paper, etc.) and their physical properties (color, size, shape, weight, texture, flexibility, etc.).

Things can be done to materials to change some of their properties, but not all materials respond the same way to what is done to them. p. 76

Heating and cooling cause changes in the properties of materials.

When a new material is made by combining two or more materials, it has properties that are different from the original materials. p. 77

Chapter 8 The Designed World
8B Materials and Manufacturing

Naturally occurring materials such as wood, clay, cotton, and animal skins may be processed or combined with other materials to change their properties. p. 188

New York City Performance Standards

S1 Physical Sciences Concepts

The student demonstrates conceptual understanding by using a concept accurately to explain observations and make predictions and by representing the concept in multiple ways (through words, diagrams, graphs, or charts, as appropriate). Both aspects of understanding—explaining and representing—are required to meet this standard.

S1 b The student produces evidence that demonstrates understanding of position and motion of objects, such as how the motion of an object can be described by tracing and measuring its position over time; and how sound is produced by vibrating objects.

Examples of activities through which students might demonstrate conceptual understanding of physical sciences include:

▲ Predict the bouncing pattern of a basketball under different throwing conditions using previous observations of force and motion. **1b**

▲ Make a musical instrument, explain the relationship between sound and shape, and compare this to a structure/function relationship in an organism. **1b, 2a**

New York State Learning Standards for Math, Science, & Technology

Standard 4 Science
Physical Setting

5. Energy and matter interact through forces that result in changes in motion.

Students:

describe the effects of common forces (pushes and pulls) on objects, such as those caused by gravity, magnetism, and mechanical forces.

describe how forces can operate across distances. p. 30

National Documents which guided New York State and New York City

NRC National Science Education Standards

Standard B Physical Science
Position and Motion of Objects

The position of an object can be described by locating it relative to another object or the background.

An object's motion can be described by tracing and measuring its position over time.

The position and motion of objects can be changed by pushing or pulling. The size of the change is related to the strength of the push or pull.

Sound is produced by vibrating objects. The pitch of the sound can be varied by changing the rate of vibration. p. 127

Project 2061, AAAS
Benchmarks for Science Literacy

Chapter 4 The Physical Setting
4F Motion

Something that is moving may move steadily or change its direction. The greater the force is, the greater the change in motion will be. The more massive an object is, the less effect a given force will have.

How fast things move differs greatly. Some things are so slow that their journey takes a long time; others move too fast for people to even see them.

Things that make sound vibrate. p. 89

4G Forces of Nature

The earth's gravity pulls any object toward it without touching it.

Without touching them, a magnet pulls on all things made of iron, and either pushes or pulls on other magnets. p. 94

Chapter 11 Common Themes
11C Constancy and Change

Things can change in different ways, such as in size, weight, color, and movement. Some small changes can be detected by taking measurements. p. 272

New York City Performance Standards

S1 Physical Sciences Concepts

The student demonstrates conceptual understanding by using a concept accurately to explain observations and make predictions and by representing the concept in multiple ways (through words, diagrams, graphs, or charts, as appropriate). Both aspects of understanding—explaining and representing—are required to meet this standard.

S1c The student produces evidence that demonstrates understanding of light, heat, electricity, and magnetism, such as the variation of heat and temperature; how light travels in a straight line until it strikes an object or how electrical circuits work.

Examples of activities through which students might demonstrate conceptual understanding of physical sciences include:

▲ Investigate heat and friction by burning, rubbing, or mixing substances together; explain similarities and differences. **1c**

▲ Use knowledge of magnetism to predict what materials will be attracted, repelled, or unaffected by a magnet, then conduct an experiment to confirm or reject their predictions. **1c, 3a**

New York State Learning Standards for Math, Science, & Technology

Standard 4 Science
Physical Setting

4. Energy exists in many forms, and when these forms change, energy is conserved.

Students:

describe a variety of forms of energy (e.g., heat, chemical, light) and the changes that occur in objects when they interact with those forms of energy.

observe the way one form of energy can be transformed into another form of energy present in common situations (e.g., mechanical to heat energy, mechanical to electrical energy chemical to heat energy).

5. Energy and matter interact through forces that result in changes in motion.

Students:

describe the effects of common forces (pushes and pulls) on objects, such as those caused by **gravity**, magnetism, and **mechanical forces**.

describe how forces can operate across distances. p. 30

National Documents which guided New York State and New York City

NRC National Science Education Standards

Standard B Physical Science
Light, Heat, Electricity, and Magnetism

Light travels in a straight line until it strikes an object. Light can be reflected by a mirror, refracted by a lens, or absorbed by the object.

Heat can be produced in many ways, such as burning, rubbing, or mixing one substance with another. Heat can move from one object to another by conduction.

Electricity in circuits can produce light, heat, sound and magnetic effects. Electrical circuits require a complete loop through which an electrical current can pass.

Magnets attract and repel each other and certain kinds of other materials. p. 127

Project 2061, AAAS
Benchmarks for Science Literacy

Chapter 4 The Physical Setting
4E Energy Transformation

Things that give off light often also give off heat. Heat is produced by mechanical and electrical machines, and any time one thing rubs against something else.

When warmer things are put with cooler ones, the warm ones lose heat and the cool ones gain it until they are all at the same temperature. A warmer object can warm a cooler one by contact or at a distance.

Some materials conduct heat much better than others. Poor conductors can reduce heat loss. p. 84

4G Forces of Nature

The earth's gravity pulls any object toward it without touching it.

Without touching them, a magnet pulls on all things made of iron and either pushes or pulls on other magnets.

Without touching them, material that has been electrically charged pulls on all other materials and may either push or pull other charged materials. p. 94

New York City Performance Standards

S2 Life Sciences Concepts

The student demonstrates conceptual understanding by using a concept accurately to explain observations and make predictions and by representing the concept in multiple ways (through words, diagrams, graphs, or charts, as appropriate). Both aspects of understanding—explaining and representing—are required to meet this standard.

S2a The student produces evidence that demonstrates understanding of characteristics of organisms, such as survival and environmental support; the relationship between structure and function; and variations in behavior.

Examples of activities through which students might demonstrate conceptual understanding of life sciences include:

▲ Predict how long a plant will live planted in a closed glass jar located by a window; and explain what additional information regarding the plant and the surrounding environment would be needed to improve the prediction. **2a, 1a, 3a, 3b**

▲ Complete a 4-H animal care project; write a report explaining the growth and development of the animal and present the animal at the county-wide fair. **2a, 2b, 2c, 7a, 8b**

▲ Explain the differences between inherited and environmental features of individuals such as flower colors or bike riding ability and describe the physical characteristics of the environment that could affect these features. **2a, 2b, 2c, 2d, 1a, 4a**

▲ Plan the supplies and equipment needed for a camping trip and explain their purposes. **2a, 2c, 4b, 4d, M8d, A1c**

▲ Explain how organisms, both human and other, cause changes in their environments and how some of these changes can be detrimental to other organisms. **2a, 2b, 2c, 2d, 1a, 4a, 4b**

▲ Describe the similarities and differences between fossils and related contemporary organisms and explain how environmental factors contributed to these similarities and differences. **2a, 2c, 2d, 1a, 3a, 3c, 4a**

New York State Learning Standards for Math, Science, & Technology

Standard 4 Science
The Living Environment

1. Living things are both similar to and different from each other and non-living things.

Students:

describe the characteristics of and variations between living and non-living things.

describe the life processes common to all living things.

5. Organisms maintain a dynamic equilibrium that sustains life.

Students:

describe the basic life functions of common living specimens (guppy, mealworm, gerbil).

describe some survival behaviors of common living species.

describe the factors that help promote good health and growth in humans. p. 31

National Documents which guided New York State and New York City

NRC National Science Education Standards

Standard C Life Science
Characteristics of Organisms

Organisms have basic needs. For example, animals need air, water, and food; plants require air, water, nutrients, and light.

Each plant or animal has different structures that serve different functions in growth, survival and reproduction.

The behavior of individual organisms is influenced by internal cues (such as hunger) and external cues (such as a change in the environment). p. 129

Project 2061, AAAS
Benchmarks for Science Literacy

Chapter 5 The Living Environment
5A Diversity of Life

A great variety of kinds of living things can be sorted into groups in many ways using various features to decide which things belong to which group. p. 103

5C Cells

Some living things consist of a single cell. Like familiar organisms, they need food, water, and air; a way to dispose of waste; and an environment they can live in. p. 111

5D Interdependence of Life

For any particular environment, some kinds of plants and animals survive well, some survive less well, and some cannot survive at all.

Changes in an organism's habitat are sometimes beneficial to it and sometimes harmful. p. 116

Chapter 6 The Human Organism
6D Learning

Human beings can use the memory of their past experiences to make judgments about new situations. p. 140

New York City Performance Standards

S2 Life Sciences Concepts

The student demonstrates conceptual understanding by using a concept accurately to explain observations and make predictions and by representing the concept in multiple ways (through words, diagrams, graphs, or charts, as appropriate). Both aspects of understanding—explaining and representing—are required to meet this standard.

S2 b The student produces evidence that demonstrates understanding of life cycles of organisms, such as how inheritance and environment determine the characteristics of an organism; and that all plants and animals have life cycles.

Examples of activities through which students might demonstrate conceptual understanding of life sciences include:

▲ Complete a 4-H animal care project; write a report explaining the growth and development of the animal and present the animal at the county-wide fair. **2a, 2b, 2c, 7a, 8b**
▲ Make drawings of observations showing the life cycle of a plant or animal. **2b**
▲ Explain the differences between inherited and environmental features of individuals such as flower colors or bike riding ability and describe the physical characteristics of the environment that could affect these features. **2a, 2b, 2c, 2d, 1a, 4a**
▲ Explain how organisms, both human and other, cause changes in their environments and how some of these changes can be detrimental to other organisms. **2a, 2b, 2c, 2d, 1a, 4a, 4b**

New York State Learning Standards for Math, Science, & Technology

Standard 4 Science
The Living Environment

2. Organisms inherit genetic information in a variety of ways that result in continuity of structure and function between parents and offspring.

Students:

recognize that traits of living things are both inherited and acquired or learned.

recognize that for humans and other living things there is genetic continuity between generations

4. The continuity of life is sustained through reproduction and development.

Students:

describe the major stages in the life cycle of selected plants and animals.

describe evidence of growth, repair, and maintenance, such as nails, hair and bone, and the healing of cuts and bruises.

6. Plants and animals depend on each other and their physical environment.

Students:

describe the relationship of the sun as an energy source for living and non-living cycles. p. 31

National Documents which guided New York State and New York City

NRC National Science Education Standards

Standard C Life Science
Life Cycles of Organisms

Plants and animals have life cycles that include being born, developing into adults, reproducing, and eventually dying. The details of this life cycle are different for different organisms.

Plants and animals closely resemble their parents.

Many characteristics of an organism are inherited from the parents of the organism, but others are a result from the environment. Inherited characteristics include the color of flowers and the number of limbs of an animal. Other features, such as the ability to ride a bicycle, are learned through interactions with the environment and cannot be passed on to the next generation. p. 129

Project 2061, AAAS
Benchmarks for Science Literacy

Chapter 5 The Living Environment
5B Heredity

Some likenesses between children and parents such as eye color in human beings or fruit or flower color in plants, are inherited. Other likenesses, such as people's table manners or carpentry skills are learned.

For offspring to resemble their parents, there must be a reliable way to transfer information from one generation to the next. p. 107

5D Interdependence of Life

For any particular environment, some kinds of plants and animals survive well, some survive less well and some cannot survive at all. p. 116

5E Flow of Matter and Energy

Over the whole earth, organisms are growing, dying and decaying and new organisms are being produced by the old ones. p. 119

5F Evolution of Life

Individuals of the same kind differ in their characteristics, and sometimes the differences give individuals an advantage in surviving and reproducing. p. 123

Chapter 6 The Human Organism
6B Human Development

There is a usual sequence of physical and mental development among human beings, although individuals differ in exactly when they learn things. p. 132

New York City Performance Standards

S2 Life Sciences Concepts

The student demonstrates conceptual understanding by using a concept accurately to explain observations and make predictions and by representing the concept in multiple ways (through words, diagrams, graphs, or charts, as appropriate). Both aspects of understanding—explaining and representing—are required to meet this standard.

S2c The student produces evidence that demonstrates understanding of organisms and environments, such as the interdependence of animals and plants in an ecosystem; and populations and their effects on the environment.

Examples of activities through which students might demonstrate conceptual understanding of life sciences include:

- Complete a 4-H animal care project; write a report explaining the growth and development of the animal and present the animal at the county-wide fair. **2a, 2b, 2c, 7a, 8b**
- Explain the differences between inherited and environmental features of individuals such as flower colors or bike riding ability and describe the physical characteristics of the environment that could affect these features. **2a, 2b, 2c, 2d, 1a, 4a**
- Plan the supplies and equipment needed for a camping trip and explain their purposes. **2a, 2c, 4b, 4d, M8d, A1c**
- Explain how organisms, both human and other, cause changes in their environments and how some of these changes can be detrimental to other organisms. **2a, 2b, 2c, 2d, 1a, 4a, 4b**
- Use more than one medium such as models, text, drawings, or oral explanations to show how various organisms have changed over time to fill a variety of niches. **2c, 2d, 4a**
- Describe the similarities and differences between fossils and related contemporary organisms and explain how environmental factors contributed to these similarities and differences. **2a, 2c, 2d, 1a, 3a, 3c, 4a**

New York State Learning Standards for Math, Science, & Technology

Standard 4 Science
The Living Environment

6. Plants and animals depend on each other and their physical environment.

Students:

describe how plants and animals, including humans, depend upon each other and the non-living environment.

describe the relationship of the sun as an energy source for living and non-living cycles.

7. Human decisions and activities have had a profound impact on the physical and living environment.

Students:

identify ways in which humans have changed their environment and the effects of those changes. p. 31

National Documents which guided New York State and New York City

NRC National Science Education Standards

Standard C Life Science
Organisms and Their Environments

All animals depend on plants. Some animals eat plants for food. Other animals eat animals that eat the plants.

An organism's patterns of behavior are related to the nature of that organism's environment, including the kinds and numbers of other organisms present, the availability of food and resources, and the physical characteristics of the environment. When the environment changes, some plants and animals survive and reproduce, and others die or move to new locations.

All organisms cause changes in the environment where they live. Some of these changes are detrimental to the organism or other organisms, whereas others are beneficial.

Humans depend on their natural and constructed environments. Humans change environments in ways that can be either beneficial or detrimental for themselves and other organisms. p. 129

Project 2061, AAAS
Benchmarks for Science Literacy

Chapter 5 The Living Environment
5D Interdependence of Life

For any particular environment, some kinds of plants and animals survive well, some survive less well, and some cannot survive at all.

Insects and various other organisms depend on dead plant and animal material for food.

Organisms interact with one another in various ways besides providing food. Many plants depend on animals for carrying their pollen to other plants for dispersing their seeds. p. 116

5F Evolution of Life

Individuals of the same kind differ in their characteristics and, sometimes, the difference give individuals an advantage in survival and reproducing. p. 123

Chapter 7 Human Society
7E Political and Economic Systems

People tend to live together in groups and therefore have to have ways of deciding who will do what. p. 168

New York City Performance Standards

S2 Life Sciences Concepts

The student demonstrates conceptual understanding by using a concept accurately to explain observations and make predictions and by representing the concept in multiple ways (through words, diagrams, graphs, or charts, as appropriate). Both aspects of understanding—explaining and representing—are required to meet this standard.

S2d The student produces evidence that demonstrates understanding of change over time, such as evolution and fossil evidence depicting the great diversity of organisms developed over geologic history.

Examples of activities through which students might demonstrate conceptual understanding of life sciences include:

- Explain the differences between inherited and environmental features of individuals such as flower colors or bike riding ability and describe the physical characteristics of the environment that could affect these features. **2a, 2b, 2c, 2d, 1a, 4a**
- Explain how organisms, both human and other, cause changes in their environments and how some of these changes can be detrimental to other organisms. **2a, 2b, 2c, 2d, 1a, 4a, 4b**
- Use more than one medium such as models, text, drawings, or oral explanations to show how various organisms have changed over time to fill a variety of niches. **2c, 2d, 4a**
- Describe the similarities and differences between fossils and related contemporary organisms and explain how environmental factors contributed to these similarities and differences. **2a, 2c, 2d, 1a, 3a, 3c, 4a**

New York State Learning Standards for Math, Science, & Technology

Standard 4 Science
The Living Environment

2. Organisms inherit genetic information in a variety of ways that result in continuity of structure and function between parent and offspring.

Students:

recognize that traits of living things are both inherited and acquired or learned.

recognize that for humans and other living things there is genetic continuity between generations.

3. Individual organisms and species change over time.

Students:

describe how the structures of plants and animals complement the environment of the plant or animal.

observe that differences within a species may give individuals an advantage in surviving and reproducing. p. 31

National Documents which guided New York State and New York City

NRC National Science Education Standards

Standard D Earth and Space Science
Properties of Earth Materials

Fossils provide evidence about the plants and animals that lived long ago and in the nature of the environment at that time. p. 134

Project 2061, AAAS
Benchmarks for Science Literacy

Chapter 5 The Living Environment
5F Evolution of Life

Individuals of the same kind differ in their characteristics, and sometimes the differences give individuals an advantage in surviving and reproducing.

Fossils can be compared to one another and to living organisms according to their similarities and differences. Some organisms that lived long ago are similar to existing organisms, but some are quite different. p. 123

New York City Performance Standards

S3 Earth and Space Sciences Concepts

The student demonstrates conceptual understanding by using a concept accurately to explain observations and make predictions and by representing the concept in multiple ways (through words, diagrams, graphs or charts, as appropriate). Both aspects of understanding—explaining and representing—are required to meet this standard.

S3a The student produces evidence that demonstrates understanding of properties of Earth materials, such as water and gases; and the properties of rocks and soils, such as texture, color, and ability to retain water.

Examples of activities through which students might demonstrate conceptual understanding of Earth and space sciences include:

▲ Investigate how the properties of soil can affect the growth of a plant. **3a, 1a, 2a, 2b, 2c, 4a**

▲ Predict what kinds of materials would be useful for different purposes, such as in buildings or as sources of fuel, because of their physical and chemical properties. **3a, 1a**

▲ Write a story that describes what happens to a drop of water and the physical environment through which it flows as it travels from a lake to a river via the Earth's atmosphere. **3a, 3b, 1a, 4a**

New York State Learning Standards for Math, Science, & Technology

Standard 4 Science Physical Setting

2. Many of the phenomena that we observe on earth involve interactions among components of air, water, and land.

Students:

describe the relationships among air, water, and land on Earth. p. 30

National Documents which guided New York State and New York City

NRC National Science Education Standards

Standard D Earth and Space Science Properties of Earth Materials

Earth materials are solid rocks and soils, water, and the gases of the atmosphere. The varied materials have different physical and chemical properties, which make them useful in different ways, for example, as building materials, as sources of fuel, or for growing the plants we use as food. Earth materials provide many of the resources that humans use.

Soils have properties of color and texture, capacity to retain water, and ability to support the growth of many kinds of plants, including those in our food supply. p. 134

Project 2061, AAAS Benchmarks for Science Literacy

Chapter 4 The Physical Setting
4B The Earth

Water can be a liquid or a solid and can be made to go back and forth from one form to the other. If water is turned into ice and then the ice is allowed to melt, the amount of water is the same as it was before freezing.

Water left in an open container disappears but water in a closed container does not disappear. p. 67

When liquid water disappears it turns into a gas (vapor) in the air and can reappear as a liquid when cooled or as a solid if cooled below the freezing point of water. Clouds and fog are made up of tiny droplets of water. p. 68

4C Processes that Shape the Earth

Rock is composed of different combinations of minerals. Smaller rocks come from the breakage and weathering of bedrock and larger rocks.

Chunks of rocks come in many sizes and shapes, from boulders to grains of sand and even smaller.

Soil is made partly from weathered rock, partly from planet remains—and also contains living organisms. p. 72

New York City Performance Standards

S3 Earth and Space Sciences Concepts

The student demonstrates conceptual understanding by using a concept accurately to explain observations and make predictions and by representing the concept in multiple ways (through words, diagrams, graphs or charts, as appropriate). Both aspects of understanding—explaining and representing—are required to meet this standard.

S3 b The student produces evidence that demonstrates understanding of objects in the sky, such as Sun, Moon, planets, and other objects that can be observed and described; and the importance of the Sun to provide the light and heat necessary for survival.

Examples of activities through which students might demonstrate conceptual understanding of Earth and space sciences include:

- Observe and keep a record of the shape of the Moon for several months; and then make drawings predicting what will happen during the next week. **3b, 3c**
- Make observations of the changes in an object's shadow during the course of a day and investigate the source of the variation. **3b, 3c**
- Write a story that describes what happens to a drop of water and the physical environment through which it flows as it travels from a lake to a river via the Earth's atmosphere. **3a, 3b, 1a, 4a**
- Collect information from a weather station and use the information to explain the patterns of change from fall to winter in terms of weather and the position and movement of objects in the sky. **3b, 3c, 4a, M1a, M1c, M1f, A1a**

New York State Learning Standards for Math, Science, & Technology

Standard 4 Science
Physical Setting

1. The earth and celestial phenomena can be described by principles of relative motion and perspectives.

Students:

describe patterns of daily, monthly, and seasonal changes in their environment.

4. Energy exist in many forms, when these forms change, energy is conserved.

Students:

describe a variety of forms of energy (e.g.. heat, chemical, light) and the changes that occur in objects when they interact with those forms of energy.

observe the way one form of energy can be transformed into another form of energy present in common situations (e.g.. mechanical to heat energy, mechanical to electrical energy, chemical to heat energy). p. 30

National Documents which guided New York State and New York City

NRC National Science Education Standards

Standard D Earth and Space Science
Objects in the Sky

The sun, moon, stars, clouds, birds, and airplanes all have properties, locations and movement that can be observed.

The sun provides the light and heat necessary to maintain the temperature of the earth. p. 134

Project 2061, AAAS Benchmarks for Science Literacy

Chapter 4 The Physical Setting
4A The Universe

There are more stars in the sky than anyone can easily count, but they are not scattered evenly, and they are not all the same in brightness or color.

The sun can only be seen in the daytime but the moon can be seen sometimes at night and sometimes during the day. The sun, moon, and stars all appear to move slowly across the sky.

The moon looks a little different every day, but looks the same again about every four weeks. p. 62

Planet change their positions against the background of stars.

The earth is one of several planets that orbit the sun, and the moon orbits around the earth.

Stars are like the sun, some being smaller and some larger, but so far away that they look like points of lights. p. 63

Chapter 8 The Designed World
8C Energy Sources and Use

The sun is the main source of energy for people and they use it in various ways. The energy in fossil fuels such as oil and coal comes from the sun indirectly, because the fuels come from plants that grew long ago. p. 193

New York City Performance Standards

S3 Earth and Space Sciences Concepts

The student demonstrates conceptual understanding by using a concept accurately to explain observations and make predictions and by representing the concept in multiple ways (through words, diagrams, graphs or charts, as appropriate). Both aspects of understanding—explaining and representing—are required to meet this standard.

S3c The student produces evidence that demonstrates understanding of changes in Earth and sky, such as changes caused by weathering, volcanism, and earthquakes; and the patterns of movement of objects in the sky.

Examples of activities through which students might demonstrate conceptual understanding of Earth and space sciences include:

▲ Observe and keep a record of the shape of the Moon for several months; and then make drawings predicting what will happen during the next week. **3b, 3c**

▲ Make observations of the changes in an object's shadow during the course of a day and investigate the source of the variation. **3b, 3c**

▲ Collect information from a weather station and use the information to explain the patterns of change from fall to winter in terms of weather and the position and movement of objects in the sky. **3b, 3c, 4a, M1a, M1c, M1f, A1a**

New York State Learning Standards for Math, Science, & Technology

Standard 4 Science
Physical Setting

1. The earth and celestial phenomena can be described by principles of relative motion and perspective.

Students:

describe patterns of daily, monthly, and seasonal changes in their environment.

2. Many of the phenomena that we observe on Earth involve interactions among components of air, water, and land.

Students:

describe the relationships among air, water, and land on Earth. p. 30

National Documents which guided New York State and New York City

NRC National Science Education Standards

Standard D Earth and Space Science
Changes in the Earth and Sky

The Surface of the earth changes. Some changes are due to slow processes, such as erosion and weathering and some changes are due to rapid processes, such as landslides, volcanic eruptions and earthquakes.

Weather changes from day to day and over the seasons weather can be described by measurable quantities, such as temperature, wind direction and speed, and precipitation.

Objects in the sky have patterns of movement. The sun for example, appears to move across the sky in the same way everyday, but its path changes slowly over the seasons. The moon moves across the sky on a daily basis much like the sun. The observable shape of the moon changes from day to day in a cycle that lasts about a month. p. 134

Project 2061, AAAS
Benchmarks for Science Literacy

Chapter 4 The Physical Setting
4A The Universe

The patterns of stars in the sky stay the same although they appear to move across the sky nightly and different stars can be seen in different seasons.

Planets change their positions against the background of stars.

The earth is one of several planets that orbits the sun, and the moon orbits around the earth. p. 63

4C Processes that Shape the Earth

Waves, wind, water, and ice shape and reshape the earth's land surface by eroding rock and soil in some areas and depositing them in other areas sometimes in seasonal layers.

Rock is composed of different combinations of minerals. Smaller rocks come from the breakage and weathering of bedrock and larger rocks. Soil is made partly from weathered rock, partly from plant remains — and also contains many living organisms. p. 72

New York City Performance Standards

S4 Scientific Connections and Applications

The student demonstrates conceptual understanding by using a concept accurately to explain observations and make predictions and by representing the concept in multiple ways (through words, diagrams, graphs or charts, as appropriate). Both aspects of understanding—explaining and representing—are required to meet this standard.

The student produces evidence that demonstrates understanding of:

S4a Big ideas and unifying concepts, such as order and organization; models, form and function; change and constancy; and cause and effect.

S4b The designed world, such as development of agricultural techniques; and the viability of technological designs.

S4c Personal health, such as nutrition, substance abuse, and exercise; germs and toxic substances; personal and environmental safety.

S4d Science as a human endeavor, such as communication, cooperation, and diverse input in scientific research; and the importance of reason, intellectual honesty, and skepticism.

Examples of activities through which students might demonstrate conceptual understanding of scientific connections and applications include:

- Conduct an experiment to determine which brand of paper towel is the best in terms of form and function, cause and effect, cost and personal preference, and write an advertisement for the brand highlighting findings of the experiment. 4a, 4b, 1a, 3a
- Earn the Webelos Engineer Badge (Boy Scouts of America) or the Brownie Building Art Try-It (Girl Scouts of the U.S.A.) and explain the design of the model. 4b, 4d, 1a, 1b, 1c
- Explain why people should wash their hands when preparing food. 4c, 3c
- Make recommendations to improve the selection of food in the school vending machines so that students can make healthier choices. 4c, 2b, M8a, A1b
- Build a solar cooker and explain what foods can or cannot be cooked safely within the temperature range achieved. 4b, 4c, 2a
- Interview a person who has a job that interests you and write a report explaining how studying science helped the person prepare for the job. 4d

New York State Learning Standards for Math, Science, & Technology

Standard 6 Interconnectedness: Common Themes

Students will understand the relationships and common themes that connect mathematics, science, and technology and apply the themes to these and other areas of learning.

Systems Thinking

1. Through systems thinking, people can recognize the commonalities that exist among all systems and how parts of a system interrelate and combine to perform specific functions.

Models

2. Models are simplified representations of objects, structures, or systems used in analysis, explanation, interpretation, or design. p. 48

Magnitude and Scale

3. The grouping of magnitudes of size, time, frequency, and pressures or other units of measurement into a series of relative order provides a useful way to deal with the immense range and the changes in scale that affect the behavior and design of systems.

Equilibrium and Stability

4. Equilibrium is a state of stability due either to a lack of changes (static equilibrium) or a balance between opposing forces (dynamic equilibrium). p. 49

Patterns of Change

5. Identifying patterns of change is necessary for making predictions about future behavior and conditions.

Optimization

6. In order to arrive at the best solution that meets criteria within constraints, it is often necessary to make trade-offs. p.50

National Documents which guided New York State and New York City

NRC National Science Education Standards

Unifying Concepts and Processes
Systems, order, and organization
Evidence, models, and explanation
Constancy, change, and measurement
Evolution and equilibrium
Form and function pp. 115-119

Standard E Science and Technology pp. 135-138

Standard F Science in Personal and Social Perspectives
Personal Health
Characteristics and Changes in Populations
Types of Resources
Changes in Environments
Science and Technology in Local Challenges pp. 138-141

Standard G History and Nature of Science p. 141

Project 2061, AAAS Benchmarks for Science Literacy

Chapter 3 The Nature of Technology pp. 41-57

Chapter 6 The Human Organism pp. 127-149

Chapter 8 The Designed World pp. 181-207

Chapter 10 Historical Perspectives pp. 237-259

Chapter 11 Common Themes
11A Systems
11B Models
11C Constancy and Change
11D Scale pp. 261-279

New York City Performance Standards

S5 Scientific Thinking

The student demonstrates scientific inquiry and problem solving by using thoughtful questioning and reasoning strategies, common sense and conceptual understanding from Science Standards 1 to 4, and appropriate methods to investigate the natural world; that is, the student:

S5 a Asks questions about natural phenomena; objects and organisms; and events and discoveries.

S5 b Uses concepts from Science Standards 1 to 4 to explain a variety of observations and phenomena.

S5 c Uses evidence from reliable sources to construct explanations.

S5 d Evaluates different points of view using relevant experiences, observations, and knowledge; and distinguishes between fact and opinion.

S5 e Identifies problems; proposes and implements solutions; and evaluates the accuracy, design, and outcomes of investigations.

S5 f Works individually and in teams to collect and share information and ideas.

Examples of activities through which students might demonstrate scientific thinking include:

▲ Evaluate the claims of a new product: describe the questions and evidence required to substantiate the claims; conduct an investigation to test ideas; and evaluate the accuracy of the conclusions. 5a, 5b, 5c, 5e

▲ Work with others to examine the changes in the flora, fauna, and environment in a one square meter plot, caused by recent construction, explain the observations, and make predictions about the future of this microsystem. 5a, 5b, 5c, 5d, 5f, 2a, 2b, 2c

▲ Use data from one investigation to generate a prediction and conduct a new investigation. 5a, 5b, 5c, 5e

▲ Summarize a series of newspaper and magazine articles on a current topic, e.g., El Niño; use multiple sources to evaluate accuracy in the articles; and write a revised article putting all the relevant ideas together. 5a, 5b, 5c, 5d, 3a

New York State Learning Standards for Math, Science, & Technology

Standard 1 Analysis, Inquiry, and Design
Scientific Inquiry

1. The central purpose of scientific inquiry is to develop explanations of natural phenomena in a continuing, creative process.

2. Beyond the use of reasoning and consensus, scientific inquiry involves the testing of proposed explanations involving the use of conventional techniques and procedures and usually requiring considerable ingenuity. p. 2

3. The observations made while testing proposed explanations, when analyzed using conventional and invented methods, provide new insights into phenomena. p. 3

National Documents which guided New York State and New York City

NRC National Science Education Standards

Standard A Science As Inquiry

Ask a question about objects, organisms, and events in the environment. Students should answer their questions by seeking information from reliable sources of scientific information and from their own observations and investigations.

Use data to construct a reasonable explanation. Students should check their explanations against scientific knowledge, experiences, and observations of others. p. 122

Scientific investigations involve asking and answering a question and comparing the answer with what scientists already know about the world.

Scientists develop explanations using observations (evidence) and what they already know about the world (scientific knowledge). Good explanations are based on evidence from investigations. p. 123

Project 2061, AAAS Benchmarks for Science Literacy

Chapter 1 The Nature of Science
1B Scientific Inquiry

Scientists' explanations about what happens in the world come partly from what they observe, partly from what they think. Sometimes scientists have different explanations for the same set of observations. That usually leads to their making more observations to resolve the differences. p. 11

1C The Scientific Enterprise

In doing science, it is often helpful to work with a team and to share findings with others. All team members should reach their own individual conclusions, however, about what the findings mean. p. 15

Chapter 12 Habits of Mind
12A Values and Attitudes

Raise questions about the world around them and be willing to seek answers to some of them by making careful observations and trying things out. p. 285

12E Critical Response Skills

Seek better reasons for believing something than "Everybody knows that..." or "I just know" and discount such reasons when given by others. p. 299

New York City Performance Standards

S6 Scientific Tools and Technologies

The student demonstrates competence with the tools and technologies of science by using them to collect data, make observations, analyze results, and accomplish tasks effectively; that is, the student:

S6 a Uses technology and tools (such as rulers, computers, balances, thermometers, watches, magnifiers, and microscopes) to gather data and extend the senses.

S6 b Collects and analyzes data using concepts and techniques in Mathematics Standard 4, such as average, data displays, graphing, variability, and sampling.

S6 c Acquires information from multiple sources, such as experimentation and print and non-print sources.

Examples of activities through which students might demonstrate competence with the tools and technologies of science include:

▲ Collect information from the United States Geological Survey and use the information to identify trends in geologic movement in your hometown or state. 6c, 3a, 3c, 5c

▲ Conduct a survey of students' electricity and gas use at home, compare the data to that of other students, and select an appropriate way to display the comparative data. 6b, 2c, 4b

▲ Use telecommunications to compare data on similar investigations with students in another school. 6c

▲ Use electronic data bases to find out about the nutritional value of food available in the cafeteria and compare with alternative selections or snack foods. 6c, 4c

New York State Learning Standards for Math, Science, & Technology

Standard 2 Information Systems

1. Information technology is used to retrieve, process, and communicate information and as a tool to enhance learning.

Students:

use a variety of equipment and software packages to enter, process, display, and communicate information in different forms using text, tables, pictures, and sound. p. 8

Standard 3 Mathematics
Modeling/Multiple Representation

4. Students use mathematical modeling/multiple representation to provide a means of presenting, interpreting, and communicating, and connecting mathematical information and relationships. p. 15

Measurement

5. Students use measurement in both metric and English measure to provide a major link between the abstractions of mathematics and the real world in order to describe and compare objects and data. p. 16

Standard 5 Technology

3. Computers, as tools for design, modeling, information processing, communication, and systems control, have greatly increased human productivity and knowledge. p. 37

Standard 7 Interdisciplinary Problem Solving

2. Solving interdisciplinary problems involves a variety of skills and strategies, including effective work habits; gathering and processing information; generating and analyzing ideas ... p. 60

National Documents which guided New York State and New York City

NRC National Science Education Standards

Standard A Science as Inquiry

Employ simple equipment and tools to gather data and extend the senses. p. 122

Simple instruments, such as magnifiers, thermometers, and rulers, provide more information than scientists obtain using only their senses. p. 123

Project 2061, AAAS Benchmarks for Science Literacy

Chapter 1 The Nature of Science
1B Scientific Inquiry

Tools such as thermometers, magnifiers, rulers, or balances often give more information about things than can be obtained by just observing things without their help. p. 10.

Chapter 12 Habits of Mind
12 C Manipulation and Observation

Measure and mix dry and liquid materials (in the kitchen, garage, or laboratory) in prescribed amounts, exercising reasonable safety. p. 293

New York City Performance Standards

S7 Scientific Communication

The student demonstrates effective scientific communication by clearly describing aspects of the natural world using accurate data, graphs, or other appropriate media to convey depth of conceptual understanding in science; that is, the student:

S7a Represents data and results in multiple ways, such as numbers, tables, and graphs; drawings, diagrams, and artwork; and technical and creative writing.

S7b Uses facts to support conclusions.

S7c Communicates in a form suited to the purpose and the audience, such as writing instructions that others can follow.

S7d Critiques written and oral explanations, and uses data to resolve disagreements.

Examples of activities through which students might demonstrate competence in scientific communication include:

- Write and illustrate a creative story to explain the food chain to a younger brother or sister. 7a, 7c, 2c
- Make a poster of charts and graphs to communicate effective nutrition and health habits. 7a, 2a, 4b
- Work with other students to create a skit depicting the sequence of events and the characters in an important scientific discovery. 7c, 4d
- Prepare a report, with graphs, charts, and diagrams, on the optimal number and placement of recycling containers, based on trash disposal data from the classroom and the entire school. 7a, 4b, 6b, M7, A1b

New York State Learning Standards for Math, Science, & Technology

Standard 1 Analysis, Inquiry, and Design Scientific Inquiry

3. The observations made while testing proposed explanations, when analyzed using conventional and invented methods, provide new insights into phenomena.

Students:

organize observations and measurements of objects and events through classification and the preparation of simple charts and tables. p. 3

National Documents which guided New York State and New York City

NRC National Science Education Standards

Standard A Science as Inquiry

Communicate investigations and explanations. Students should begin developing the abilities to communicate, critique, and analyze their work and the work of others. This communication might be spoken or drawn as well as written. p. 122

Scientists make the results of their investigations public; they describe the investigations in ways that enable others to repeat the investigations.

Scientists review and ask questions about the results of other scientists' work. p. 123

Project 2061, AAAS Benchmarks for Science Literacy

Chapter 1 The Nature of Science
1B Scientific Inquiry

Describing things as accurately as possible is important in science because it enables people to compare their observations with those of others. p. 10

Scientists do not pay much attention to claims about how something they know about works unless the claims are backed up with evidence that can be confirmed and with a logical argument. p. 11

1C The Scientific Enterprise

Clear communication is an essential part of doing science. It enables scientists to inform others about their work, expose their ideas to criticism by other scientists, and stay informed about scientific discoveries around the world. p. 16

Chapter 9 The Mathematical World
9B Symbolic Relationships

Tables and graphs can show how values of one quantity are related to values of another. p. 218

Chapter 12 Habits of Mind
12D Communication Skills

Write instructions that others can follow in carrying out a procedure.

Make sketches to aid in explaining procedures or ideas.

Use numerical data in describing and comparing objects and events. p 296

12E Critical Response Skills

Buttress their statements with facts found in books, articles, and databases, and identify the sources used and expect others to do the same. p. 299

New York City Performance Standards

S8 Scientific Investigation

The student demonstrates scientific competence by completing projects drawn from the following kinds of investigations, including at least one full investigation each year and, over the course of elementary school, investigations that integrate several aspects of Science Standards 1 to 7 and represent all four of the kinds of investigation:

S8a An experiment, such as conducting a fair test.

S8b A systematic observation, such as a field study.

S8c A design, such as building a model or scientific apparatus.

S8d Non-experimental research using print and electronic information, such as journals, video, or computers.

A single project may draw on more than one kind of investigation.

A full investigation includes:

• Questions that can be studied using the resources available.

• Procedures that are safe, humane, and ethical; and that respect privacy and property rights.

• Data that have been collected and recorded (see also Science Standard 6) in ways that others can verify and analyze using skills expected at this grade level (see also Mathematics Standard 4).

• Data and results that have been represented (see also Science Standard 7) in ways that fit the context.

• Recommendations, decisions, and conclusions based on evidence.

• Acknowledgment of references and contributions of others.

• Results that are communicated appropriately to audiences.

• Reflection and defense of conclusions and recommendations from other sources and peer review.

Examples of projects through which students might demonstrate competence in scientific investigation include:

▲ Design, make, and fly kites; modifying the kites so they fly higher, maneuver more easily, or achieve some other goal. 8a, 8c

▲ Investigate why different plants live in the cracks of the sidewalk in different areas around the school. 8b, 2a

▲ Design and build a Rube Goldberg device and explain how changing aspects of the design made it work better. 8c, 4b

▲ Research a particular disease; compare local with national risk factors; and produce an information pamphlet that communicates the characteristics and risk associated with the disease. 8d, 4c

▲ Make a series of drawings and explain the seasonal succession of plants in a field near the school. 8d, 2b

▲ With a partner, select an endangered plant or animal in your area; collect information from reference books, magazines, video; debate whether the plant or animal should be saved or allowed to disappear, and why. 8d, 2c, 6c

New York State Learning Standards for Math, Science, & Technology

Standard 1 Analysis, Inquiry, and Design
Scientific Inquiry

1. The central purpose of scientific inquiry is to develop explanations of natural phenomena in a continuing, creative process.

2. Beyond the use of reasoning and consensus, scientific inquiry involves the testing of proposed explanations involving the use of conventional techniques and procedures and usually requiring considerable ingenuity. p. 2

3. The observations made while testing proposed explanations, when analyzed using conventional and invented methods, provide new insights into phenomena. p. 3

Engineering Design

1. Engineering design is an iterative process involving modeling and optimization finding the best solution within given constraints which is used to develop technological solutions to problems within given constraints. p. 3

National Documents which guided New York State and New York City

NRC National Science Education Standards

Standard A Science as Inquiry

Plan and conduct a simple investigation. In the earliest years, investigations are largely based on systematic observations. As students develop, they may design and conduct simple experiments to answer questions. The idea of a fair test is possible for many students to consider by fourth grade. p. 122

Scientists use different kinds of investigations depending on the questions they are trying to answer. Types of investigations include describing objects, events, and organisms, classifying them and doing a fair test (experimenting). p. 123

Standard E Science and Technology

Identify a simple problem.

Propose a solution.

Implementing proposed solutions.

Evaluate a product or design.

Communicate a problem, design, and solution. pp. 137-138.

Project 2061, AAAS Benchmarks for Science Literacy

Chapter 1 The Nature of Science
1B Scientific Inquiry

Scientific investigations may take many different forms, including observing what things are like or what is happening somewhere, collecting specimens for analysis, and doing experiments. Investigations can focus on physical, biological, and social questions. p. 11

Chapter 3 The Nature of Technology
3B Design and Systems

There is no perfect design. Designs that are best in one respect (safety or ease of use, for example) may be inferior in other ways (cost or appearance). Usually some features must be sacrificed to get others. How such trade-offs are received depends on which features are emphasized and which are down-played. p. 49

Chapter 12 Habits of Mind
12E Critical Response Skills

Recognize when comparisons might not be fair because some conditions are not kept the same. p. 299

Work Sample & Commentary: *Light or Dark?*

Physical
Sciences
Concepts **S1**

Life
Sciences
Concepts

Earth and
Space Sciences
Concepts

Scientific
Connections and **S4**
Applications

Scientific
Thinking **S5**

Scientific Tools
and **S6**
Technologies

Scientific
Communication **S7**

Scientific
Investigation

The quotations from the
Science performance
descriptions in this com-
mentary are excerpted.
The complete perfor-
mance descriptions are
shown on pages
18-32.

The task

Student teams compared the absorption of solar
energy by light and dark surfaces. Students performed an initial procedure and then followed it
with two experiments, changing one variable in
each experiment. Data were collected and recorded
on table matrices provided by the publisher of this
particular investigation.

Circumstances of performance

This sample of student work was produced under
the following conditions:

alone

√ in class

√ with teacher feedback

timed

√ in a group

as homework

√ with peer feedback

√ opportunity for
revision

What the work shows

S1c Physical Sciences Concepts: The student
produces evidence that demonstrates understanding of light, heat...such as the variation of
heat and temperature....

A The student collected and recorded data
showing variations in temperature.

B The student interprets the data in terms of
temperature increase.

C The student makes a prediction based on the
data interpretation.

**This work sample illustrates a standard-setting
performance for the following
parts of the standards:**

S1c **Physical Sciences Concepts: Light, heat, electricity,
and magnetism.**

S4a **Scientific Connections and Applications: Big ideas
and unifying concepts.**

S5b **Scientific Thinking: Use concepts from Standards
1 to 4.**

S6a **Scientific Tools and Technologies: Use technology
and tools.**

S7a **Scientific Communication: Represent data and
results in multiple ways.**

Name _____

Energy Sources
Section 5 • Chapter 16

A.
◆ Add a tumblerful of water to each tray.
◆ Pour the water all over the tray.
◆ Put the trays out in the sun for 30 minutes.

Record
starting
time:

11.10

Record
ending
time:

11:40

A

	Starting temperature	Final temperature	Change in temperature
Open black tray	25°C	26°C	+1°C
Closed black tray	25°C	37°C	+12°C
Closed white tray	25°C	30°C	+5°C

B.
◆ Describe what your team found out.

My team found that all of the trays (Open black tray, closed
black tray and a closed white tray) showed an increase in
temperature. It also showed that a covered black tray absorbs
more heat than the other trays. The uncovered tray had the lowest increase in temperature.

C.
◆ Suppose you put water into an open white tray and leave it out in the sun for 30 minutes. What
do you think will happen to the water temperature?

I think the water temperature will stay the same because
the opened black tray only went up 1°C and white reflects
the suns rays.

SCIS3+ © 1998 Delta Education, Inc. Permission granted to purchaser to photocopy for classroom use

39

Name _____

Energy Sources
Section 5 • Chapter 17

A. How does the amount of water in a tray affect the rise in temperature?
◆ Everyone will use covered black trays.
◆ All trays will be left out for 30 minutes.
◆ The amount of water in each tray will be different.

starting time _____

ending time _____

E

Amount of water	Starting temperature	Final temperature	Temperature change
½ tumbler	26°C	38°C	+12°C
1 tumbler	26°C	40°C	+14°C
1½ tumblers	26°C	39°C	+13°C
2 tumblers	26°C	38°C	+12°C

B.
◆ Make a graph of the results for your team. **F**

(graph: Temperature change (°C) vs Amount of water in tumblers)

◆ What variables were not changed in this experiment? Every one used covered
black trays for the experiment and all of the water
stayed out for the same amount of time.

SCIS3+

40 © 1998 Delta Education, Inc. Permission granted to purchaser to photocopy for classroom use

Reproduced by permission. *SCIS3* Chapter 16, Section 5, Energy Sources, "Transferring Solar Energy to Water". Delta Education, Inc., 80 Northwest Blvd., Nashua, NH 03060.

Light or Dark?

S4a Scientific Connections and Applications: The student produces evidence that demonstrates understanding of big ideas and unifying concepts such as...cause and effect.

C The student recognizes the causal relationship between color of materials and the amount of change in temperature in the presence of sunlight.

D In the conclusion, the student correctly applies the causal relationship noted in C.

S5b Scientific Thinking: The student uses concepts from Science Standards 1 to 4 to explain a variety of observations and phenomena.

D The student applied understanding of the concept of heat variation from S1c by explaining "that light trays reflect the sunlight and the black trays don't reflect the sunlight." The student's confidence in his/her understanding of the concept is evident in the use of the words, "I know this is true...."

S6a Scientific Tools and Technologies: The student uses technology and tools (such as...thermometers...) to gather data and extend the senses.

A E The work clearly illustrates use of the thermometers and watches as tools to gather data.

S7a Scientific Communication: The student represents data and results in multiple ways, such as numbers, tables, and graphs...and technical and creative writing.

A E F G H The student presents data in charts and line graphs, and uses narrative writing to describe outcomes and conclusions. Note that in F and H, the student begins each line graph at 0°. The student needs some minor assistance to understand how to record the initial data on a line graph. However, recordings after the initial one on each graph are correct.

Name _____

Energy Sources
Section 5 • Chapter 17

A.
◆ How does changing the time affect the temperature of the water?
◆ Everyone will use covered black trays.
◆ All trays will be filled with 1 tumblerful of water.
◆ The time you leave your trays out will be different.

Time left out	Starting temperature	Final temperature	Temperature change
15 minutes	25 °C	28 °C	+ 3 °C
30 minutes	25 °C	30 °C	+ 5 °C
45 minutes	25 °C	35 °C	+ 10 °C
60 minutes (optional)			
90 minutes (optional)			
120 minutes (optional)			

B.
◆ Make a graph of the results for your team.

◆ What variables were not changed in this experiment? We used black covered trays and all of them were filled with 1 tumbler of water.

SCIS3+
© 1998 Delta Education, Inc. Permission granted to purchaser to photocopy for classroom use.

41

NAME _____

WHITE CARS OR DARK CARS?

Suppose a friend is moving to southern Arizona or Florida. On the basis of the evidence from the experiments with the solar trays, what color car would you advise him or her to buy?

D I would tell my friend to buy a white car because it would reflect the sunlight. I know this is true because I learned during our experiments with the trays that light trays reflect the sunlight and the black trays dont reflect the sunlight. If I were to do another experiment I would test different types of cloth to see if the same was true for clothing.

Work Sample & Commentary: *The Come Back Can*

Physical Sciences Concepts **S1**

Life Sciences Concepts

Earth and Space Sciences Concepts

Scientific Connections and Applications **S4**

Scientific Thinking **S5**

Scientific Tools and Technologies

Scientific Communication **S7**

Scientific Investigation

For related work on Force and Motion, see "Mechanical Nut", page 86, and "Challenger", page 153.

The quotations from the Science performance descriptions in this commentary are excerpted. The complete performance descriptions are shown on pages 18-32.

The task

Students were instructed to construct several model energy cans. After constructing the original model can, students were asked to make a change in the design of the can that would affect its performance (e.g., different rubber band, different mass suspended from the rubber band, different size of can). The task calls for the student to design and carry out the task; to compare and contrast the behavior of the original and the modified can; and to describe the effect of the changed variable. Within this explanation, the student needed to demonstrate an understanding of potential and kinetic energy.

Circumstances of performance

This sample of student work was produced under the following conditions:

alone	√ in a group
√ in class	as homework
√ with teacher feedback	√ with peer feedback
timed	√ opportunity for revision

What the work shows

S1a **Physical Sciences Concepts:** The student produces evidence that demonstrates understanding of properties of objects and materials, such as similarities and differences in the size, weight...of objects....

Ⓐ The student observed, "The sinkers twist the rubber band when you push it away from you. The rubber band, as it is twisted, contains the stored or potential energy." This observation demonstrates an

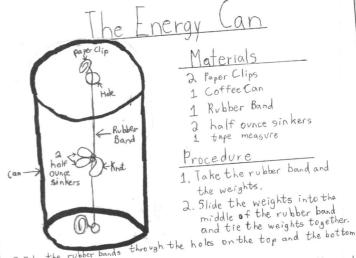

> # The Energy Can
>
> Paper clip
> Hole
> Rubber Band
> Can
> 2 half ounce sinkers
> Knot
>
> ## Materials
> 2 Paper Clips
> 1 Coffee Can
> 1 Rubber Band
> 2 half ounce sinkers
> 1 tape measure
>
> ## Procedure
> 1. Take the rubber band and the weights.
> 2. Slide the weights into the middle of the rubber band and tie the weights together.
> 3. Poke the rubber bands through the holes on the top and the bottom of the can.
> 4. Slide a paperclip into the rubber band. do the same to the other side.
> 5. Now test it. Will the can roll back?
>
> ## Explanation of Results
> Ⓐ The sinkers twist the rubber band when you push it away from you. The rubber band, as it is twisted, contains the stored or potential energy. The potential energy is going to turn into kinetic energy as it is twisted backwards. The force moves it backwards.
>
> Roll Back Result: <u>404 centimeters or 160 inches</u>

This work sample illustrates a standard-setting performance for the following parts of the standards:

S1a **Physical Sciences Concepts: Properties of objects and materials.**

S1b **Physical Sciences Concepts: Position and motion of objects.**

S4a **Scientific Connections and Applications: Big ideas and unifying concepts.**

S5b **Scientific Thinking: Use concepts from Science Standards 1 to 4.**

S7a **Scientific Communication: Represent data and results in multiple ways.**

S7b **Scientific Communication: Use facts to support conclusions.**

understanding of properties of the sinker (weight) and the rubber band (elasticity).

Ⓑ The student noted a difference in the size of the sinker.

Ⓒ The student hypothesized that the heavier weight will work better because "...the rubber band will store more potential energy." This indicates an understanding of the differences in weight and the effect of increasing the weight.

Ⓓ The student stated that the rubber band did not store the potential energy because the heavier weight did not allow the rubber band to twist, indicating an understanding of the property of weight.

S1b **Physical Sciences Concepts:** The student produces evidence that demonstrates understanding of position and motion of objects....

Ⓐ The student observed, "The sinkers twist the rubber band when you push it away from you. The rubber band, as it is twisted, contains the stored or potential energy." This explanation indicates an understanding that the positions and motions of objects can be changed by pushing or pulling.

The Come Back Can

S1 Physical Sciences Concepts

Life Sciences Concepts

Earth and Space Sciences Concepts

S4 Scientific Connections and Applications

S5 Scientific Thinking

Scientific Tools and Technologies

S7 Scientific Communication

Scientific Investigation

C The student hypothesized that the heavier weight "will work because it will store more potential energy." Although the student's use of the word "it" leaves the object unclear (clarified later), it is apparent that the student grasps the relationship between potential energy and motion.

D The student implied that the heavier weight did not impel the can further, as hypothesized. The student stated that the rubber band did not store potential energy because of the effect of the weight. These statements indicate understanding of the cause and effect relationship between the weight, the rubber band, and the motion (or lack thereof) of the can.

E The student suggests tightening the rubber band in order to store more potential energy, once again indicating an understanding of the relationship between the weight, the rubber band, and the motion of the can.

S4a Scientific Connections and Applications: The student produces evidence that demonstrates understanding of big ideas and unifying concepts, such as...cause and effect.

D The statement concerning the effect of the weight on the rubber band is evidence of a specific understanding of cause and effect.

E The student's "remedy" is distinguished by the informed judgment that another variable, tightness of the rubber band, needs to be changed, evidence of a specific understanding of cause and effect.

S5b Scientific Thinking: The student uses concepts from Science Standards 1 to 4 to explain a variety of observations and phenomena....

A C D The student presents several applications of **S1**b (position and motion of objects).

S7a Scientific Communication: The student represents data and results in multiple ways, such as...drawings, diagrams...and technical writing.

B C D E Writing and diagrams are significantly clearer in the recording of the second procedure.

S7b Scientific Communication: The student uses facts to support conclusions.

A The student accurately uses facts related to position and motion of objects in the statements concerning the effects of the sinkers on the rubber band.

The Energy Can Part II

The Change in Materials

B I had the same can and the same rubber band plus the same paper clips. I changed the weight to a 2 ounce heavy sinker.

C Hypothesis

I think it will roll back more. I think it will work because the rubber band will store more potential energy, because of the additional weight.

Procedure

1. Take the rubber band and weight. Slide the weight into the center of the rubber band and tie it.

2. Poke the rubber band into the 2 holes and slide each paper clip onto each loop on the rubber band.

D Explanation of Results

The can did not come back. The different weight matters because the rubber band doesn't really support the 2 ounce weight and the weight hangs down on the bottom and doesn't really twist the rubber band to store the potential energy. The potential energy in the other can quickly turned into kinetic energy because it was half the weight in the can.

E Remedy

You need to tighten the rubber band to make the 2 ounce heavy sinker come up instead of dragging down on the bottom. I tested it and it worked almost as good as the original can.

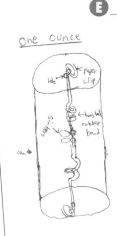

one ounce

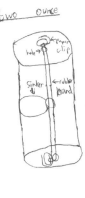

two ounce

Roll Back Result with a tightened rubber band:

392 centimeters or 155 inches

Work Sample & Commentary: *Pendulum*

Physical Sciences Concepts **S1**

Life Sciences Concepts

Earth and Space Sciences Concepts

Scientific Connections and Applications **S4**

Scientific Thinking **S5**

Scientific Tools and Technologies **S6**

Scientific Communication **S7**

Scientific Investigation **S8**

For related work on Pendula, see "Pendulum Experiment", page 144.

The quotations from the Science performance descriptions in this commentary are excerpted. The complete performance descriptions are shown on pages 18-32.

The task

Student teams made pendulums and were asked to hypothesize about how to increase the number of swings during a given period of time (15 seconds). Students tested their hypotheses, collected data, and presented the data in the form of written reports.

Circumstances of performance

This sample of student work was produced under the following conditions:

√ alone   √ in a group

√ in class   √ as homework

  with teacher feedback   with peer feedback

  timed   opportunity for revision

What the work shows

S1a Physical Sciences Concepts: The student produces evidence that demonstrates understanding of properties of objects and materials, such as similarities and differences in the size [and] weight...of objects....

A **B** The student describes how changing the properties of the system affected the data. In changing the variables of weight and string length and by describing the effects of those changes, the student demonstrates an understanding of those properties.

G <u>Pendulums</u>

In science class we made pendulums. The materials were string, a penny, tape and a pen or pencil. First we taped the pen or pencil to the desk. After that we made a loop a little bit bigger than the pen or pencil. Then we tied a paper clip to the other end of the string. We finally put the penny in the clip.

H We then timed our pendulums to see how many swings it made. One full swing was back and forth.

After that we wanted to find out how the pendulum would go faster. One variable was the **F** release position. We tried a 45°, 90° (desk height), and 135° angle. We recorded the data. This **C** variable did not make a difference. All of the positions made my pendulum swing 14 times in 15 seconds.

A We tried another variable. It was the weight of the pendulum. Instead of one penny, we put two in the clip. It turned out that this variable didn't change the number of swings.

This work sample illustrates a standard-setting performance for the following parts of the standards:

S1a **Physical Sciences Concepts: Properties of objects and materials.**

S1b **Physical Sciences Concepts: Position and motion of objects.**

S4a **Scientific Connections and Applications: Big ideas and unifying concepts.**

S5f **Scientific Thinking: Work individually and in teams.**

S6a **Scientific Tools and Technologies: Use technology and tools.**

S7a **Scientific Communication: Represent data and results in multiple ways.**

S7c **Scientific Communication: Communicate in a form suited to the purpose and the audience.**

S8a **Scientific Investigation: An experiment.**

S1b Physical Sciences Concepts: The student produces evidence that demonstrates understanding of position and motion of objects, such as how the motion of an object can be described by measuring its position over time....

C The student's observation about the consistent number of swings (oscillations) over the same period of time clearly meets the standard.

D The student demonstrates an understanding of position over time when comparing the effects of long and short strings on the number of swings.

S4a Scientific Connections and Applications: The student produces evidence that demonstrates understanding of big ideas and unifying concepts, such as...cause and effect.

E The student clearly understands the causal relationship between the length of the string and the number of swings. (The substitution of "effect" for "affect," a minor error that occurs in two places, should be corrected in a revision.)

Pendulum

S1 ▸ Physical Sciences Concepts

Life Sciences Concepts

Earth and Space Sciences Concepts

S4 ▸ Scientific Connections and Applications

S5 ▸ Scientific Thinking

S6 ▸ Scientific Tools and Technologies

S7 ▸ Scientific Communication

S8 ▸ Scientific Investigation

S5f Scientific Thinking: The student works individually and in teams to collect and share information and ideas.

A **B** **F** The use of the word "we" throughout the work indicates that the student worked in a group.

G The entire written report is an individual effort.

S6a Scientific Tools and Technologies: The student uses technology and tools (such as rulers,…watches) to gather data and extend the senses.

Although the student neglects to mention these tools, it is evident from the description of the procedure that the student used a centimeter ruler **B**, a protractor **F**, and a watch **H**.

S7a Scientific Communication: The student represents data and results in multiple ways, such as numbers, tables, and graphs;…and technical and creative writing.

G **I** **J** The entire narrative is well-written and accurately describes the investigation. The student represents data in both table and graph formats. By convention, the dependent variable, number of swings, would be plotted on the y-axis, and the independent variable, length of string, would be plotted on the x-axis. This is not necessarily expected of elementary students.

S7c Scientific Communication: The student communicates in a form suited to the purpose and the audience, such as writing instructions that others can follow.

G Other students could easily replicate the investigation by following the procedure described in the narrative.

S8a Scientific Investigation: The student demonstrates scientific competence by completing…an experiment, such as conducting a fair test.

G This work sample is evidence that the student conducted a fair test. Each of three variables was tested separately to determine which variable affected the speed (period of oscillation) of the pendulum.

B We finally tried the length of the string. We measured our first pendulum. (43cm). Then we made a smaller (20cm) and a larger (60cm) pendulum. We finally found out our answer. The length of the string effects the number of swings. **E**

D It turned out that my hypothesis was right. I guessed it would effect the number of swings because a long string would have a very wide swing. A little size string would move much faster because it does not have a wide swing.

I

Length of String	# of swings
20 cm	19
43 cm	12
60 cm	10

J

CENTIMETRE GRAPH PAPER

My Pendulum's Progress of Swings

Length of String (in cm) — Number of Swings

Work Sample & Commentary: *Acid/Base*

Physical Sciences Concepts **S1**

Life Sciences Concepts

Earth and Space Sciences Concepts

Scientific Connections and Applications **S4**

Scientific Thinking **S5**

Scientific Tools and Technologies **S6**

Scientific Communication **S7**

Scientific Investigation

For related work on Acids and Bases, see "Acid Rain", page 89, and "Buffer Lab", page 156.

The quotations from the Science performance descriptions in this commentary are excerpted. The complete performance descriptions are shown on pages 18-32.

The task

As an assessment of prior investigations working with red cabbage juice as an indicator, the teacher asked students to see what would happen when they blew through a straw with BTB (bromthymol blue) solution. Students were given BTB, water, cups, and straws. They designed and recorded their own procedures and observations and were asked to explain what happened. When they were done, they conducted a further exploration with vinegar and BTB solution to test their initial conclusion that the color change of BTB from blue to yellow indicated the presence of an acid.

Circumstances of performance

This sample of student work was produced under the following conditions:

alone	√ in a group
√ in class	as homework
√ with teacher feedback	√ with peer feedback
timed	√ opportunity for revision

The students were asked to re-write steps 8, 9, and 10 of their original procedure as a second experiment.

What the work shows

S1a Physical Sciences Concepts: The student produces evidence that demonstrates understanding of properties of objects and materials, such as similarities and differences in...color...[and] the ability of materials to react with other substances....

This work sample illustrates a standard-setting performance for the following parts of the standards:

S1a **Physical Sciences Concepts: Properties of objects and materials.**

S4a **Scientific Connections and Applications: Big ideas and unifying concepts.**

S5b **Scientific Thinking: Use concepts to explain observations.**

S5e **Scientific Thinking: Identify problems, propose and implement solutions, and evaluate the accuracy, design, and outcomes of investigations.**

S6a **Scientific Tools and Technologies: Use technologies and tools.**

S7a **Scientific Communication: Represent data and results in multiple ways.**

S7c **Scientific Communication: Communicate in a form suited to the purpose and audience.**

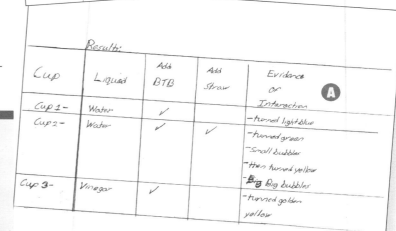

Materials: 3 cups, BTB, water, straw, vinegar, goggles

Procedure
1. We got the materials.
2. We labelled the cups - 1. BTB and water, 2. straw, BTB, water.
3. We put 5 mls. of water into cup1, then 5 mls. of water into cup2.
4. Our group member put the goggles on.
5. We put 10 drops of BTB into cup1 then into cup2.
6. After that one group member put the straw into cup2, then put it near his mouth and blew into the straw.
7. Next we observed what happened.
8. We got another cup labelled 3 BTB and vinegar.
9. We got the vinegar bottle and poured 5 mls. into the cup.
10. And then after we observed it.

Cup	Liquid	Add BTB	Add Straw	Evidence of Interaction	**A**
Cup 1 -	Water	√		-turned light blue	
Cup 2 -	Water	√	√	-turned green, -small bubbles, -then turned yellow	
Cup 3 -	Vinegar	√		-big bubbles, -turned golden yellow	

Results:

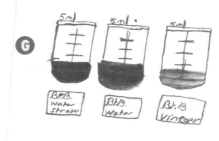

Acid/Base

S1 Physical Sciences Concepts

Life Sciences Concepts

Earth and Space Sciences Concepts

S4 Scientific Connections and Applications

S5 Scientific Thinking

Scientific Tools and Technologies

S6

S7 Scientific Communication

Scientific Investigation

A The data table indicates recognition of a change of color and the ability of materials to react with different substances.

B In the conclusion, the students state, "The color of the liquid changed, so there was a chemical change."

C In light of **B**, the students' connection of color change to acid/base determination is evidence of an understanding that a chemical reaction has occurred between the materials.

S4a Scientific Connections and Applications: The student produces evidence that demonstrates understanding of big ideas and unifying concepts, such as…cause and effect.

C **D** The students recognized that the color change was caused by the addition of certain chemicals and that similar chemicals will have similar effects.

S5b Scientific Thinking: The student uses concepts from Science Standards 1 to 4 to explain…observations and phenomena.

C **D** The students applied an understanding of **S1**a, properties of objects and materials, and **S4**a, cause and effect, to explain the results of the experiment.

S5e Scientific Thinking: The student identifies problems, proposes and implements solutions, and evaluates the accuracy, design, and outcomes of investigations.

E The students developed another experiment, hypothesized, and evaluated the outcome based on previous knowledge and the results of both experiments.

S6a Scientific Tools and Technologies: The student uses tools…to gather data.

E Use of the BTB in the students' follow-up experiment is evidence of accurate use of BTB as a tool.

F "…the BTB was an indicator…" demonstrates understanding that indicators can be used to detect acids and bases.

S7a Scientific Communication: The student represents data and results in multiple ways, such as…tables…drawings, diagrams, and art work.

A **G** Both the table and the student's color diagram clearly show the results of the experiment.

S7c Scientific Communication: The student communicates in a form suited to the purpose and audience, such as writing instructions that others can follow.

A **B** **D** **F** Throughout the work, appropriate scientific vocabulary is applied, such as accurate use of "interaction", "chemical change", "exhaled", "carbon dioxide", and "indicator".

E The procedure in the students' follow-up experiment clearly describes the steps of the experiment in a way that would allow replication by another elementary student.

Conclusion

First, when we observed Cup 1, there was a little change in color. Then when we observed Cup 2, the color of the liquid changed, so there was a chemical change. **B**

F We thought that the BTB was an indicator because the liquid that the BTB was in changed colors just like the cabbage juice did to the lemon juice, vinegar, seltzer, and the detergent.

We wanted to find out if it was an acid or a base so, we put the vinegar and BTB together to see if it would change colors just like it did with the cabbage juice. It turned golden yellow. **C**

D Cup 2 - water, BTB, and straw, and air that my group members exhaled called Carbon Dioxide. I had almost the same property as the vinegar and BTB. They were similar colors of yellow. The vinegar is an acid so the air is an acid to.

E

We wanted to find out if it was an acid or a base. So we did another experiment.

Problem: Is breath an acid or base?

Hypothesis: If we add BTB to vinegar, then it might change color like cup two.

Materials: Cup 2, 1 cup, BTB, vinegar.

Procedure: 1. We got the materials.
2. We labelled the cup - Cup 3
3. We put 5 mls. of vinegar into cup 3.
4. Our group member put the goggles on.
5. A group member put 10 drops of BTB into cup 3.
6. After that, we observed cup 3.
7. We compared cup 2 to cup 3.

Results: Cup 3 turned golden yellow. Cup 2 was yellow and had big bubbles.

Work Sample & Commentary: *Flinkers*

Physical
Sciences
Concepts **S1**

Life
Sciences
Concepts

Earth and
Space Sciences
Concepts

Scientific
Connections and
Applications

Scientific
Thinking

Scientific Tools
and
Technologies

Scientific
Communication

Scientific
Investigation

For related work on
Density, see
"Discovering Density",
page 93, "Density of
Sand", page 169, and
"Density", page 173.

The quotations from the
Science performance
descriptions in this com-
mentary are excerpted.
The complete perfor-
mance descriptions are
shown on pages
18-32.

The task

Students were instructed to complete a laboratory activity in which they adjusted the
mass and/or the volume of an object so that
the object would not float on top of water or
sink…it would "flink."

The task calls for the student to explore the
range of available floating and sinking objects.
In order to accomplish the task, it is necessary
to combine floating and sinking objects to construct one of the correct density.

Circumstances of performance

This sample of student work was produced
under the following conditions:

alone	√ in a group
in class	√ as homework
with teacher feedback	with peer feedback
timed	opportunity for revision

What the work shows

S1a Physical Sciences Concepts: The student produces evidence that demonstrates understanding of
properties of objects and materials, such as similarities and differences in the size, weight, and color
of objects….

The drawings provide evidence of sorting objects
by observable properties and representing the findings.

A The students sorted common objects into those
that floated and those that sank and recorded their
findings.

B They used trial and error to find combinations
that were neutrally buoyant (that "flinked") and
drew the results.

The written summary provides evidence of conceptual understanding of density, an observable and measurable property of objects and materials.

SCIENCE ENTRY SLIP
Your name_____

Date work was completed _Feb. 6_
Date work placed in portfolio _Feb 6_

What was the assignment? (Attach a copy if possible)
To get the mass and volume of an object to equal 1 so it wouldn't float or sink, it would flink.

Is this part of a long-term investigation or a shorter task?
A short task.

Who selected this piece of work?

What tools or resources did you use? How much feedback or help did you get from your teacher or other adults?
We used things from home that would float and others that sank and put them together just right. My partners mom helped us try out different combinations.

Did you work alone or with a group?
I worked with a partner.

What do you want the reader to notice about this work? Why did you select this piece of work?
That it took determination and patience to get an object to flink, but it was also fun.

What were the important scientific ideas in this task?
To learn about floating, sinking, and density.

C The statement, "To make something flink, the
mass and volume had to equal one," is acceptable for
the elementary school level. At the middle school
level, one would expect the student to discuss density
in terms of a ratio; for example, "To make something
flink, the ratio of the mass and the volume had to
equal one," or "To make something flink, the mass
divided by the volume had to equal one." Further,
and although this is perhaps taken for granted, an
adequate middle school response would make explicit the density of water, which equals one.

**This work sample illustrates a standard-setting
performance for the following
part of the standards:**

S1a **Physical Sciences Concepts: Properties of objects
and materials.**

Flinkers

S1 Physical Sciences Concepts

Life Sciences Concepts

Earth and Space Sciences Concepts

Scientific Connections and Applications

Scientific Thinking

Scientific Tools and Technologies

Scientific Communication

Scientific Investigation

D Additional evidence of understanding the concept of density is provided in this sentence which says that the addition of mass changes the buoyancy of the object.

E The final sentence completes the summary with reference to observable properties.

This work is an unrevised piece of homework. There are three spelling errors ("prosess," "absorbe," and "detirmination") and a missing apostrophe ("partners").

Work Sample & Commentary: *Bean Farmers*

Physical
Sciences
Concepts

Life
Sciences
Concepts **S2**

Earth and
Space Sciences
Concepts

Scientific
Connections and
Applications

Scientific
Thinking **S5**

Scientific Tools
and
Technologies **S6**

Scientific
Communication **S7**

Scientific
Investigation **S8**

For related work on
Response to Environment,
see "Water Tolerance",
page 50, "Toasted
Bread", page 54,
"Snails", page 104, and
"Endocrine Feedback
Exercise ", page 183.

The quotations from the
Science performance
descriptions in this com-
mentary are excerpted.
The complete perfor-
mance descriptions are
shown on pages
18-32.

The task

A fourth grade class designed a controlled
experiment, under the guidance of their science cluster teacher, to compare and contrast
the structures and growth of six different varieties of bean plants during the plants' life
cycles. The students were asked to select two
of the varieties and to determine which of the
two they would want to plant, if they were
farmers, and why. Each student was given an
individual opportunity during science class to
observe the plants by using magnifying lenses
and to take measurements using string and
rulers. Each student kept a log of findings and
wrote a conclusion based on them.

Circumstances of performance

This sample of student work was produced
under the following conditions:

√ alone   in a group

√ in class   as homework

   with teacher feedback   with peer feedback

   timed   opportunity for
                  revision

What the work shows

S2 b Life Sciences Concepts: The student produces
evidence that demonstrates understanding of life
cycles of organisms...and that all plants and animals have life cycles.

A The student began the documentation of the
bean plant life cycle with a drawing of the germination of five seeds.

**This work sample illustrates a standard-setting
performance for the following
parts of the standards:**

S2 b   **Life Sciences Concepts: Life cycles of organisms.**

S5 b   **Scientific Thinking: Use concepts to explain observations.**

S6 a   **Scientific Tools and Technologies: Use technology
and tools.**

S7 a   **Scientific Communication: Represent data and
results in multiple ways.**

S7 b   **Scientific Communication: Use facts to support
conclusions.**

S7 c   **Scientific Communication: Communicate in a form
suited to audience and purpose.**

S8 a   **Scientific Investigation: An experiment, such as a
fair test.**

The Bean Farmer's Experiment

Which bean seed is best to plant

Problem: because it will produce the hardiest
plant and the most beans?

Hypothesis: I think the Bush Bean plant will
be the hardiest and produce the most seeds
because the seed is bigger to begin with.

Materials: 5 Bush Bean seeds, 5 Kidney Bean seeds, 2 clear
cups, rulers, magnifying lens, plastic pea fence, two
bamboo stakes, string, twist ties, crayons, drawing
paper, log paper, pots, and soil

I Procedure: 1. Crumple 2 paper towels and put
them in a clear cup.
2. Add water to make the towels damp.
3. Place five Kidney Beans halfway down
the cup between the cup and the paper towels.
4. Repeat for the Bush Beans.
J 5. Keep moist-out of the light. Check each
day. Fill in the log every few days, as needed.
6. When leaves appear, move to a sunny location. 7. Plant the seedlings in soil when
the plant is established. 8. Add support when the
plants get tall. Fill two pots with moist soil.
Put a bamboo pole in each pot. Attach pea fence
between the poles. Secure the fence with twist ties.
Place the bean plants next to the fence.
9. When the plants produce beans, germinate them
starting back at #1. of this procedure.

Observation: See log entries

B Understanding of a subsequent stage in the bean
plant life cycle is demonstrated in the entry for
9/25/98 in both the labeled diagram and in the word-
ing: "Three [of the initial five seeds] are now
seedlings."

C Evidence of understanding of other life cycle
stages is found in the conclusion. The student notes
that the bush bean plants produced more flowers and
pods than the kidney bean plants did. The student
clearly understands that pods produce beans. The
student also uses the term "life cycle" in a correct
comparison based on observations.

S5 b Scientific Thinking: The student uses concepts
from Science Standards 1 to 4 to explain a variety of
observations and phenomena.

C The student's conclusion applies concepts
from **S2 b**.

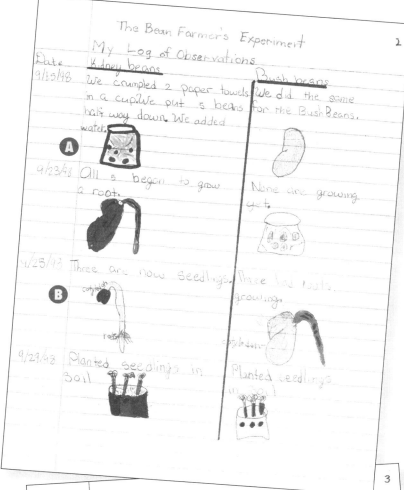

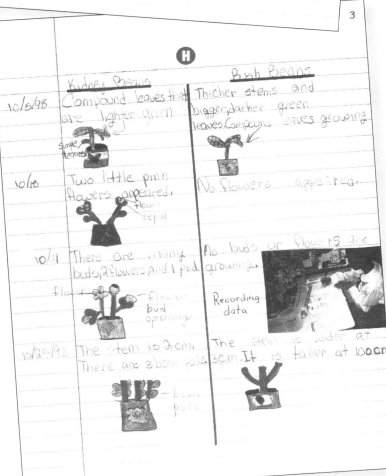

S6a Scientific Tools and Technologies: The student uses…tools (such as rulers,…magnifiers) to gather data and extend the senses.

D In the 11/2/98 entry, the measurements for pod length and width are recorded next to a diagram of the bean pods. The student used a metric ruler to measure lengths and widths of pods.

E F The student measured and recorded plant height and circumference using a metric ruler and string.

G The student used a magnifying lens to examine the structures of the flowers and the emergent pods.

S7a Scientific Communication: The student represents data and results in multiple ways, such as…drawings, diagrams, and artwork, and…technical writing.

D The student used a labeled drawing to communicate measurement of the bean pods and used two sentences to convey these observations.

H In all of the entries from 10/5/98 through 10/27/98, the student used labeled drawings in brief log entries to illustrate understanding of differences between compound and simple leaves and to note the development of flowers and pods.

S7b Scientific Communication: The student uses facts to support conclusions.

A B D G H Observations and data recorded in the log kept over the course of the experiment support the conclusion.

C The student observed that the bush beans produced the greater number of flowers. To arrive at the conclusion, the student combined this fact with an understanding, explicitly indicated in the conclusion, that bean flowers produce bean pods and pods produce seeds.

S7c Scientific Communication: The student communicates in a form suited to the purpose and the audience, such as writing instructions that others can follow.

I The work includes a step-by-step procedure that would allow for replication of the experiment by another elementary student.

S8a Scientific Investigation: The student demonstrates scientific competence by…an experiment, such as conducting a fair test.

J The procedure indicates that all factors were kept the same in the germination and growth of the two kinds of bean plants. In the conclusion, the student cites observations of differences in the relative hardiness of the plants that resulted from the procedure.

Bean Farmers

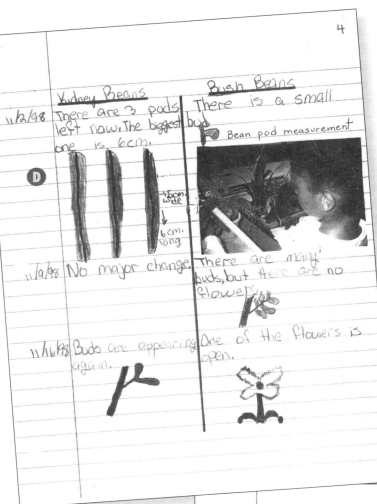

Page 4

Kidney Beans | **Bush Beans**

D 11/2/98 There are 3 pods left now. The biggest one is 6cm.

There is a small bud.

Bean pod measurement

→5cm wide
↓ 6cm. long

11/9/98 No major change.

There are many buds, but there are no flowers.

11/16/98 Buds are appearing again.

One of the flowers is open.

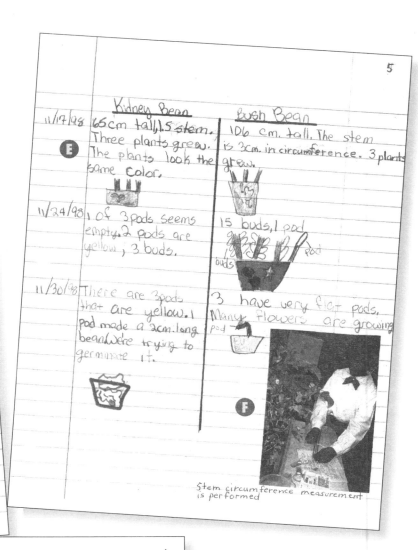

Page 5

Kidney Bean | **Bush Bean**

E 11/17/98 65cm tall, 1.5 stem. Three plants grew. The plants look the same color.

106 cm. tall. The stem is 3cm. in circumference. 3 plants grew.

11/24/98 1 of 3 pods seems empty. 2 pods are yellow, 3 buds.

15 buds, 1 pod, buds, pod

11/30/98 There are 3 pods that are yellow. 1 pod made a 2cm. long bean. We're trying to germinate it.

3 have very flat pods. Many flowers are growing. pod

F

Stem circumference measurement is performed

Page 6

My Conclusion

C Based on my log I would plant the Bush Beans. They grew the tallest and the widest. They also had more flowers and pods than the Kidney Beans. The Bush Beans may have a longer life cycle but right now I think they will produce more beans. I think it pays to wait longer to get more beans.

G

Bush bean plants showing many flowers.

Work Sample & Commentary: *Butterflies*

Physical Sciences Concepts

S2 Life Sciences Concepts

Earth and Space Sciences Concepts

Scientific Connections and Applications

S5 Scientific Thinking

S6 Scientific Tools and Technologies

S7 Scientific Communication

S8 Scientific Investigation

The task

Students investigated the life cycle of butterflies by observing a live butterfly as it developed through its life cycle stages in a commercially prepared butterfly habitat; and by accessing information in reference materials. Students recorded their observations in journals and reported what they learned in writing and artwork.

Circumstances of performance

This sample of student work was produced under the following conditions:

√ alone   √ in a group

√ in class   as homework

    with teacher feedback   with peer feedback

    timed   opportunity for revision

What the work shows

S2b Life Sciences Concepts: The student produces evidence that demonstrates understanding of life cycles of organisms,…that all plants and animals have life cycles.

A B The student provides evidence of understanding of the butterfly's life cycle by keeping a narrative journal of observations and by making a diagram that illustrates the four stages of the life cycle, three of which were personally observed.

C D The student summarized information about butterfly life cycles from reference sources in narrative form and in a diagram.

This work sample illustrates a standard-setting performance for the following parts of the standards:

S2a Life Sciences Concepts: Characteristics of organisms.

S2b Life Sciences Concepts: Life cycles of organisms.

S5c Scientific Thinking: Use evidence from reliable sources.

S6c Scientific Tools and Technologies: Acquire information from multiple sources.

S7a Scientific Communication: Represent data and results in multiple ways.

S8b Scientific Investigation: Systematic observation.

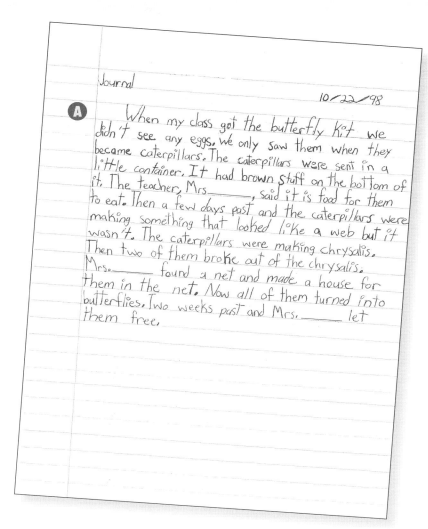

A

> Journal
>
> 10/22/98
>
> When my class got the butterfly kit we didn't see any eggs, we only saw them when they became caterpillars. The caterpillars were sent in a little container. It had brown stuff on the bottom of it. The teacher, Mrs._____, said it is food for them to eat. Then a few days past and the caterpillars were making something that looked like a web but it wasn't. The caterpillars were making chrysalis. Then two of them broke out of the chrysalis. Mrs._____ found a net and made a house for them in the net. Now all of them turned into butterflies. Two weeks past and Mrs._____ let them free.

S2a Life Sciences Concepts: The student produces evidence that demonstrates understanding of characteristics of organisms, such as…the relationship between structure and function.

E F The student relates the structure of a butterfly's probe to its function of getting nectar. This relationship is described in both written form and in an illustration.

S5c Scientific Thinking: The student uses evidence from reliable sources.

A B The student reports from personal observations.

G The student's bibliography lists several references used in developing the report.

For related work on Reproduction, see "It's All in the Genes", page 106, "DNA Models", page 176, and "DNA Concept Map", page 179.

The quotations from the Science performance descriptions in this commentary are excerpted. The complete performance descriptions are shown on pages 18-32.

Butterflies

S6c Scientific Tools and Technologies: The student acquires information from multiple sources, such as experimentation and print and non-print sources.

G The student's bibliography lists references, both print and software, used in developing the report.

S7a Scientific Communication: The student represents data and results in multiple ways, such as...diagrams and artwork; and technical and creative writing.

The student presents data in narrative form (**A**, **C**, **E**) accompanied by diagrams (**B**, **D**) and artwork (**F**).

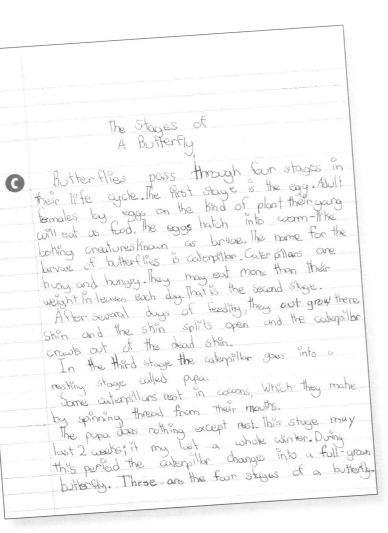

The Stages of
A Butterfly

Butterflies pass through four stages in their life cycle. The first stage is the egg. Adult females lay eggs on the kind of plant their young will eat as food. The eggs hatch into worm-like looking creatures known as larvae. The name for the larvae of butterflies is caterpillar. Caterpillars are busy and hungry. They may eat more than their weight in leaves each day. That is the second stage.

After several days of feeding, they out grew there skin and the skin splits open and the caterpillar crawls out of the dead skin.

In the third stage the caterpillar goes into a resting stage called pupa.

Some caterpillars rest in cocoons, which they make by spinning thread from their mouths.

The pupa does nothing except rest. This stage may last 2 weeks; it my last a whole winter. During this period the caterpillar changes into a full-grown butterfly. These are the four stages of a butterfly.

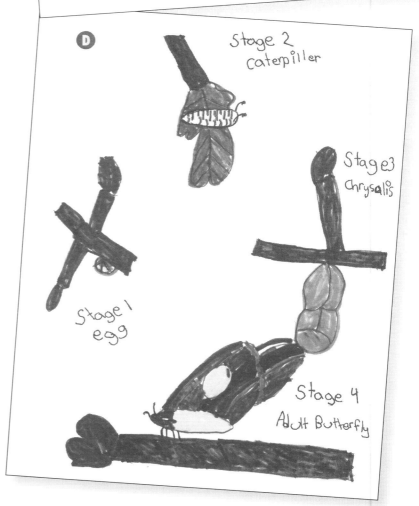

Stage 2
caterpiller

Stage 3
Chrysalis

Stage 1
egg

Stage 4
Adult Butterfly

Butterflies

Physical Sciences Concepts

S2 Life Sciences Concepts

Earth and Space Sciences Concepts

Scientific Connections and Applications

S5 Scientific Thinking

S6 Scientific Tools and Technologies

S7 Scientific Communication

S8 Scientific Investigation

E

Butterflies

Butterflies are a group of insects. During the daytime they eat and fly. During the night they sleep with their wings held upright and closed. Butterflies drink nectar from flowers by using their long slender sucking tubes. They are called probes. That is how butterflies live.

S8 b Scientific Investigation: The student demonstrates scientific competence by completing…a systematic observation….

A **B** The student's observations of a closed habitat were made systematically over a period of weeks. During this time, the student recorded observations of three of the stages of development of a butterfly, and used reference materials to find out about the unobserved stage.

F

G Bibliography

Book of Knowledge. 1979, 468-470.

Encyclopedia Britannica. Computer disc. 1998.

Getzoff, Melissa, Butterfly Magic, 1998.

World Book Encyclopedia. Vol. 2. 1967. 622-629.

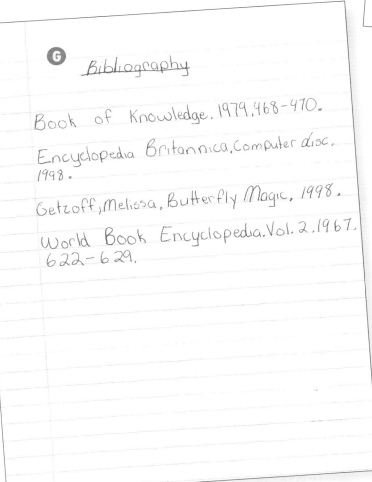

Work Sample & Commentary: *Water Tolerance*

Physical
Sciences
Concepts

Life
Sciences **S2**
Concepts

Earth and
Space Sciences
Concepts

Scientific
Connections and **S4**
Applications

Scientific **S5**
Thinking

Scientific Tools
and **S6**
Technologies

Scientific **S7**
Communication

Scientific
Investigation

For related work on
Response to Environment,
see "Bean Farmers",
page 44, "Toasted
Bread", page 54,
"Snails", page 104, and
"Endocrine Feedback
Exercise", page 183.

The quotations from the
Science performance
descriptions in this com-
mentary are excerpted.
The complete perfor-
mance descriptions are
shown on pages
18-32.

The task

In a seed germination and plant growth
experiment, students were required to keep all
conditions equal except for a single variable,
the volume of water. Each student team was
required to monitor growth of four sets of
seeds; each set included seeds of four different
plant species. The four seed sets were grown in
four cups, with each cup receiving a different
volume of water. Over the course of the investigation, students observed the cups at regular
intervals to determine the most favorable water
quantity (of the quantities used) for seed germination and growth.

Circumstances of performance

This sample of student work was produced
under the following conditions:

√ alone   √ in a group

√ in class   as homework

√ with teacher feedback   with peer feedback

timed   √ opportunity for
revision

What the work shows

S2a   Life Sciences Concepts: The student produces
evidence that demonstrates understanding of characteristics of organisms, such as survival and environmental support....

A   Throughout the observations and especially in
the conclusion, the student demonstrates understanding of the impacts of different volumes of water on
seed germination and plant growth.

This work sample illustrates a standard-setting performance for the following parts of the standards:

S2a   **Life Sciences Concepts: Survival and environmental
support.**

S4a   **Scientific Connections and Applications: Big ideas
and unifying concepts.**

S5f   **Scientific Thinking: Work individually and in teams.**

S6a   **Scientific Tools and Technologies: Use tools to
gather data.**

S7a   **Scientific Communication: Represent data and
results in multiple ways.**

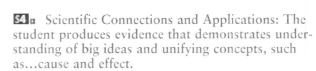

Date 10/8/98

Names _____

PLANT EXPERIMENT SETUP

1. Environmental factor tested
Water Tolerance

2. Planting date 10/8/98

3. Number of each seed planted
Barley 3 seeds
Corn 3 seeds
Pea 3 seeds
Radish 3 seeds

4. Map where each seed is planted.

5. Plant all four containers in
exactly the same way.

KEY

| ▲ Barley | ■ Corn | ● Pea | ✚ Radish |

Comments On the planting date we have set up 4 planter cups.
All 4 cups have 3 of each seed the same way. The label for
the water amount is on the front eg (20ml). I am planting corn
in each cup. The other three students will plant pea, Radish, and Barley
the same. The only difference is the water amounts. The first cup,
black gets 10ml 2x a week. The second cup, blue gets 20ml 2x a week.
The third cup, green gets 40 ml 2x a week. The fourth cup, red 80ml 2x
a week.

Environments Module   FOSS 1992 Edition   Copyright © 1992 U.C. Regents   WATER TOLERANCE/SALT OF THE EARTH 4
PART NO. 542-0117 (no. 4 of 10)   This sheet may be reproduced for classroom use.   Week

S4a   Scientific Connections and Applications: The
student produces evidence that demonstrates understanding of big ideas and unifying concepts, such
as...cause and effect.

B   The conclusion states, "By observing the four
cups over three weeks, we saw that the plants that
were watered 40 ml 2 x a week grew best..." In comparison, the student goes on to explicitly describe the
relationship between too much water and lack of germination in the 80ml cup. While use of the word
"drowned" is technically incorrect, it doesn't detract
from the student's understanding that a causal relationship exists.

S5f   Scientific Thinking: The student works individually and in teams to collect and share information
and ideas.

C   The student places individual work within the
context of the team assignment: "I am planting corn
in each cup. The other students are planting pea,
radish and barley." (In a revision, it would be appropriate to have the student go on to explain that data
were collected individually and analyzed cooperatively to reach the conclusion.)

Water Tolerance

Physical Sciences Concepts

S2 Life Sciences Concepts

Earth and Space Sciences Concepts

S4 Scientific Connections and Applications

S5 Scientific Thinking

S6 Scientific Tools and Technologies

S7 Scientific Communication

Scientific Investigation

S6 a Scientific Tools and Technologies: The student uses...tools...to gather data.

D The "Environment" columns in the "Data Table" imply evidence of the use of graduated cylinders for measuring volume.

E The "Height..." columns in the Data Table provide evidence of the use of rulers.

S7 a Scientific Communication: The student represents data and results in multiple ways, such as numbers, tables...drawings...and technical and creative writing.

A The written conclusion presents the outcome and data analysis clearly, concisely.

F G The two tables ("Plant Observations" and "Plant Profile") required students to organize and present their data in graphic formats that encompass numbers, tables, drawings, and written statements.

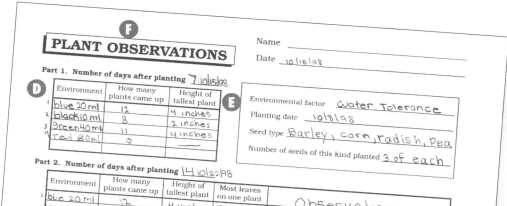

F

PLANT OBSERVATIONS

Name _____
Date 10/16/98

Part 1. Number of days after planting 7 10/15/98

D

Environment	How many plants came up	Height of tallest plant
1 blue 20 ml	12	4 inches
2 black 10 ml	8	2 inches
3 green 40 ml	11	4 inches
4 red 80 ml	0	—

E Environmental factor Water Tolerance
Planting date 10/8/98
Seed type Barley, corn, radish, Pea
Number of seeds of this kind planted 3 of each

Part 2. Number of days after planting 14 10/22/98

Environment	How many plants came up	Height of tallest plant	Most leaves on one plant	Observations
1 blue 20 ml	12	4 inches	12 leaves	The soil is dry but Plants are growing.
2 black 10 ml	8	3 inches	10 leaves	Look very small. Color is different.
3 green 40 ml	11	6 inches	13 leaves	Doing very well, soil is wet,
4 red 80 ml	0			Flooded, not grown, drowned

Part 3. Number of days after planting 21 10/29/98

Environment	How many plants came up	Height of tallest plant	Most leaves on one plant	Length of longest leaf	Length of longest root	Observations
1 blue 20 ml	12	7 inches	12 leaves		8 inches	Green, well grown
2 black 10 ml	8	4 inches	10 leaves		4 inches	not grown looks sick
3 green 40 ml	11	8 inches	13 leaves		8 inches	Did very well
4 red 80 ml	0					

Environments Module FOSS 1992 Edition
PART NO. 542-0117 (no. 5 of 10)

Copyright © 1992 U.C. Regents

WATER TOLERANCE/SALT OF THE EARTH
This sheet may be reproduced for classroom use.

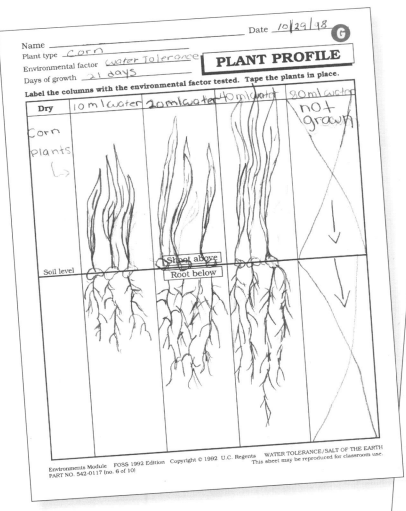

Name _____
Plant type Corn
Environmental factor Water Tolerance
Days of growth 21 days
Date 10/29/98 **G**

PLANT PROFILE

Label the columns with the environmental factor tested. Tape the plants in place.

Dry	10 ml water	20 ml water	40 ml water	80 ml water not grown
Corn plants				
Soil level		Shoot above / Root below		

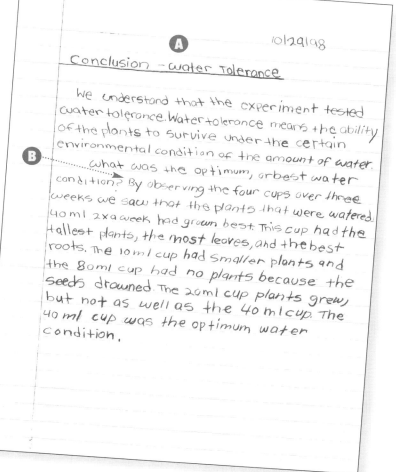

A 10/29/98

Conclusion - Water Tolerance

We understand that the experiment tested water tolerance. Water tolerance means the ability of the plants to survive under the certain environmental condition of the amount of water.

B .... What was the optimum, or best water condition? By observing the four cups over three weeks we saw that the plants that were watered 40 ml 2 x a week had grown best. This cup had the tallest plants, the most leaves, and the best roots. The 10 ml cup had smaller plants and the 80 ml cup had no plants because the seeds drowned. The 20 ml cup plants grew, but not as well as the 40 ml cup. The 40 ml cup was the optimum water condition.

Environments Module FOSS 1992 Edition Copyright © 1992 U.C. Regents WATER TOLERANCE/SALT OF THE EARTH
PART NO. 542-0117 (no. 6 of 10) This sheet may be reproduced for classroom use.

Work Sample & Commentary: *Biomes*

Physical
Sciences
Concepts

Life
Sciences **S2**
Concepts

Earth and
Space Sciences
Concepts

Scientific
Connections and
Applications

Scientific
Thinking

Scientific Tools **S6**
and
Technologies

Scientific **S7**
Communication

Scientific
Investigation

For related work on Interdependence, see "Bio Box", page 98, "Owl Pellets", page 101, "Eagles", page 186, and "The Invincible Cockroach", page 188.

The quotations from the Science performance descriptions in this commentary are excerpted. The complete performance descriptions are shown on pages 18-32.

The task

Each student was asked to research an animal species using a variety of reference sources, including accessing information on a CD-ROM, and to prepare a brief written report about the animal. The reports were then used collectively to help teams of students create murals that depicted animals representing the major biomes.

Circumstances of performance

This sample of student work was produced under the following conditions:

√ alone   √ in a group

√ in class   √ as homework

√ with teacher feedback   with peer feedback

    timed   √ opportunity for revision

What the work shows

S2a Life Sciences Concepts: The student produces evidence that demonstrates understanding of characteristics of organisms, such as...the relationship between structure and function.

A B C The students clearly describe the functions of specific structures.

S2a Life Sciences Concepts: The student produces evidence that demonstrates understanding of organisms and environments, such as the interdependence of animals and plants in an ecosystem....

D E F G The students provide specific examples of interdependence of species.

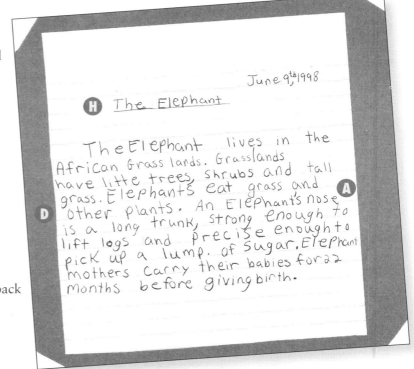

June 9th, 1998

H The Elephant

The Elephant lives in the African Grass lands. Grasslands have little trees, shrubs and tall grass. Elephants eat grass and other plants. An Elephant's nose is a long trunk, strong enough to lift logs and precise enough to pick up a lump of sugar. Elephant mothers carry their babies for 22 months before giving birth.

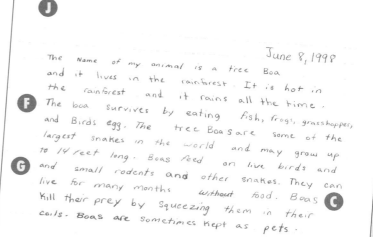

June 8, 1998

The Name of my animal is a tree Boa and it lives in the rainforest. It is hot in the rainforest and it rains all the time. The boa survives by eating fish, frogs, grasshoppers, and Birds egg. The tree Boas are some of the largest snakes in the world and may grow up to 14 feet long. Boas feed on live birds and small rodents and other snakes. They can live for many months without food. Boas Kill their prey by squeezing them in their coils. Boas are sometimes Kept as pets.

This work sample illustrates a standard-setting performance for the following parts of the standards:

S2a **Life Sciences Concepts: Characteristics of organisms.**

S6a **Scientific Tools and Technologies: Acquire information from multiple sources.**

S7a **Scientific Communication: Represent data and results in multiple ways.**

S6a Scientific Tools and Technologies: The student acquires information from multiple sources, such as experimentation and print and non-print sources.

H I J It is evident from the description of the task and the tone of the writing that the students used print and software resources. In a further revision, however, students should be asked to include a bibliography with the written piece.

Biomes

Physical Sciences Concepts

Life Sciences Concepts **S2**

Earth and Space Sciences Concepts

Scientific Connections and Applications

Scientific Thinking

Scientific Tools and Technologies **S6**

Scientific Communication **S7**

Scientific Investigation

June 8, 1998

I OCTOPUS

The Octopus lives in the ocean. They live in the Atlantic, Pacific and Indian oceans. **E** The Octopus eats crabs lobsters and shellfish. The Octopus has eight strong tentacles. The common **B** Octopus can hide by changing its color from pinkish to brown.

S7a Scientific Communication: The student represents data and results in multiple ways, such as…drawings, diagrams, and artwork; and technical and creative writing.

H **I** **J** **K** The students presented data in narrative form and in artwork.

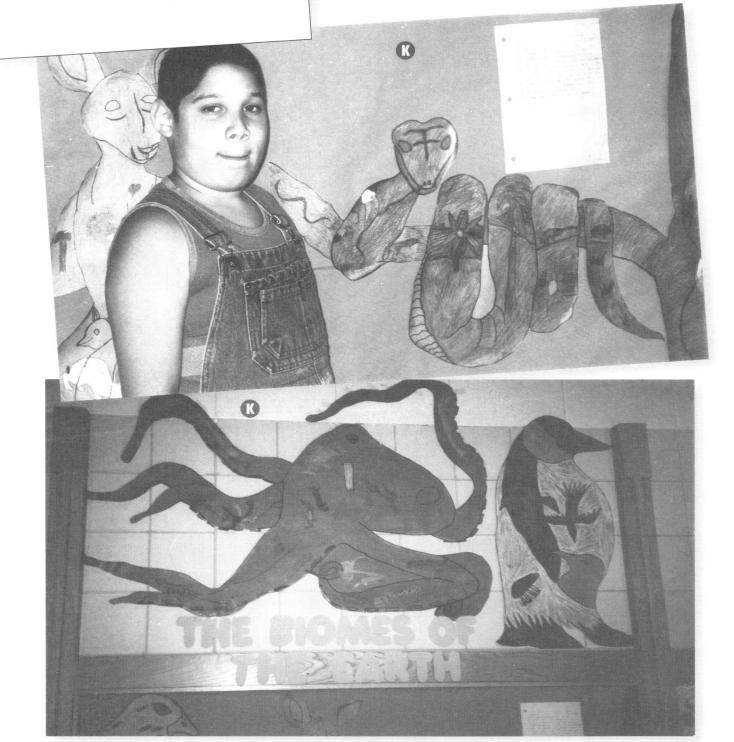

Work Sample & Commentary: *Toasted Bread vs. Non-Toasted Bread*

Physical
Sciences
Concepts

Life
Sciences **S2**
Concepts

Earth and
Space Sciences
Concepts

Scientific
Connections and
Applications

Scientific
Thinking

Scientific Tools
and
Technologies

Scientific **S7**
Communication

Scientific **S8**
Investigation

For related work on
Response to Environment,
see "Bean Farmers",
page 44, "Water
Tolerance", page 50,
"Snails", page 104, and
"Endocrine Feedback
Exercise", page 183.

The task
Students were asked to conduct a controlled experiment.

Circumstances of performance
This sample of student work was produced under the following conditions:

alone	√ in a group
√ in class	√ as homework
with teacher feedback	with peer feedback
timed	opportunity for revision

What the work shows

S2a Life Sciences Concepts: The student produces evidence that demonstrates understanding of characteristics of organisms, such as survival and environmental support.

Ⓐ The students indicated that there is a relationship between heat and the growth of mold.

S7a Scientific Communication: The student represents data and results in multiple ways, such as drawings...and...writing.

Ⓑ Ⓒ Both in the "Observation" section of the text and the illustration, the results are clearly communicated.

The quotations from the
Science performance
descriptions in this com-
mentary are excerpted.
The complete perfor-
mance descriptions are
shown on pages
18-32.

---

①

Tit: Pen Ki toste ak Pen Ki Pa toste.

Qwestion: Ki Pen Ki ap gaté avan 10 Jou, Pen Ki toste oubyen Pen Ki Pa tosté.

Ypotez: nou Panse si nou mete 6 moso Pen Ki Pa tosté nan yon shache Plastik epi Kitel nan Klass la Pou 10 Jou, yo tout ap gaté. Men si nou meté Pen Ki tosté nan shache Plastik yo Pap gaté.

Materyel: 12 moso Pen blan, 12 shache Plastik ak yon tosté.

Eksperimantasyon: Ⓓ ①nou Pran 12 moso Pen blan nan yon shaché Pen yo te ashté nan mache.
② nou Pran sis moso Pen epi nou mete yo chak nan yon shache Plastik.
③ nou Pran sis lot moso Pen nou tosté yo epi nou Ⓔ mete yo chak nan yon shaché Plastik.
④ nou Pa vlé Pen Ki sho yo boulé Plastik la nou tan yo frét avan nou mete yo nan shache Plastik la.
⑤ nou Kité tout 12 shaché yo sou tab anndan Klass la Pou 10 Jou.

Obsèvasyon: Ⓑ nou obsevé Pen yo Pandan 10 Jou men sa nou wé

Premye Jou: Pa te genyen ankan chanJman nan tout

S7c Scientific Communication: The student communicates in a form suited to the purpose and the audience, such as writing instructions that others can follow.

Ⓒ Ⓓ The "Experimentation" section of the text is clear and supported by the illustration.

Toasted Bread vs. Non-Toasted Bread

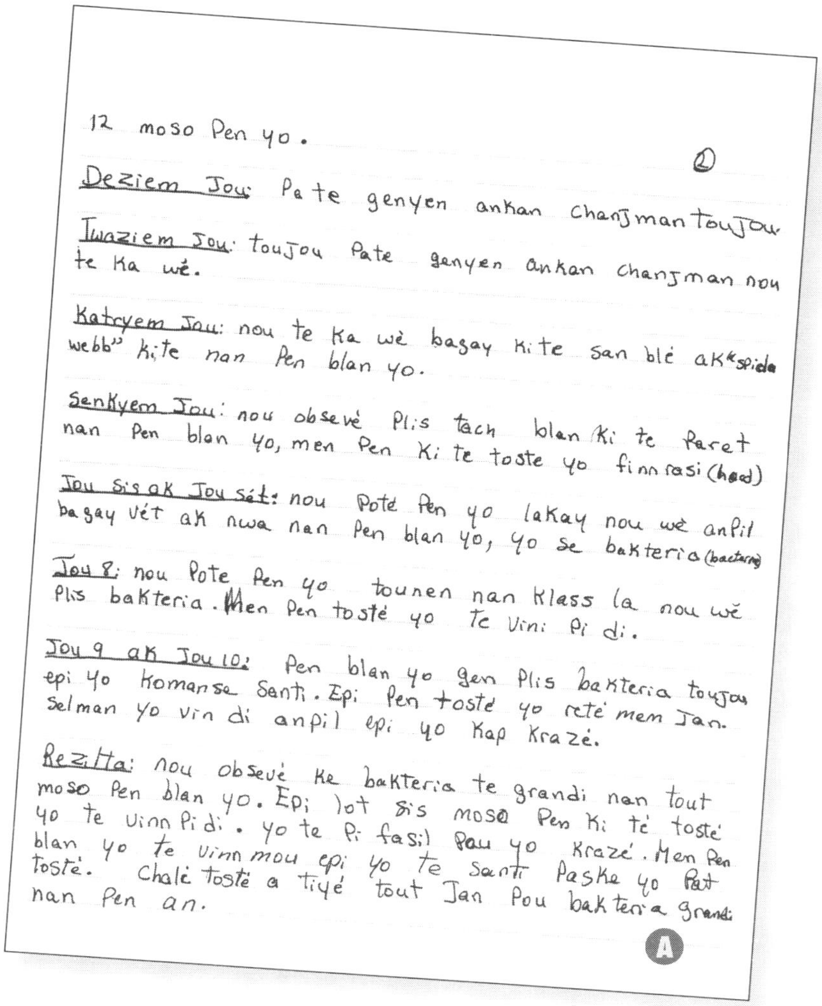

Physical Sciences Concepts

S2 Life Sciences Concepts

Earth and Space Sciences Concepts

Scientific Connections and Applications

Scientific Thinking

Scientific Tools and Technologies

S7 Scientific Communication

S8 Scientific Investigation

Paper A (handwritten, Haitian Creole):

12 moso Pen yo.

Deziem Jou: Pate genyen ankan chanjman toujou

Twaziem Jou: toujou Pate genyen ankan chanjman nou te ka we.

Katryem Jou: nou te ka we bagay kite san blé akk"spide webb" kite nan Pen blan yo.

Senkyem Jou: nou obsevé Plis tach blan ki te paret nan Pen blan yo, men Pen ki te toste yo finn rasi (hard)

Jou sis ak Jou sét: nou Poté Pen yo lakay nou we anpil bagay vét ak nwa nan Pen blan yo, yo se bakteria (bacteria)

Jou 8: nou Pote Pen yo tounen nan klass la nou wé Plis bakteria. Men Pen tosté yo te vini Pi di.

Jou 9 ak Jou 10: Pen blan yo gen Plis bakteria toujou epi yo komanse santi. Epi Pen tosté yo reté mem Jan. Selman yo vin di anpil epi yo kap kraze.

Rezilta: nou obsevé ke bakteria te grandi nan tout moso Pen blan yo. Epi lot sis moso Pen ki té tosté yo te vinn Pi di. yo te Pi fasil Pou yo kraze. Men Pen blan yo te vinn mou epi yo te santi Paske yo Pat tosté. Chalé tosté a tiyé tout Jan Pou bakteria grandi nan Pen an.

A

Paper F (handwritten, Haitian Creole):

Konklusyon: nou te byen Predi ke Pen blan yo ki Pat tosté ka pab fé bakteria apre 10 Jou femen nan yon Shaché Plastik. Men nou Pat ka di ke Pen tosté yo te ka Pab kraze. Vwasi nou ka ize Pen kraze yo Pou fe Bread Crumbs?!

F

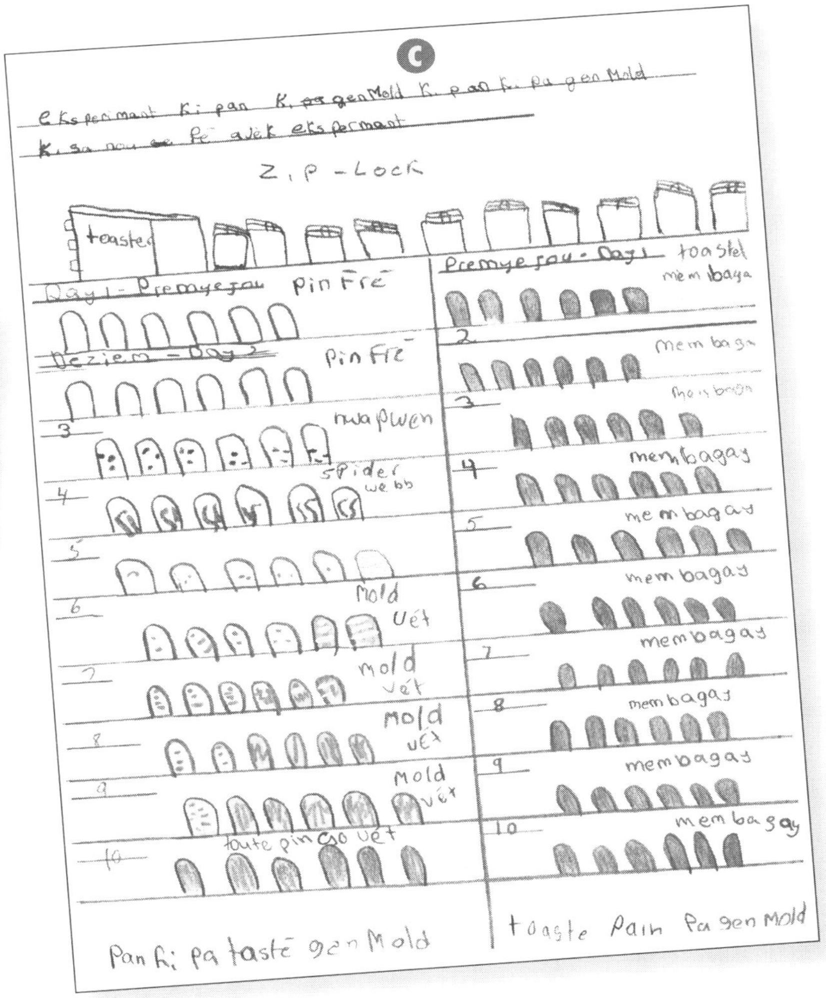

S8a Scientific Investigation: The student demonstrates scientific competence by completing an experiment, such as a fair test.

E The "Experimentation" section, particularly the third step, shows that the only variable that was changed was the toasting condition.

F The conclusion provides evidence that the students recognized that their results were different from what they expected.

Note: Although the student has made some grammatical errors in Haitian (capitalization, punctuation, misuse of the accent, etc.) the content of the work remains intact. It can be understood by a Haitian reader.

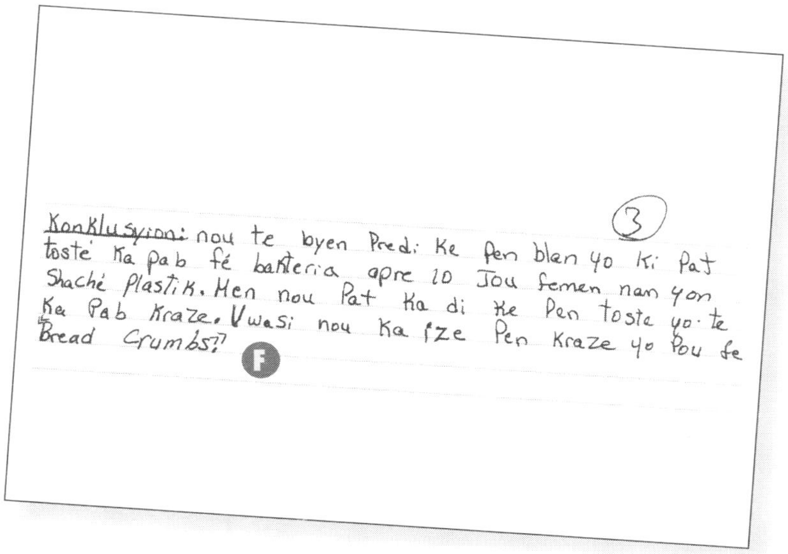

Paper C (handwritten chart):

eksperimant ki pan k. pa gen Mold k. pan f. pa gen Mold k. sa nou we fé avek eksperimant

ZIP-LOCK

toasted

Day 1 - Premye jou: pin Frè | Premye jou - Day 1: toastel mem bagay

Deziem - Day 2: Pin Frè | 2. mem bagay

3. nwa plwen | 3. mo.n brown

4. spider web | 4. mem bagay

5. | 5. mem bagay

6. mold vét | 6. mem bagay

7. mold vét | 7. mem bagay

8. mold vét | 8. mem bagay

9. mold vét | 9. mem bagay

10. toute pin gao vét | 10. mem bagay

Pan fi pa tasté gen Mold | toasté Pain Pa gen Mold

C

Toasted Bread vs. Non-Toasted Bread

Translation

Sidebar navigation:
Physical Sciences Concepts
Life Sciences Concepts — S2
Earth and Space Sciences Concepts
Scientific Connections and Applications
Scientific Thinking
Scientific Tools and Technologies
Scientific Communication — S7
Scientific Investigation — S8

Panel ①

Title: Toasted Bread vs. non-toasted bread.

Question: Which bread is more likely to grow mold? Toasted bread or non-toasted bread?

Hypothesis: We think if we put some slices of white plain bread in plastic bags and leave them in the classroom for ten days, they will most likely grow mold. However, if they are toasted they will not develop mold after ten days.

Materials: twelve regular slices of white bread, 12 plastic bags, toaster.

Experimentation: We take six slices of plain white bread from a bag that was bought from the local grocery store.
② We put each slice into a zip-lock bag.
③ We take six other slices of the same plain white bread from the same bag. Then we toasted them up until they turn really

Panel ②

brown.
④ We do not want the hot bread to burn the plastic bag, so we let the bread cool off a bit before we put them one in each zip-lock bag as we did for the plain white or non-toasted bread.
⑤ We let all 12 bags on a table in the classroom for ten days.

Observation: This is what we observe during the ten days of the experiment.
Day #1: There is no change in all 12 slices of bread.
Day #2: There is no change.
Day #3: Still there is no visible in all 12 slices of bread.
Day #4: Some white thing like tiny spider webb appear in some places on all six slices of the plain white bread, while the toasted bread remain the same.

Panel ③

Day #5 we observe more white things on more spots on the plain white bread. But the toasted bread get harder.
Day #6 and day #7. We take the bread home. We see round and greenish and black spots with spongy white thing on the white bread. They are molds. They are similar bacteria.
Day #8 We take the experiment back into the classroom. We see more molds. They are darker. But the toasted bread become harder and harder.
Day #9 and day #10 The white plain bread with more molds became smelly. The toasted breads have not grown mold, but they are easier to crunch.

Result: We have seen that the six slices of white bread grew mold. And the six slices of toasted bread gets harder and easier to crunch. The plain white bread that also

Panel ④

saggy and smelly because it was not toasted. Maybe the heat from the toaster destroys ways for mold to grow.

Conclusion: We were right to predict that the plain white (non-toasted) bread would develop mold. But we did not predict the toasted bread would get, instead, crunchy.

Physical Sciences Concepts

Life Sciences Concepts

S3 Earth and Space Sciences Concepts

Scientific Connections and Applications

Scientific Thinking

S6 Scientific Tools and Technologies

S7 Scientific Communication

Scientific Investigation

Work Sample & Commentary: *Weather Watch*

The task

Students studied weather and learned to use instruments such as the thermometer, barometer, hygrometer, wind meter, and compass. They learned how to record temperature, barometric pressure, humidity, wind speed, and wind direction and to observe cloud cover. They also learned to interpret weather data in a local newspaper. They were then given the opportunity to use these skills in a field study wherein they collected and recorded weather data outdoors for five consecutive school days. Each student team was then asked to choose weather factors and represent each factor visually using appropriate charts or graphs of their choice. The students reflected on their experience through narrative writing. While the narratives are not intended to be conclusive, they do reflect understanding of key concepts.

Circumstances of performance

This sample of student work was produced under the following conditions:

alone	√ in a group
√ in class	as homework
√ with teacher feedback	√ with peer feedback
timed	√ opportunity for revision

DATE	TIME	TEMP.	BAR. PRESS.	WIND DIRECTION	WIND SPEED	REL. % HUM.	CLOUD COVER	FORECAST FOR DAY WAS:	STUDENT INITIALS
10/6	1 PM	66°F	1,030	North	4	43%	●	◑	
10/7	1:15	70°F	1,039	East	5	43%	◑	◑	
10/8	1 PM	76°F	992		0	89%	Ⓡ	Ⓡ	
10/9	1:15	75°F	990		0	78%	Ⓡ	Ⓡ	
10/13	1:20	70°F	998	South	5	67%	●	◑	

Ⓐ

What the work shows

S3c Earth Sciences Concepts: The student produces evidence that demonstrates understanding of changes in Earth and sky, such as changes caused by weather….

Ⓐ Ⓑ Ⓒ Ⓓ The chart, bar graphs, and narratives provide evidence that the children have used weather instruments to collect quantifiable data outdoors.

S6a Scientific Tools and Technologies: The student uses technology and tools…to gather data and extend the senses.

Ⓐ Ⓔ Ⓕ Ⓖ The students used instruments (thermometer, barometer, hygrometer, wind meter, compass) to collect data. They described their work with these instruments in their narratives.

S6b Scientific Tools and Technologies: The student collects and analyzes data using concepts and techniques in Mathematics Standard 4, such as…data displays…[and] graphing.

Ⓑ Ⓒ Ⓓ The students collected and analyzed data and used the information to construct graphs.

This work sample illustrates a standard-setting performance for the following parts of the standards:

S3c Earth Sciences Concepts: Changes in Earth and sky.

S6a Scientific Tools and Technologies: Use tools and technology.

S6b Scientific Tools and Technologies: Collect and analyze data.

S7a Scientific Communication: Represent data and results in multiple ways.

The quotations from the Science performance descriptions in this commentary are excerpted. The complete performance descriptions are shown on pages 18-32.

Weather Watch

S7a Scientific Communication: The student represents data and results in multiple ways, such as numbers, tables, and graphs…and technical and creative writing.

A B C D The students completed charts and generated graphs based on the collected data. On two of the graphs (Temperature of the Week and Relative Humidity) students added extra numbers to the y axis so that they could accurately interpret and display the data they collected, indicating a clear understanding of the incremental organization of the graph formats. Note that the Wind Speed graph has a minor flaw in that the bars are not all an equal width, and on the Temperature of the Week graph the increment between 0 and 10 is different, however this does not detract from the students' accurate representation of the data collected.

In the narratives, the students describe their work with various instruments and their surprise at some of their results. In **H**, for example, the student explains how a hygrometer works. The writing contains some spelling and grammatical errors, but these do not detract from the quality of the students' narratives.

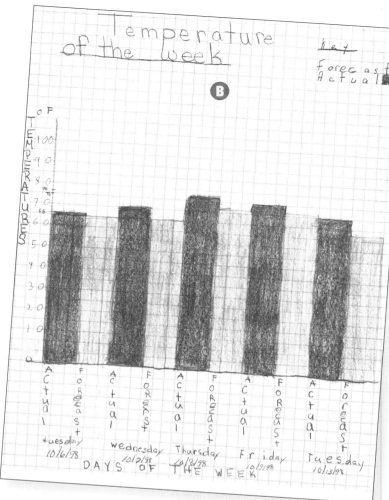

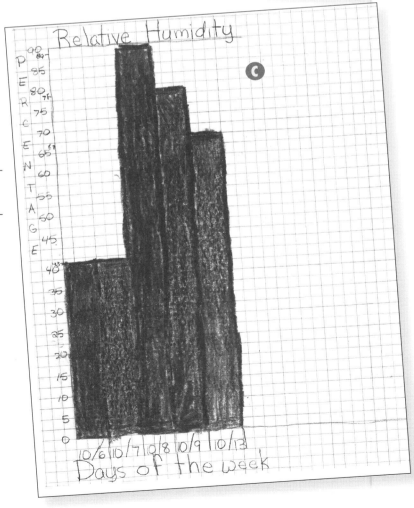

Weather Watch

Physical Sciences Concepts

Life Sciences Concepts

S3 Earth and Space Sciences Concepts

Scientific Connections and Applications

Scientific Thinking

S6 Scientific Tools and Technologies

S7 Scientific Communication

Scientific Investigation

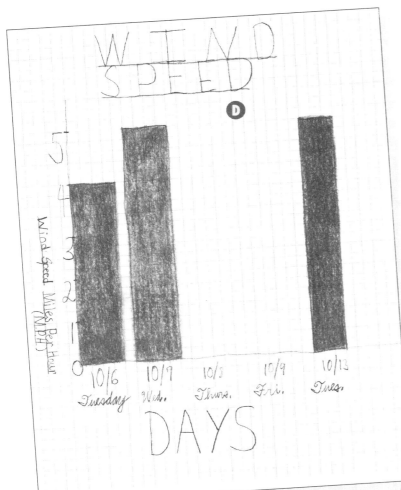

D

WIND SPEED

Wind Speed Miles Per Hour (MPH)

| 10/6 Tuesday | 10/9 Web. | 10/8 Thurs. | 10/9 Fri. | 10/13 Tues. |

DAYS

E

Is the Weatherman Always Right?

When my table went out to check the weather, the weatherman never got the temperature right. My favorite was the wind speed with the little ball. It was fun doing the wind direction also. I learned how to use the hygrometer. I learned a few sings for when it was cloudy. ☁ means cloudy. ◑ means partly cloudy. ☂ means rainy. Inside the hygrometer is a long strand of blond straigh hair. We didnt use the weather bunny but when it turns pink its going to rain. When it turns blue its a nice day. I learned alot about weather when we did the weather check.

F

Weather Watch

What I learned is that not all predictions are right. The newspaper was different from our predictions. I also learned how to read the compass. I learned to use all the instruments. I used to think that the compasses would point in the direction of my house. But now I know it points north. It was fun yet educational. I learned so much. I think I'll like science this year.

weather Watch

H

G

I had fun testing the weather. My favorite thing was using the Wind Speed Meter to test the wind speed. I also was interested in what was in the hygrometer. I learned that there was a long straight blond hair inside the hygrometer and when the air had alot of moisture in the air the hair will get longer and the hygrometer would show a higher persentage of moisture in the air. At the end of testing the weather my group graphed the tempwratune. It was fun.

Work Sample & Commentary: *Drop of Water*

The quotations from the Science performance descriptions in this commentary are excerpted. The complete performance descriptions are shown on pages 18-32.

The task

Students who had been studying weather were asked to write a story about a drop of water that goes through the water cycle.

Circumstances of performance

These samples of student work were produced under the following conditions:

√ alone   in a group

√ in class   as homework

√ with teacher feedback   with peer feedback

   timed   √ opportunity for revision

What the work shows

S3 b Earth and Space Sciences Concepts: The student produces evidence that demonstrates understanding of objects in the sky, such as...the importance of the Sun to provide the light and heat necessary for survival.

A B The stories begin with the important role of the Sun in the water cycle.

S1 a Physical Sciences Concepts: The student produces evidence that demonstrates understanding of properties of objects and materials, such as...different states of materials.

C Conceptual understanding of different states of matter is demonstrated in the consistent and accurate relationships among phase, temperature and volume, particularly the recognition that gases rise, and in the descriptions of how it "feels" to be a gas ("getting bigger"), to be a solid ("smaller"), and to condense from gas to liquid ("getting really crowded"). The student is correct that the drop of water is smaller as a solid than it is as a gas; it should be noted, however, that solid water (ice) takes up more space than liquid water.

These work samples illustrate standard-setting performances for the following parts of the standards:

S1 a Physical Sciences Concepts: Properties of objects and materials.

S3 a Earth and Space Sciences Concepts: Properties of Earth materials.

S3 b Earth and Space Sciences Concepts: Objects in the sky.

S4 a Scientific Connections and Applications: Big ideas and unifying concepts.

Sample 1

My Big Trip
by Jason

Good morning, I am Mr. H. Tuoh. I just woke up and the sun is coming up. I have been swimming with my friends in a nice lake in Nebraska. Since I am on top of this pile of sleeping friends the sun is going to take me for a ride today. **A**

Wow, that was fast. I am climbing really fast. I feel **C** bigger. That's because I am a gas . It happens every time I get hot. When I get cold I get smaller. They call me a solid. Being solid gives me a headache. This is better than World's of fun! There is a big cloud ahead and we are slowing down. I am getting smaller now because my pants fit better. But, it's getting really crowded!!! I can hardly move. Who let in the ugly dust family? I think I will hang on to this dust guy so I **F** can rest up. Hey, everybody is coppying my idea and we are getting heavy. Oh Noooooooooooooooooo we are falling!!! But that's OK because I was getting really cold.

What a trip. I am almost back to the lake. Wait, where is the lake. This looks like a big river . I don't think I am going to hit the river. Oh noooooooooo .I better put on my crash helmet and prepare for a land landing. OUCH! That hurt. But, at least I am down. hey, we are moving again. These dirt and rock hurt. Do they have to come along on MY trip?

H Wow, I am in the Mississipi river! There are lots of us and mud and rocks and stuff. I feel kind of dirty. I wish I could go up to sit in the clouds a while. I will just sit back and float a while. Oh, **J** here comes the sun. Here I go again. I wonder where I will end up this time.

The End...not really

Drop of Water

S1 Physical Sciences Concepts

Life Sciences Concepts

S3 Earth and Space Sciences Concepts

S4 Scientific Connections and Applications

Scientific Thinking

Scientific Tools and Technologies

Scientific Communication

Scientific Investigation

D Conceptual understanding of different states of matter is demonstrated by the relationship between temperature and form.

E Strictly speaking, a single drop of water is not "converted into a white beautiful cloud," but one may grant the author poetic license.

S3a Earth and Space Sciences Concepts: The student produces evidence that demonstrates understanding of properties of Earth materials, such as water and gases….

F Noting that water can condense dust particles is evidence of understanding the water cycle.

G An understanding of the role of gravity in precipitation is implicit in the statement that "someone is pulling me."

H The arrival in the Mississippi River, not in the original lake in Nebraska, shows further understanding of the water cycle in that water precipitates elsewhere from its evaporative source.

I The final sentence denotes the cyclical concept.

Sample 2 Translation

The Adventures of a Drop of Water That Falls

I am a drop of water that falls on the grass, flowers, and people who don't have umbrellas. You might wonder how I could be at some many different places. Here is what happens, **B** the heat of the sun makes me feel like an airplane that starts to fly and fly like a feather when it is blown. I start to elevate to the atmosphere. While I'm flying I encounter my friends the birds. They tell me that I am too hot and I am changing and I evaporate like smoke. **D** I then arrive to a very cold place in the atmosphere it feels as if I were inside a freezer. When I open my eyes I realize that I am no longer a drop of water. I have been converted to a white beautiful cloud. **E** When I'm in the sky I feel happy but sometimes I feel lonely because I want to return to the earth. Now I am heavy and I think that I can't be up here much longer. I think I am going to fall. Sometimes I think that someone is pulling me by the legs. I'm so heavy that I really **G** think that I am going to precipitate to the ground. So I can see my friends: the flowers, the grass, the birds, the countryside, and other friends. My drop sisters are happy because I can join them and become rain. We are no longer drops but a beautiful rain that fills the countryside, oceans, rivers, and lakes. Soon the sun will **I** come back and my adventure will start again.

Sample 2

Las Aventuras de una gota de agua que cae

Yo Soy la gota que le cae a la grama, las flores y las personas que no tienen sombrillas. Ustedes se preguntarán como yo puedo estar en tantas partes **B** diferentes. El calor del sol me hace sentir como si fuera un avión que empieza a volar y a volar como una pluma cuando la soplan y me empiezo a elevar en la atmósfera. Cuando voy volando me encuentro con mis amigas las aves. Me dicen que estoy muy caliente y **D** que estoy cambiando y me evaporo como humo. Después llego a un lugar muy frio en la atmósfera siento como si estuviera dentro de un congelador. Cuando abro mis ojos me doy cuenta de que ya no **E** soy una gota de agua. Me he convertido en una blanca y bella nube. Cuando estoy en el cielo me siento feliz pero a veces me siento muy sola porque quiero volver a la tierra. Ahora estoy pesada y creo que ya no puedo estar mas tiempo aquí arriba. Creo que me voy a caer. **G** A veces creo que alguien me esta jalando de los pies. Estoy tan pesada que ahora si creo que me precipitaré al suelo. Podré ver a mis amigos: las flores, la grama, las aves, los campos y otros amigos. Mis hermanas las gotas están feliz porque al juntarme con ellas nos convertimos en lluvia. Ahora ya no somos gotas sino una hermosa lluvia que llena de agua los campos, **I** mares, rios y lagos. Pronto regresará el sol y mi aventura epezará otra vez.

S4a Scientific Connections and Applications: The student produces evidence that demonstrates understanding of big ideas and unifying concepts, such as…change and constancy….

J The final sentences, especially the conclusion, "The End…not really," go beyond an understanding of the water cycle to suggest understanding of a unifying concept, change and constancy.

Work Sample & Commentary: *Erosion*

Physical Sciences Concepts

Life Sciences Concepts

Earth and Space Sciences Concepts **S3**

Scientific Connections and Applications **S4**

Scientific Thinking **S5**

Scientific Tools and Technologies **S6**

Scientific Communication **S7**

Scientific Investigation

For related work on Erosion, see "River Cutters", page 112.

The quotations from the Science performance descriptions in this commentary are excerpted. The complete performance descriptions are shown on pages 18-32.

The task

An elementary class was involved in a year-long, interdisciplinary study of their state. On a field trip to a conservation center, they learned about wind and water erosion. When they returned, they wanted to learn more about erosion and which combinations of soil and grass were most effective in preventing erosion.

Circumstances of performance

This sample of student work was produced under the following conditions:

    alone   √ in a group

√ in class   as homework

    with teacher feedback   √ with peer feedback

    timed   opportunity for revision

What the work shows

The first page explains that this group of students examined Tall Fescue grass. Other groups in their class studied Perennial Rye, Crested Wheat, and Irrigated Pasture Mix (a mixture of these three and two other types). The second, third, and fourth pages explain the question, hypothesis, and procedures. The fifth page shows the plan for studying soils; the sixth, seventh, and eighth pages show the observations from the three soil types.

This work sample illustrates a standard-setting performance for the following parts of the standards:

S3 a   **Earth and Space Sciences Concepts: Properties of Earth materials.**

S4 a   **Scientific Connections and Applications: Big ideas and unifying concepts.**

S5 a   **Scientific Thinking: Ask questions about natural phenomena; objects and organisms; and events and discoveries.**

S5 e   **Scientific Thinking: Identify problems; propose and implement solutions; and evaluate the accuracy, design, and outcomes of investigations.**

S6 a   **Scientific Tools and Technologies: Use technology and tools.**

S7 a   **Scientific Communication: Represent data and results in multiple ways.**

S7 b   **Scientific Communication: Use facts to support conclusions.**

S7 c   **Scientific Communication: Communicate in a form suitable to the purpose and audience.**

Native Colorado Soils and Grasses — A Water Erosion Experiment
Our class has been studying the effects of erosion. We broke into groups and did erosion experiments. In our group, we had four people, _____, _____, _____, and _____. For our experiment, we decided to plant Tall Fescue grass seeds in three different types of soils. During our experiments we learned how Tall Fescue grows in different soils and how the grass effects soil erosion.

The results of the soils' analysis (without grass) are summarized on page 9. The next three pages (10-12) show the results of the same procedure for the same soils planted with Tall Fescue. The final page (13) summarizes the work.

S3 a   Earth and Space Sciences Concepts: The student produces evidence that demonstrates understanding of properties of Earth materials, such as...the properties of rocks and soils such as texture, color, and ability to retain water.

A **B** **C** There is ample evidence that the students have an understanding of erosion.

S4 a   Scientific Connections and Applications: The student produces evidence that demonstrates understanding of big ideas and unifying concepts such as...cause and effect.

A **B** **C** **D** These pieces and the ending also show a good understanding of cause and effect.

S5 a   Scientific Thinking: The student asks questions about natural phenomena; objects and organisms; and events and discoveries.

D The entire investigation came from students' questions about natural phenomena. The question and hypothesis are clearly stated.

S5 e   Scientific Thinking: The student identifies problems; proposes and implements solutions; and evaluates the accuracy, design, and outcomes of investigations.

E The conclusion shows that students were focused on the best combination of grasses and soils to prevent erosion.

S6 a   Scientific Tools and Technologies: The student uses technology and tools....

F **G** **H** **I** **J** **K** **L** The stream table was used effectively to gather data.

M **N** Attention to accuracy is evident throughout; these are but two examples.

Erosion

Physical
Sciences
Concepts

Life
Sciences
Concepts

S3 Earth and
Space Sciences
Concepts

S4 Scientific
Connections and
Applications

S5 Scientific
Thinking

S6 Scientific Tools
and
Technologies

S7 Scientific
Communication

Scientific
Investigation

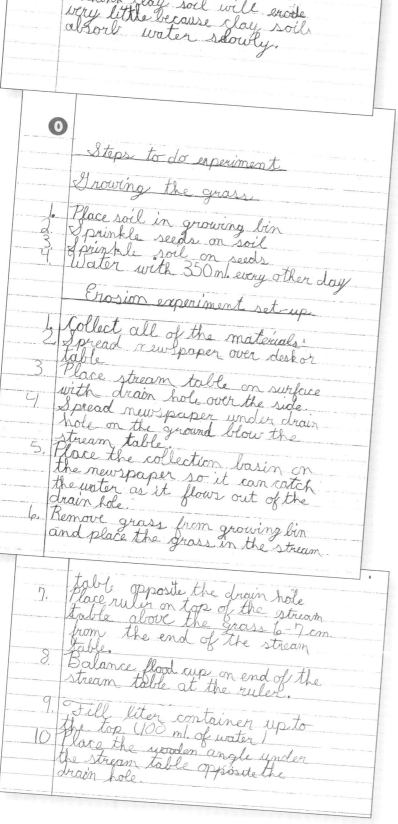

D Question:
What type of soil will erode least with Tall Fescue grass.

Hypothesis:
I think clay soil will erode very little because clay soil absorb water slowly.

O

Steps to do experiment

Growing the grass

1. Place soil in growing bin
2. Sprinkle seeds on soil
3. Sprinkle soil on seeds
4. Water with 350 ml. every other day

Erosion experiment set-up

1. Collect all of the materials
2. Spread newspaper over desk or table
3. Place stream table on surface with drain hole over the side.
4. Spread newspaper under drain hole on the ground blow the stream table.
5. Place the collection basin on the newspaper so it can catch the water as it flows out of the drain hole.
6. Remove grass from growing bin and place the grass in the stream

7. table opposite the drain hole Place ruler on top of the stream table above the grass 6-7cm. from the end of the stream table.
8. Balance flood cup on end of the stream table at the ruler.
9. Fill liter container up to the top (400 ml. of water)
10. Place the wooden angle under the stream table opposite the drain hole.

S7a Scientific Communication: The student represents data and results in multiple ways, such as... diagrams...and...writing.
F G H I J K L The diagrams and accompanying explanations clearly describe the results of the investigations.

S7b Scientific Communication: The student uses facts to support conclusions.
C Throughout the work, but particularly in the conclusion, the generalizations follow directly from the data.

S7c Scientific Communication: The student communicates in a form suited to the purpose and the audience, such as writing instructions that others can follow.
O The procedures are well explained.

The attention to detail, and the recording and use of qualitative and quantitative data, support the judgment of this work as standard setting. Evidence of conceptual and applied understanding of Earth science is shown throughout.

Names _____ Date _____

STREAM TABLE PLAN

We are trying to find out what happens when We put houses at the end of the sand.

We will need these materials:

stream table	water
cup with hole	duct tape
ruler	3 houses
sand	

F

We will set up our tray like this:

Drain hole

Landforms Module
PART NO. 542-0106 (no. 7 of 12)

GO WITH THE FLOW
This sheet may be reproduced for classroom use.

Erosion

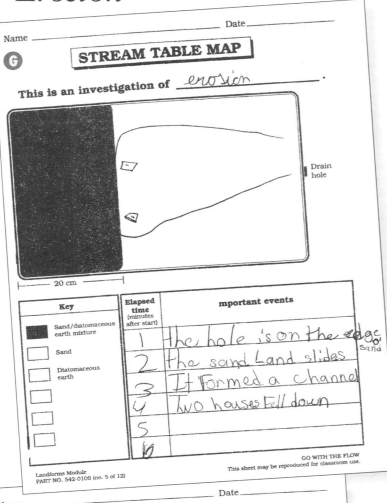

G STREAM TABLE MAP

Name _____ Date _____

This is an investigation of _erosion_ .

20 cm

Drain hole

Key	Elapsed time (minutes after start)	Important events
■ Sand/diatomaceous earth mixture	1	the hole is on the edge sand
☐ Sand	2	the sand Land slides
☐ Diatomaceous earth	3	It Formed a channel
☐	4	Two houses Fell down
☐	5	
☐	6	

Landforms Module
PART NO. 542-0106 (no. 5 of 12)

GO WITH THE FLOW
This sheet may be reproduced for classroom use.

H STREAM TABLE MAP

Name _____ Date _____

This is an investigation of _erosion_ .

20 cm

Drain hole

Key	Elapsed time (minutes after start)	Important events
■ Sand/diatomaceous earth mixture	1	Holes formed
☐ Sand	2	land channeled
☐ Diatomaceous earth	3	tunnel closed
☐	4	tunnel opened again
☐	5	teok more sand down
☐	6	

Landforms Module
PART NO. 542-0106 (no. 5 of 12)

GO WITH THE FLOW
This sheet may be reproduced for classroom use.

I STREAM TABLE MAP

Name _____ Date _____

This is an investigation of _erosion_ .

20 cm

Drain hole

Key	Elapsed time (minutes after start)	Important events
■ Sand/diatomaceous earth mixture	1	made a little hole
☐ Sand	2	hole little bigger
☐ Diatomaceous earth	3	water going to side
☐	4	water going Forward
☐	5	hole's cubic inch
☐	6	water looks like milk

Landforms Module
PART NO. 542-0106 (no. 5 of 12)

GO WITH THE FLOW
This sheet may be reproduced for classroom use.

Experiment Results
(Soils without grass)

° The sandy soil eroded through two channels that the water made.

° The topsoil eroded through one channel. At the bottom of stream Table, is where you could find silt and organic materials.

M ➔

° The clay soil eroded just a little bit. A little channel was made and little organic material eroded.

Erosion

Physical Sciences Concepts

Life Sciences Concepts

S3 Earth and Space Sciences Concepts

S4 Scientific Connections and Applications

S5 Scientific Thinking

S6 Scientific Tools and Technologies

S7 Scientific Communication

Scientific Investigation

Results - Sandy Soil with grass

There was a land slide on the right and in the middle. As the water was coming out of the flood cup, a hole was made in the soil carring a lot of silt and soil materials down the stream table. Most of the water went to the right and a sand bar was formed on the right of the drain hole. The erosion we collected was 2 cm.   ← N

Before — Flood cup / grass / ruler grass

After — Flood cup / grass / ruler grass / Stream table   ← J

Results - Topsoil with grass

There were channels being made both above ground and below ground. There were pebbles and rocks deposited into the collection basin. It is carring the silt and lighter materials into the collection basin. The soil did not erode much because the roots are holding the soil and letting the water leak out. The erosin we collected was 1 cm.   ← A

Before — Flood Cup / grass / ruler grass

After — Flood Cup / stream table   ← K

Results - Clay soil with grass

There were under ground tunnels made during the experiment. Little pebbles were carried in the under ground tunnels. It was looking like a land slide would occur. Most of the water went under the soil and it came out clear. There was not enough erosion to measure.   ← B

Before — Flood Cup / grass / ruler grass

After — Flood Cup / ruler grass / Stream table   ← L

Conclusion

I learned that Tall Fescue grass grows best in clay and topsoil. I also learned that soils erode less with grass growing in them.   ← C

I learned that clay soils do not erode a lot and the water that came out of the stream table was pretty clear. Topsoil erodes more than clay soil but less than sandy soil. Sandy soil erodes a lot. I would suggest that people plant Tall Fescue to help pervent erosion. You may plant Tall Fescue in sandy soil at your own risk. You may want to mix sandy soil with clay to help grow grass and pervent erosion.   ← E

The middle school standards are set at a level of performance approximately equivalent to the end of eighth grade. It is expected that some students might achieve this level earlier and others later than this grade. (See "Deciding what constitutes a standard-setting performance," page 9.)

S Science

S1 Physical Sciences Concepts

S1a Demonstrates understanding of properties and changes of properties in matter.

S1b Demonstrates understanding of position and motion and forces.

S1c Demonstrates understanding of transfer of energy and the nature of a chemical reaction.

S2 Life Sciences Concepts

S2a Demonstrates understanding of structure and function in living systems.

S2b Demonstrates understanding of reproduction and heredity and the role of genes and environment on trait expression.

S2c Demonstrates understanding of regulation and behavior and response to environmental stimuli.

S2d Demonstrates understanding of populations and ecosystems and the effects of resources and energy transfer on populations.

S2e Demonstrates understanding of evolution, diversity, and adaptation of organisms.

S3 Earth and Space Sciences Concepts

S3a Demonstrates understanding of structure of the Earth system.

S3b Demonstrates understanding of Earth's history.

S3c Demonstrates understanding of Earth in the Solar System.

S3d Demonstrates understanding of natural resource management.

S4 Scientific Connections and Applications

S4a Demonstrates understanding of big ideas and unifying concepts.

S4b Demonstrates understanding of the designed world.

S4c Demonstrates understanding of health.

S4d Demonstrates understanding of impact of technology.

S4e Demonstrates understanding of impact of science.

S Science

S5 Scientific Thinking

S5a Frames questions to distinguish cause and effect; and identifies or controls variables.

S5b Uses concepts from Science Standards 1 to 4 to explain a variety of observations and phenomena.

S5c Uses evidence from reliable sources to to develop descriptions, explanations, and models.

S5d Proposes, recognizes, analyzes, considers, and critiques alternative explanations; and distinguishes between fact and opinion.

S5e Identifies problems; proposes and implements solutions; and evaluates the accuracy, design, and outcomes of investigations.

S5f Works individually and in teams to collect and share information and ideas.

S6 Scientific Tools and Technologies

S6a Uses technology and tools to observe and measure objects, organisms, and phenomena, directly, indirectly, and remotely.

S6b Records and stores data using a variety of formats.

S6c Collects and analyzes data using concepts and techniques in Mathematics Standard 4.

S6d Acquires information from multiple sources.

S6e Recognizes sources of bias in data.

S7 Scientific Communication

S7a Represents data and results in multiple ways.

S7b Argues from evidence.

S7c Critiques published materials.

S7d Explains a scientific concept or procedure to other students.

S7e Communicates in a form suited to the purpose and the audience.

S8 Scientific Investigation

S8a Demonstrates scientific competence by completing a controlled experiment.

S8b Demonstrates scientific competence by completing fieldwork.

S8c Demonstrates scientific competence by completing a design.

S8d Demonstrates scientific competence by completing secondary research.

New York City Performance Standards

S1 Physical Sciences Concepts

The student demonstrates conceptual understanding by using a concept accurately to explain observations and make predictions and by representing the concept in multiple ways (through words, diagrams, graphs, or charts, as appropriate). Both aspects of understanding—explaining and representing—are required to meet this standard.

S1 a The student produces evidence that demonstrates understanding of properties and changes of properties in matter, such as density and boiling point; chemical reactivity; and conservation of matter.

Examples of activities through which students might demonstrate conceptual understanding of physical sciences include:

▲ Use the concept of density to explain why some things float and others sink in water. **1a**

▲ Investigate the characteristics that are necessary to obtain an electric current from an electrochemical cell of metal(s) and a fluid medium. **1a**

▲ Explain the difference between recycling and reusing in terms of mass and energy conservation. **1a, 1c, 3a, 4b**

New York State Learning Standards for Math, Science, & Technology

Standard 4 Science
Physical Setting

3. Matter is made up of particles whose properties determine the observable characteristics of matter and its reactivity.

Students:

observe and describe properties of materials, such as density, conductivity, and solubility.

distinguish between chemical and physical changes.

develop their own mental models to explain common chemical reactions and changes in states of matter.

National Documents which guided New York State and New York City

NRC National Science Education Standards

Standard B Physical Science
Properties and Changes of Properties in Matter

A substance has characteristic properties, such as density, a boiling point, and solubility, all of which are independent of the amount of the sample. A mixture of substances often can be separated into the original substances using one or more of the characteristic properties.

Substances react chemically in characteristic ways with other substances to form new substances (compounds) with different characteristic properties. In chemical reactions, the total mass is conserved. Substances often are placed in categories or groups if they react in similar ways; metals is an example of such a group.

Chemical elements do not break down during normal laboratory reactions involving such treatments as heating, exposure to electric current, or reaction with acids. There are more than 100 known elements that combine in a multitude of ways to produce compounds, which account for the living and nonliving substances that we encounter. p. 154

Project 2061, AAAS
Benchmarks for Science Literacy

Chapter 4 The Physical Setting
4D Structure of Matter

When a new material is made by combining two or more materials, it has properties that are different from the original materials. For that reason, a lot of different materials can be made from a small number of basic kinds of materials. p. 77

All matter is made up of atoms, which are far too small to see directly through a microscope. The atoms of any element are alike but are different from atoms of other elements. Atoms may stick together in well-defined molecules or may be packed together in large arrays. Different arrangements of atoms into groups compose all substances.

Equal volumes of different substances usually have different weights.

Atoms and molecules are perpetually in motion. Increased temperature means greater average energy of motion, so most substances expand when heated. In solids, the atoms are closely locked in position and can only vibrate. In liquids, the atoms or molecules have higher energy of motion, are more loosely connected, and can slide past one another; some molecules may get enough energy to escape into a gas. In gases, the atoms or molecules have still more energy of motion and are free of one another except during occasional collisions.

There are groups of elements that have similar properties, including highly reactive metals, less-reactive metals, highly reactive nonmetals (such as chlorine, fluorine, and oxygen), and some almost completely nonreactive gases (such as helium and neon). An especially important kind of reaction between substances involves combination of oxygen with something else—as in burning or rusting. Some elements don't fit into any of the categories; among them are carbon and hydrogen, essential elements of living matter.

No matter how substances within a closed system interact with one another, or how they combine or break apart, the total weight of the system remains the same. The idea of atoms explains the conservation of matter: If the number of atoms stays the same no matter how they are rearranged, then their total mass stays the same. p. 78

New York City Performance Standards

S1 Physical Sciences Concepts

The student demonstrates conceptual understanding by using a concept accurately to explain observations and make predictions and by representing the concept in multiple ways (through words, diagrams, graphs, or charts, as appropriate). Both aspects of understanding—explaining and representing—are required to meet this standard.

S1 b The student produces evidence that demonstrates understanding of motions and forces, such as inertia and the net effects of balanced and unbalanced forces.

Examples of activities through which students might demonstrate conceptual understanding of physical sciences include:
▲ Use the concept of force to explain the roles of front and rear brakes on a bicycle. **1b, 4d**
▲ Build a grandfather clock and explain how it works. **1b, 4d, 8c, A1a**

New York State Learning Standards for Math, Science, & Technology

Standard 4 Science
Physical Setting

5. Energy and matter interact through forces that result in changes in motion.

Students:

describe different patterns of motion of objects.

observe, describe, and compare effects of forces (gravity, electric current, and magnetism) on the motion of objects. p. 32

National Documents which guided New York State and New York City

NRC National Science Education Standards

Standard B Physical Science
Motions and Forces

The motion of an object can be described by its position, direction of motion, and speed. That motion can be measured and represented on a graph

An object that is not being subjected to a force will continue to move at a constant speed and in a straight line. If more than one force acts on an object along a straight line, then the forces will reinforce or cancel one another, depending on their direction and magnitude. Unbalanced forces will cause changes in the speed or direction of an object's motion. p. 154

Project 2061, AAAS
Benchmarks for Science Literacy

Chapter 4 The Physical Setting
4F Motion

An unbalanced force acting on an object changes its speed or direction of motion, or both. If the force acts toward a single center, the object's path may curve into an orbit around the center. p. 90

New York City Performance Standards

S1 Physical Sciences Concepts

The student demonstrates conceptual understanding by using a concept accurately to explain observations and make predictions and by representing the concept in multiple ways (through words, diagrams, graphs, or charts, as appropriate). Both aspects of understanding—explaining and representing—are required to meet this standard.

S1 c The student produces evidence that demonstrates understanding of transfer of energy, such as transformation of energy as heat; light, mechanical motion, and sound; and the nature of a chemical reaction.

Examples of activities through which students might demonstrate conceptual understanding of physical sciences include:
- Explain the difference between recycling and reusing in terms of mass and energy conservation. **1a, 1c, 3a, 4b**
- Conduct an energy audit of the classroom and develop procedures for reducing waste. **1c, 4a, 4b, A1b**
- Evaluate the claims and potential benefits of sunglasses that are advertised to screen out ultraviolet light. **1c, 4a, 4b, 4c**

New York State Learning Standards for Math, Science, & Technology

National Documents which guided New York State and New York City

NRC National Science Education Standards

Project 2061, AAAS Benchmarks for Science Literacy

Standard 4 Science Physical Setting

4. Energy exists in many forms, and when these forms change energy is conserved.

Students:

describe the sources and identify the transformations of energy observed in everyday life.

observe and describe heating and cooling events.

observe and describe energy changes as related to chemical reactions.

observe and describe the properties of sound, light, magnetism, and electricity.

describe situations that support the principle of conservation of energy. p. 32

Standard B Physical Science Transfer of Energy

Energy is a property of many substances and is associated with heat, light, electricity, mechanical motion, sound, nuclei, and the nature of a chemical. Energy is transferred in many ways.

Heat moves in predictable ways, flowing from warmer objects to cooler ones, until both reach the same temperature.

Light interacts with matter by transmission (including refraction), absorption, or scattering (including reflection). To see an object, light from that object—emitted by or scattered from it—must enter the eye

Electrical circuits provide a means of transferring electrical energy when heat, light, sound, and chemical changes are produced.

In most chemical and nuclear reactions, energy is transferred into or out of a system. Heat, light, mechanical motion, or electricity might all be involved in such transfers.

The sun is a major source of energy for changes on the earth's surface. The sun loses energy by emitting light. A tiny fraction of that light reaches the earth, transferring energy from the sun to the earth. The sun's energy arrives as light with a range of wavelengths, consisting of visible light, infrared, and ultraviolet radiation. p. 155

Chapter 4 The Physical Setting 4E Energy Transformations

Most of what goes on in the universe—from exploding stars and biological growth to the operation of machines and the motion of people—involves some form of energy being transformed into another. Energy in the form of heat is almost always one of the products of an energy transformation. p. 84

4F Motion

Light from the sun is made up of a mixture of many different colors of light, even though to the eye the light looks almost white. Other things that give off or reflect light have a different mix of colors.

Something can be "seen" when light waves emitted or reflected by it enter the eye—just as something can be "heard" when sound waves from it enter the ear.

Vibrations in materials set up wavelike disturbances that spread away from the source.

Human eyes respond to only a narrow range of wavelengths of electromagnetic radiation—visible light. Differences of wavelength within that range are perceived as differences in color. p. 90

Chapter 8 The Designed World 8C Energy Sources and Use

Energy can change from one form to another, although in the process some energy is always converted to heat. Some systems transform energy with less loss of heat than others

Electrical energy can be produced from a variety of energy sources and can be transformed into almost any other form of energy. Moreover, electricity is used to distribute energy quickly and conveniently to distant locations. p. 194

New York City Performance Standards

S2 Life Sciences Concepts

The student demonstrates conceptual understanding by using a concept accurately to explain observations and make predictions and by representing the concept in multiple ways (through words, diagrams, graphs, or charts, as appropriate). Both aspects of understanding—explaining and representing—are required to meet this standard.

S2 a The student produces evidence that demonstrates understanding of structure and function in living systems, such as the complementary nature of structure and function in cells, organs, tissues, organ systems, whole organisms, and ecosystems.

Examples of activities through which students might demonstrate conceptual understanding of life sciences include:

- Explain the effects of a particular disease (e.g., common cold) on an organism's internal structures and their related functions. **2a, 4a, 4c**
- Use drawings to demonstrate the structure and function relationships among a group of cells, tissues, or organs. **2a, 2c**
- Predict how long a plant will live planted in a closed glass jar located by a window; and explain what additional information regarding the plant and the surrounding environment would be needed to improve the prediction. **2a, 1a, 3a, 3b**
- Conduct an investigation to determine the kinds of seeds best suited to germination in a hydroponic system. **2a, 2d, 2e, 4b, 8a**

New York State Learning Standards for Math, Science, & Technology

Standard 4 Science
The Living Environment

1. Living things are both similar to and different from each other and nonliving things.

Students:

compare and contrast the parts of plants, animals, and one-celled organisms.

explain the functioning of the major human organ systems and their interactions.

5. Organisms maintain a dynamic equilibrium that sustains life.

Students:

compare the way a variety of living specimens carry out basic life functions and maintain dynamic equilibrium.

describe the importance of major nutrients, vitamins, and minerals in maintaining health and promoting growth and explain the need for a constant input of energy for living organisms. p. 33

National Documents which guided New York State and New York City

NRC National Science Education Standards

Standard C Life Science
Structure and Function in Living Systems

Living systems at all levels of organization demonstrate the complementary nature of structure and function.

All organisms are composed of cells—the fundamental unit of life.

Cells carry on the many functions needed to sustain life.

Specialized cells perform specialized functions in multicellular organisms.

The human organism has systems for digestion, respiration, reproduction, circulation, excretion, movement, control, and coordination, and for the protection from disease.

Disease is a breakdown in structures or functions of an organism. pp. 156-157

Project 2061, AAAS Benchmarks for Science Literacy

Chapter 5 The Living Environment
5C Cells

Within cells many of the basic functions of organisms—such as extracting energy from food and getting rid of waste—are carried out. The way in which cells function is similar in all living organisms. p. 112

Chapter 6 The Human Organism
6A Human Identity

Like other animals, human beings have body systems for obtaining and providing energy, defense, reproduction, and the coordination of body functions. p. 129

6C Basic Functions

Organs and organ systems are composed of cells and help to provide all cells with basic needs.

For the body to use food for energy and building materials, the food must first be digested into molecules that are absorbed and transported to cells.

To burn food for the release of energy stored in it, oxygen must be supplied to cells, and carbon dioxide removed.

Specialized cells and the molecules they produce identify and destroy microbes that get inside the body. p. 137

New York City Performance Standards

S2 Life Sciences Concepts

The student demonstrates conceptual understanding by using a concept accurately to explain observations and make predictions and by representing the concept in multiple ways (through words, diagrams, graphs, or charts, as appropriate). Both aspects of understanding—explaining and representing—are required to meet this standard.

S2 b The student produces evidence that demonstrates understanding of reproduction and heredity, such as sexual and asexual reproduction; and the role of genes and environment on trait expression.

Examples of activities through which students might demonstrate conceptual understanding of life sciences include:
▲ Write a story about how a person learned to overcome an inherited physical limitation. **2b, 4b**
▲ Explain why offspring of organisms that reproduce sexually never look exactly like their parents. **2b, 2e**
▲ Explain the lines of evidence showing that dogs and cats are related by common ancestors. **2b, 2c, 4a, 5c**
▲ Compare and contrast historical situations where species became extinct with situations where species survived due to differences in adaptive characteristics and the degree of environmental stress or change. **2b, 2c, 2d, 2e, 4a**

New York State Learning Standards for Math, Science, & Technology

Standard 4 Science
The Living Environment

2. Organisms inherit genetic information in a variety of ways that result in continuity of structure and function between parents and offspring.

Students:

describe sexual and asexual mechanisms for passing genetic materials from generation to generation.

describe simple mechanisms related to the inheritance of some physical traits in offspring.

4. The continuity of life is sustained through reproduction and development.

Students:

observe and describe the variations in reproductive patterns of organisms, including asexual and sexual reproduction.

explain the role of sperm and egg cells in sexual reproduction.

observe and describe developmental patterns in selected plants and animals (e.g., insects, humans, seed bearing plants).

observe and describe cell division at the microscopic level and its macroscopic effects. p. 33

National Documents which guided New York State and New York City

NRC National Science Education Standards

Standard C Life Science
Reproduction and Heredity

Reproduction is a characteristics of all living systems; because no living organism lives forever, reproduction is essential to the continuation of every species.

In many species, including humans, females produce eggs and males produce sperm. Plants also reproduce sexually—the egg and sperm are produced in the flowers of flowering plants. An egg and sperm unite to begin development of a new individual. That new individual receives genetic information from its mother (via the egg) and its father (via the sperm). Sexually produced offspring never are identical to either of their parents.

Every organism requires a set of instructions for specifying its traits. Heredity is the passage of these instructions from one generation to another.

Heredity information is contained in genes, located in the chromosomes of each cell.

The characteristics of an organism can be described in terms of a combination of traits. Some traits are inherited and others result from interactions with the environment. p. 157

Project 2061, AAAS
Benchmarks for Science Literacy

Chapter 5 The Living Environment
5B Heredity

In some kinds of organisms, all the genes come from a single parent, whereas in organisms that have seeds, typically half of the genes come from each parent.

In sexual reproduction, a single specialized cell from a female merges with a specialized cell from a male. As the fertilized egg, carrying the genetic information from each parent, multiplies to form the complete organism with about a trillion cells, the same genetic information is copied in each cell.

New varieties of cultivated plants and domestic animals have resulted from selective breeding for particular traits. p. 108

New York City Performance Standards

S2 Life Sciences Concepts

The student demonstrates conceptual understanding by using a concept accurately to explain observations and make predictions and by representing the concept in multiple ways (through words, diagrams, graphs, or charts, as appropriate). Both aspects of understanding—explaining and representing—are required to meet this standard.

S2c The student produces evidence that demonstrates understanding of regulation and behavior, such as senses and behavior; and response to environmental stimuli.

Examples of activities through which students might demonstrate conceptual understanding of life sciences include:

▲ Use drawings to demonstrate the structure and function relationships among a group of cells, tissues, or organs. **2a, 2c**

▲ Earn the Bird Study Merit Badge (Boy Scouts of America) or complete the Plant Culture Project (Girl Scouts of the U.S.A.) and explain how it helped you to understand animal behavior, ecology, or regulation. **2c, 2d, 2e, 4a**

▲ Explain the physiology of sneezes, tears, or what happens when people laugh. **2c**

▲ Explain the lines of evidence showing that dogs and cats are related by common ancestors. **2b, 2c, 4a, 5c**

▲ Compare and contrast historical situations where species became extinct with situations where species survived due to differences in adaptive characteristics and the degree of environmental stress or change. **2b, 2c, 2d, 2e, 4a**

New York State Learning Standards for Math, Science, & Technology

Standard 4 Science
The Living Environment

5. Organisms maintain a dynamic equilibrium that sustains life.

Students:

compare the way a variety of living specimens carry out basic life functions and maintain dynamic equilibrium. p. 33

National Documents which guided New York State and New York City

NRC National Science Education Standards

Standard C Life Science
Regulation and Behavior

All organisms must be able to obtain and use resources, grow, reproduce and maintain stable internal conditions while living in a constantly changing external environment.

Regulation of an organism's internal environment involves sensing the internal environment and changing physiological activities to keep conditions within the range required to survive.

Behavior is one kind of response an organism can make to an internal or environmental stimulus.

An organism's behavior evolves through adaptation to its environment. How a species moves, obtains food, reproduces, and responds to danger are based in the species' evolutionary history. p. 157

Project 2061, AAAS
Benchmarks for Science Literacy

Chapter 6 The Human Organism
6A Human Identity

Specialized roles of individuals within other species are genetically programmed, whereas human beings are able to invent and modify a wider range of social behaviors. p. 130

6C Basic Functions

Hormones are chemicals from glands that affect other body parts. They are involved in helping the body respond to danger and in regulating human growth, development, and reproduction.

Interactions among the senses, nerves, and brain make possible the learning that enables human beings to cope with changes in their environment. p. 137

New York City Performance Standards

S2 Life Sciences Concepts

The student demonstrates conceptual understanding by using a concept accurately to explain observations and make predictions and by representing the concept in multiple ways (through words, diagrams, graphs, or charts, as appropriate). Both aspects of understanding—explaining and representing—are required to meet this standard.

S2 d The student produces evidence that demonstrates understanding of populations and ecosystems, such as the roles of producers, consumers, and decomposers in a food web; and the effects of resources and energy transfer on populations.

Examples of activities through which students might demonstrate conceptual understanding of life sciences include:

▲ Earn the Bird Study Merit Badge (Boy Scouts of America) or complete the Plant Culture Project (Girl Scouts of the U.S.A.) and explain how it helped you to understand animal behavior, ecology, or regulation. **2c, 2d, 2e, 4a**

▲ Identify a pest in the immediate environment; and use an understanding of food webs to propose and test a way to eliminate the pest without introducing environmental poisons. **2d, 2e, 1c, 4b, 4c, 4d, 4e**

▲ Conduct an investigation to determine the kinds of seeds best suited to germination in a hydroponic system. **2a, 2d, 2e, 4b, 8a**

▲ Compare and contrast historical situations where species became extinct with situations where species survived due to differences in adaptive characteristics and the degree of environmental stress or change. **2b, 2c, 2d, 2e, 4a**

New York State Learning Standards for Math, Science, & Technology

Standard 4 Science
The Living Environment

6. Plants and animals depend on each other and their physical environment.

Students:

describe the flow of energy and matter through food chains and food webs

provide evidence that green plants make food and explain the significance of this process to other organisms. p. 33

National Documents which guided New York State and New York City

NRC National Science Education Standards

Standard C Life Science
Populations and Ecosystems

A population consists of all individuals of a species that occur together at a given place and time. All populations living together and the physical factors with which they interact compose an ecosystem.

Populations of organisms can be categorized by the function they serve in the ecosystem. Plants and some microorganisms are producers—they make their own food. All animals, including humans, are consumers, which obtain food by eating other organisms. Decomposers, primarily bacteria and fungi, are consumers that use waste materials and dead organisms for food. Food webs identify the relationships among producers, consumers, and decomposers in an ecosystem.

For ecosystems, the major source of energy is sunlight.

The number of organisms an ecosystem can support depends on the resources and abiotic factors, such as quantity of light and water, range of temperatures, and soil composition. p. 157-158

Project 2061, AAAS
Benchmarks for Science Literacy

Chapter 5 The Living Environment
5A Diversity of Life

One of the most general distinctions among organisms is between plants, which use sunlight to make their own food, and animals, which consume energy–rich foods.

All organisms, including the human species, are part of and depend on two main global food webs. One includes microscopic ocean plants, the animals that feed on them, and finally the animals that feed on those animals. p. 104

5D Interdependence of Life

In all environments—freshwater, marine, forest, grassland, mountain, and others— organisms with similar needs may compete with one another for resources including food, space, water, air, and shelter.

Two types of organisms may interact with each other in several ways: They may be in a producer/consumer, predator/prey, or parasite/host relationship. Or one organism may scavenge or decompose another. p. 117

5E The Flow of Matter and Energy

Food provides molecules that serves as fuel and building material for all organisms. Plants use the energy from light to make sugars out of carbon dioxide and water.

Over a long time, matter is transferred from one organism to another repeatedly and between organisms and their physical environment.

Energy can change from one form to another in living things. p. 120

New York City Performance Standards

S2 Life Sciences Concepts

The student demonstrates conceptual understanding by using a concept accurately to explain observations and make predictions and by representing the concept in multiple ways (through words, diagrams, graphs, or charts, as appropriate). Both aspects of understanding—explaining and representing—are required to meet this standard.

S2e The student produces evidence that demonstrates understanding of evolution, diversity, and adaptation of organisms, such as common ancestry, speciation, adaptation, variation, and extinction.

Examples of activities through which students might demonstrate conceptual understanding of life sciences include:

▴ Explain why offspring of organisms that reproduce sexually never look exactly like their parents. **2b, 2e**

▴ Earn the Bird Study Merit Badge (Boy Scouts of America) or complete the Plant Culture Project (Girl Scouts of the U.S.A.) and explain how it helped you to understand animal behavior, ecology, or regulation. **2c, 2d, 2e, 4a**

▴ Identify a pest in the immediate environment; and use an understanding of food webs to propose and test a way to eliminate the pest without introducing environmental poisons. **2d, 2e, 1c, 4b, 4c, 4d, 4e**

▴ Conduct an investigation to determine the kinds of seeds best suited to germination in a hydroponic system. **2a, 2d, 2e, 4b, 8a**

▴ Compare and contrast historical situations where species became extinct with situations where species survived due to differences in adaptive characteristics and the degree of environmental stress or change. **2b, 2c, 2d, 2e, 4a**

New York State Learning Standards for Math, Science, & Technology

Standard 4 Science
The Living Environment

3. Individual organisms and species change over time.

Students:

describe sources of variation in organisms and their structures and relate the variations to survival.

describe factors responsible for competition within species and the significance of that competition.

7. Human decisions and activities have had a profound impact on the physical and living environment.

Students:

describe how living things, including humans, depend upon the living and nonliving environment for their survival.

describe the effects of environmental changes on humans and other populations. p. 33

National Documents which guided New York State and New York City

NRC National Science Education Standards

Standard C Life Science
Diversity and Adaptations of Organisms

Millions of species of animals, plants, and microorganisms are alive today. Although different species might look dissimilar, the unity among organisms becomes apparent from an analysis of internal structures, the similarity of their chemical processes, and the evidence of common ancestry.

Biological evolution accounts for the diversity of species developed through gradual processes over many generations. Biological adaptations include changes in structures, behaviors, or physiology that enhance survival and reproductive success in a particular environment.

Extinction of a species occurs when the environment changes and the adaptive characteristics of a species are insufficient to allow its survival. p. 158

Project 2061, AAAS
Benchmarks for Science Literacy

Chapter 5 The Living Environment
5A Diversity of Life

One of the most general distinctions among organisms is between plants, which use sunlight to make their own food, and animals, which consume energy-rich foods.

Animals and plants have a great variety of body plans and internal structures that contribute to their being able to make or find food and reproduce.

In classifying organisms, biologists consider details of internal and external structures to be more important than behavior or general appearance.

For sexually reproducing organisms, a species includes all organisms that can mate with one another to produce fertile offspring. p. 104

5F Evolution of Life

Small differences between parents and offspring can accumulate (selective breeding) in successive generations so that descendants are very different from their ancestors.

Individual organisms with certain traits are more likely than others to survive and have offspring.

Many thousands of sedimentary rock layers provide evidence for the long history of the earth, and of changing life forms whose remains are found in rocks. p. 124

New York City Performance Standards

S3 Earth and Space Sciences Concepts

The student demonstrates conceptual understanding by using a concept accurately to explain observations and make predictions and by representing the concept in multiple ways (through words, diagrams, graphs, or charts, as appropriate). Both aspects of understanding—explaining and representing—are required to meet this standard.

S3a The student produces evidence that demonstrates understanding of structure of the Earth system, such as crustal plates and land forms; water and rock cycles; oceans, weather, and climate.

Examples of activities through which students might demonstrate conceptual understanding of Earth and space sciences include:

- Explain how earthquakes, volcanoes, and sea-floor spreading have a common cause. **3a, 3b, 4a, 4c**
- Write a story that describes what happens to a drop of water and the physical environment through which it flows as it travels from a lake to a river via the Earth's atmosphere. **3a, 3c, 1a, 4a**
- Complete the Geology Project (Girl Scouts of the U.S.A.) or earn the Astronomy Merit Badge (Boy Scouts of America) and explain what it helped you to understand about Earth processes and structures; fossil evidence; or aspects of the Solar System. **3a, 3b, 3c**

New York State Learning Standards for Math, Science, & Technology

Standard 4 Science
Physical Setting

2. Many of the phenomena that we observe on earth involve interactions among components of air, water and land.

Students:

explain how the atmosphere (air), hydrosphere (water) and lithosphere (land) interact , evolve, and change.

describe volcano and earthquake patterns, the rock, and weather. p. 34

National Documents which guided New York State and New York City

NRC National Science Education Standards

Standard D Earth and Space Science
Structure of the Earth System

The solid earth is layered with a lithosphere; hot, convecting mantle; and dense metallic core.

Lithospheric plates on the scales of continents and oceans constantly move at rates of centimeters per year in response to movements in the mantle.

Land forms are the result of a combination of constructive and destructive forces. Constructive forces include crustal deformation, volcanic eruption, and deposition of sediment, while destructive forces include weathering an erosion.

Water circulates through the crust, oceans, and atmosphere in what is known as the "water cycle." Water evaporates from the earth's surface, rises and cools as it moves to higher elevations, condenses as rain or snow and falls to the surface where it collects in lakes oceans, soil, and in rocks underground.

Some changes in the solid earth can be described as the "rock cycle." Old rocks at the earth's surface weather, forming sediments that are buried, then compacted, heated, and often re crystallized into new rock. Eventually, those new rocks may be brought to the surface by the forces that drive plate motions, and the rock cycle continues.

Soil consists of weathered rocks and decomposed organic material from dead plants, animals, and bacteria. Soils are often found in layers, with each having a different chemical composition and texture.

Water, which covers the majority of the earth's surface, circulates through the crust, oceans, and atmosphere in what is known as the "water cycle."

Water is a solvent. As it passes through the "water cycle" it dissolves minerals and gases and carries them to the oceans.

The atmosphere is a mixture of nitrogen, oxygen, ad trace gases that include water vapor. The atmosphere has different properties at different elevations.

Clouds, formed by the condensation of water vapor, affect weather and climate.

Global patterns of atmospheric movements influence local weather. p. 159-160

Project 2061, AAAS
Benchmarks for Science Literacy

Chapter 4 The Physical Setting
4B The Earth

The earth is mostly rock. Three-fourths of its surface is covered by a relatively thin layer of water (some of it frozen), and the entire planet is surrounded by a relatively thin blanket of air. It is the only body is the solar system that appears able to support life. The other planets have compositions and conditions very different from the earth's.

Climates have sometimes changed abruptly in the past as a result of changes in the earth's crust, such as volcanic eruptions or impacts of huge rocks from space. Even relatively small changes in atmospheric or ocean content can have widespread effects on climate if the change lasts long enough.

The cycling of water in and out of the atmosphere plays an important role in determining climatic patterns. Water evaporates from the surface of the earth, rises and cools, condenses into rain or snow, and falls again to the surface. The water falling on land collects in rivers and lakes, soil, and porous layers of rock, and much of it flows back into the ocean. p. 69

S3 Earth and Space Sciences Concepts

The student demonstrates conceptual understanding by using a concept accurately to explain observations and make predictions and by representing the concept in multiple ways (through words, diagrams, graphs, or charts, as appropriate). Both aspects of understanding—explaining and representing—are required to meet this standard.

S3 b The student produces evidence that demonstrates understanding of Earth's history, such as Earth processes including erosion and movement of plates; change over time and fossil evidence.

Examples of activities through which students might demonstrate conceptual understanding of Earth and space sciences include:

▲ Explain how earthquakes, volcanoes, and sea-floor spreading have a common cause. **3a, 3b, 4a, 4c**

▲ Complete the Geology Project (Girl Scouts of the U.S.A.) or earn the Astronomy Merit Badge (Boy Scouts of America) and explain what it helped you to understand about Earth processes and structures; fossil evidence; or aspects of the Solar System. **3a, 3b, 3c**

New York State Learning Standards for Math, Science, & Technology

Standard 4 Science
Physical Setting

2. Many of the phenomena that we observe on earth involve interactions among components of air, water and land.

Students:

explain how the atmosphere (air), hydrosphere (water) and lithosphere (land) interact, evolve, and change.

describe volcano and earthquake patterns, the rock cycle, and weather and climate changes. p. 32

National Documents which guided New York State and New York City

NRC National Science Education Standards

Standard D Earth and Space Science
Earth History

The earth processes we see today, including erosion, movement of lithospheric plates, and changes in atmospheric composition are similar to those that occurred in the past. Earth history is also influenced by occasional catastrophes, such as the impact of an asteroid or comet. Fossils provide important evidence of how life and environmental conditions have changed.

Structure of the Earth System

Living organisms have played many roles in the earth system, including affecting the composition of the atmosphere, producing some types of rocks, and contributing to the weathering of rocks. p. 160

Project 2061, AAAS
Benchmarks for Science Literacy

Chapter 4 The Physical Setting
4C Processes that Shape the Earth

The interior of the earth is hot. Heat flow and movement of materials within the earth cause earthquakes ad volcanic eruptions and create mountains and ocean basins. Gas and dust form large volcanoes can change the atmosphere.

Some changes in the earth's surface are abrupt (such as earthquakes and volcanic eruptions) while other changes happen very slowly (such as uplift and wearing down of mountains). The earth's surface is shaped in part by the motion of water and wind over very long times, which act to level mountain ranges.

Sediments of sand and smaller particles (sometimes containing the remains of organisms) are gradually buried and are cemented together by dissolved minerals to form solid rock again.

Sedimentary rock buried deep enough may be reformed by pressure and heat, perhaps melting and re crystallizing into different kinds of rock. These re-formed rock layers may be forced up again to become land surface and even mountains. Subsequently this new rock too will erode. Rock bears evidence of the minerals, temperatures and forces that created it.

Thousands of layers of sedimentary rock confirm the long history of the changing surface of the earth and the changing life forms whose remains are found in successive layers. p. 73

New York City Performance Standards

S3 Earth and Space Sciences Concepts

The student demonstrates conceptual understanding by using a concept accurately to explain observations and make predictions and by representing the concept in multiple ways (through words, diagrams, graphs, or charts, as appropriate). Both aspects of understanding—explaining and representing—are required to meet this standard.

S3c The student produces evidence that demonstrates understanding of Earth in the solar system, such as the predictable motion of planets, moons, and other objects in the solar system including days, years, moon phases, and eclipses; and the role of the Sun as the major source of energy for phenomena on the Earth's surface.

Examples of activities through which students might demonstrate conceptual understanding of Earth and space sciences include:

▲ Write a story that describes what happens to a drop of water and the physical environment through which it flows as it travels from a lake to a river via the Earth's atmosphere. **3a, 3c, 1a, 4a**

▲ Complete the Geology Project (Girl Scouts of the U.S.A.) or earn the Astronomy Merit Badge (Boy Scouts of America) and explain what it helped you to understand about Earth processes and structures; fossil evidence; or aspects of the Solar System. **3a, 3b, 3c**

▲ Create a storybook to explain to a younger child how occasional catastrophes, such as the impact of an asteroid or comet, can influence the Earth's history. **3b, 3c, 2b, 2c, 2d, 2e**

▲ Predict what will happen to the reading of your weight on a bathroom scale while riding in an elevator, investigate your predication, and explain why the prediction was or was not accurate. **3c, 1b**

▲ Use the concept of gravity to explain why people can jump higher on the Moon than they can on Earth. **3c**

New York State Learning Standards for Math, Science, & Technology

Standard 4 Science
Physical Setting

1. The earth and celestial phenomena can be described by principles of relative motion and perspective.

Students:

explain daily, monthly, and seasonal changes on earth. p. 32

National Documents which guided New York State and New York City

NRC National Science Education Standards

Standard D Earth and Space Science
Earth in the Solar System

The earth is the third planet from the sun in a system that includes the moon, the sun, eight other planets and their moons, and smaller objects, such as asteroids and comets The sun, an average star, is the central and largest body in the solar system.

Most objects in the solar system are in regular and predictable motion. Those motions explain such phenomena as the day, the year, phases of the moon, and eclipses.

Gravity is the force that keeps planets in orbit around the sun and governs the rest of the motion in the solar system. Gravity alone holds us to the earth's surface and explains the phenomena of the tides.

The sun is the major source of energy for phenomena on the earth's surface such as growth of plants, wind, ocean currents, and the water cycle. Seasons result from variations in the amount of the sun's energy hitting the surface, due to the tilt of the earth's rotation on its axis and the length of the day. p. 160-161

Project 2061, AAAS
Benchmarks for Science Literacy

Chapter 4 The Physical Setting
4A The Universe

Nine planets of very different size, composition and surface features move around the sun in nearly circular orbits. Some planets have a great variety of moons and even flat rings of rock and ice particles orbiting around them. Some of these planets and moons show evidence of geologic activity. The earth is orbited by one moon, many artificial satellites, and debris. p. 64

4B The Earth

We live on a relatively small planet, the third from the sun, in the only system of planets definitely known to exist (although other similar systems may be discovered in the universe).

Everything on or anywhere near the earth is pulled toward the earth's center by gravitational force.

Because the earth turns daily on an axis that is tilted relative to the plane of the earth's yearly orbit around the sun, sunlight falls more intensely on different parts of the earth during the year. The difference in heating of the earth's surface produces the planet's seasons and weather patterns.

The moon's orbit around the earth once in about 28 days changes what part of the moon is lighted by the sun and how much of that part can be seen from the earth—the phases of the moon.

The moon's orbit around the earth, once in about 28 days, changes what part of the moon is lighted by the sun and how much of that part can be seen from the earth—the phases of the moon. pp. 68-69

New York City Performance Standards

S3 Earth and Space Sciences Concepts

The student demonstrates conceptual understanding by using a concept accurately to explain observations and make predictions and by representing the concept in multiple ways (through words, diagrams, graphs, or charts, as appropriate). Both aspects of understanding—explaining and representing—are required to meet this standard.

S3d The student produces evidence that demonstrates understanding of natural resource management.

Examples of activities through which students might demonstrate conceptual understanding of Earth and space sciences include:

▲ Identify a place that is subject to periodic flooding, evaluate its positive and negative consequences, and study different ways of maintaining, reducing or eliminating the likelihood of flooding. **3d**

New York State Learning Standards for Math, Science, & Technology

Standard 4 Science
The Living Environment

7. Human decisions and activities have had a profound impact on the physical and living environment.

Students:

describe how living things, including humans, depend upon the living and non living environment for their survival.

describe the effects of environmental changes on humans and other populations. p. 33

National Documents which guided New York State and New York City

NRC National Science Education Standards

Standard C Life Science
Populations and Ecosystems

The number of organisms an ecosystem can support depends on the resources available and abiotic factors, such as quantity of light and water, range of temperature, and soil composition. Given adequate biotic and abiotic resources and no disease or predators, populations (including humans) increase at rapid rates. Lack of resources and other factors, such as predation and climate, limit the growth of populations in specific niches in the ecosystem. p. 158

Standard F Science in Personal and Social Perspectives
Personal Health

Natural environments may contain substances (for example, radon and lead) that are harmful to human beings. Maintaining environmental health involves establishing or monitoring quality standards related to use of soil, water, and air.

Populations, Resources, and Environments

When an area becomes overpopulated, the environment will become degraded due to the increased use of resources.

Causes of environmental degradation and resource depletion vary from region to region and from country to country.

Natural Hazards

Human activities also can induce hazards through resource acquisitions, urban growth, land-use decisions, and waste disposal. Such activities can accelerate many natural changes. p. 168

Project 2061, AAAS
Benchmarks for Science Literacy

Chapter 4 The Physical Setting
4B The Earth

The benefits of the earth's resources—such as fresh water, air, soil, and trees—can be reduced by using them wastefully or by deliberately or inadvertently destroying them. The atmosphere and the oceans have a limited capacity to absorb wastes and recycle materials naturally. Cleaning up polluted air, water, or soil or restoring depleted soil, forests, or fishing grounds can be very difficult and costly. p. 69

4C Processes that Shape the Earth

Human activities, such as reducing the amount of forest cover, increasing the amount and variety of chemicals released into the atmosphere, and intensive farming, have changed the earth's land, oceans and atmosphere. Some of these changes have decreased the capacity of the environment to support some life forms. p. 73

Chapter 5 The Living Environment
5D Interdependence of Life

In all environments--freshwater, marine, forest, desert, grassland, mountain, and other--organisms with similar needs may compete with one another for resources, including food, space, water air, and shelter. In any particular environment, the growth ad survival of organisms depend on the physical conditions. p. 117

New York City Performance Standards

S4 Scientific Connections and Applications

The student demonstrates conceptual understanding by using a concept accurately to explain observations and make predictions and by representing the concept in multiple ways (through words, diagrams, graphs, or charts, as appropriate). Both aspects of understanding—explaining and representing—are required to meet this standard.

The student produces evidence that demonstrates understanding of:

S4a Big ideas and unifying concepts, such as order and organization; models, form, and function; change and constancy; and cause and effect.

S4b The designed world, such as the reciprocal nature of science and technology; the development of agricultural techniques; and the viability of technological designs.

S4c Health, such as nutrition, exercise, and disease; effects of drugs and toxic substances; personal and environmental safety; and resources and environmental stress.

S4d Impact of technology, such as constraints and trade-offs; feedback; benefits and risks; and problems and solutions.

S4e Impact of science, such as historical and contemporary contributions; and interactions between science and society.

Examples of activities through which students might demonstrate conceptual understanding of scientific connections and applications include:

- Create a health pamphlet for a track team that travels around North America to help them adjust to altitudes different from the place where they usually train, and explain why these adjustments are necessary. 4a, 4d, 2c
- Develop a plan to modify the school's fire warning system for students with disabilities. 4b, 4d
- Analyze an automatic ice maker and explain how its design takes into account the differences in the properties of water in liquid and solid states. 4b, 4d, 1a
- Identify a pest in a local agricultural setting; and compare and contrast the risks and benefits of chemical and biological pest control. 4b, 4c, 4d, 4e, 2d
- Hypothesize why people tend to get more colds and flu in the winter and discuss ways to prevent the spread of illness. 4c, 2c
- Investigate local water quality standards and make recommendations to school officials about water quality on and near the campus. 4c, 3a, A1b

New York State Learning Standards for Math, Science, & Technology

Standard 6 Interconnectedness: Common Themes

Students will understand the relationships and common themes that connect mathematics, science, and technology and apply the themes to these and other areas of learning.

Systems Thinking

1. Through systems thinking, people can recognize the commonalities that exist among all systems and how parts of a system interrelate and combine to perform specific functions. p. 52

Models

2. Models are simplified representations of objects, structures, or systems used in analysis, explanation, interpretation, or design. p. 52

Magnitude and Scale

3. The grouping of magnitudes of size, time, frequency, and pressures or other units of measurement into a series of relative order provides a useful way to deal with the immense range and the changes in scale that affect the behavior and design of systems. p. 53

Equilibrium and Stability

4. Equilibrium is a state of stability due either to a lack of changes (static equilibrium) or a balance between opposing forces (dynamic equilibrium). p. 53

Patterns of Change

5. Identifying patterns of change is necessary for making predictions about future behavior and conditions. p. 54

Optimization

6. In order to arrive at the best solution that meets criteria within constraints, it is often necessary to make trade-offs. p.54

National Documents which guided New York State and New York City

NRC National Science Education Standards

Unifying Concepts and Processes
  Systems, order, and organization
  Evidence, models, and explanation
  Constancy, change, and measurement
  Evolution and equilibrium
  Form and function pp. 115-119

Standard E Science and Technology pp. 161-166

Standard F Science in Personal and Social Perspectives
  Personal Health
  Characteristics and Changes in Populations
  Types of Resources
  Changes in Environments
  Science and Technology in Local Challenges pp. 166-170

Standard G History and Nature of Science pp. 170-171

Project 2061, AAAS Benchmarks for Science Literacy

Chapter 3 The Nature of Technology pp. 41-57

Chapter 6 The Human Organism pp. 127-149

Chapter 8 The Designed World pp. 181-207

Chapter 10 Historical Perspectives pp. 237-259

Chapter 11 Common Themes
11A Systems
11B Models
11C Constancy and Change
11D Scale pp. 261-279

New York City Performance Standards

S5 Scientific Thinking

The student demonstrates scientific inquiry and problem solving by using thoughtful questioning and reasoning strategies, common sense and conceptual understanding from Science Standards 1 to 4, and appropriate methods to investigate the natural world; that is, the student:

S5a Frames questions to distinguish cause and effect; and identifies or controls variables in experimental and non-experimental research settings.

S5b Uses concepts from Science Standards 1 to 4 to explain a variety of observations and phenomena.

S5c Uses evidence from reliable sources to develop descriptions, explanations, and models.

S5d Proposes, recognizes, analyzes, considers, and critiques alternative explanations; and distinguishes between fact and opinion.

S5e Identifies problems; proposes and implements solutions; and evaluates the accuracy, design, and outcomes of investigations.

S5f Works individually and in teams to collect and share information and ideas.

Examples of activities through which students might demonstrate skill in scientific thinking include:

▲ Investigate the results of two fellow students' plant growth experiments and recommend ways to enhance the information. 5a, 5b, 5c, 5d, 5e, 5f, 2a

▲ Determine if the scientific evidence in the summary data chart in Consumer Reports substantiates recommendations about the "Best Buy" for a particular purchase. 5a, 5b, 5c, 5d, 5e

▲ Work with another student to investigate the effects of several variables on oxygen production in an aquatic plant, e.g., nutrients, light, color of container. 5a, 5b, 5c, 5d, 5e, 5f, 2a, 2c

▲ Evaluate the claims and potential risks and benefits of a newly advertised "diet pill." 5b, 5c, 5d, 5e, 2c, 4c

---

New York State Learning Standards for Math, Science, & Technology

Standard 1 Analysis, Inquiry, and Design
Scientific Inquiry

1. The central purpose of scientific inquiry is to develop explanations of natural phenomena in a continuing, creative process. p. 2

2. Beyond the use of reasoning and consensus, scientific inquiry involves the testing of proposed explanations involving the use of conventional techniques and procedures and usually requiring considerable ingenuity. p. 2

3. The observations made while testing explanations, when analyzed using conventional and invented methods, provide new insights into phenomena. p. 3

National Documents which guided New York State and New York City

NRC National Science Education Standards

Standard A Science as Inquiry

Identify questions that can be answered through scientific investigations. p. 145

Develop descriptions, explanations, predictions, and models using evidence. p. 145

Think critically and logically to make the relationships between evidence and explanations. p. 145

Recognize and analyze alternative explanations and predictions. p. 148

Scientific explanations emphasize evidence, have logically consistent arguments, and use scientific principles, models, and theories. p. 148

Project 2061, AAAS Benchmarks for Science Literacy

Chapter 1 The Nature of Science
1B Scientific Inquiry

If more than one variable changes at the same time in an experiment, the outcome of the experiment may not be clearly attributable to any one of the variables. It may not always be possible to prevent outside variables from influencing the outcome of an investigation (or even to identify all of the variables), but collaboration among investigators can often lead to research designs that are able to deal with such situations. p. 12

Chapter 12 Habits of Mind
12E Critical Response Skills

Notice and criticize the reasoning in arguments in which (1) fact and opinion are intermingled or the conclusions do not follow logically from the evidence given, (2) an analogy is not apt, (3) no mention is made of whether the control groups are very much like the experimental group, or (4) all members of a group (such as teenagers or chemists) are implied to have nearly identical characteristics that differ from those of other groups. p. 299

New York City Performance Standards

S6 Scientific Tools and Technologies

The student demonstrates competence with the tools and technologies of science by using them to collect data, make observations, analyze results, and accomplish tasks effectively; that is, the student:

S6a Uses technology and tools (such as traditional laboratory equipment, video, and computer aids) to observe and measure objects, organisms, and phenomena, directly, indirectly, and remotely.

S6b Records and stores data using a variety of formats, such as data bases, audiotapes, and videotapes.

S6c Collects and analyzes data using concepts and techniques in Mathematics Standard 4, such as mean, median, and mode; outcome probability and reliability; and appropriate data displays.

S6d Acquires information from multiple sources, such as print, the Internet, computer data bases, and experimentation.

S6e Recognizes sources of bias in data, such as observer and sampling biases.

Examples of activities through which students might demonstrate competence with the tools and technologies of science include:

▲ Use a microcomputer-based investigation to compare the rates at which different carbonated beverages in a variety of containers lose their fizz. 6a, 1a, 4b, 5a
▲ Complete the Animal Observation Project (Girl Scouts of the U.S.A.) and teach another student how to conduct field observations. 6a, 2d
▲ Conduct a field research project to compare the distribution of birds near the school with a field guide for the region to see if local distributions are the same as regional. 6c, 6d, 2d
▲ Compare the accuracy and timeliness of local weather information from a variety of sources. 6d, 3a
▲ Exchange data on the acidity of rain with students from other states or countries. Figure out why the data differ, if they do. 6d, 1a, 3a
▲ Use electronic data bases to get current information on the health effects of long-term space travel. 6d, 3c, 4c

New York State Learning Standards for Math, Science, & Technology

Standard 2 Information Systems

1. Information technology is used to retrieve, process, and communicate information and as a tool to enhance learning.

Students:

use spreadsheets and data-base software to collect, process, display, and analyze information. p. 10

Standard 3 Mathematics
Modeling/Multiple Representation

4. Students use mathematical modeling/multiple representation to provide a means of presenting, interpreting, communicating, and connecting mathematical information and relationships. p. 19

Measurement

5. Students use measurement in both metric and English measure to provide a major link between the abstractions of mathematics and the real world in order to describe and compare objects and data. p. 20

National Documents which guided New York State and New York City

NRC National Science Education Standards

Standard A Science as Inquiry

Develop appropriate tools and techniques to gather, analyze, and interpret data. p. 145

Use mathematics in all aspects of scientific inquiry. p. 148

Project 2061, AAAS Benchmarks for Science Literacy

Chapter 12 Habits of Mind
12C Manipulation and Observation

Use computers to store and retrieve information in topical, alphabetical, numerical, and key-word files, and create simple files of their own devising.

Read analog and digital meters on instruments used to make direct observations of length, volume, weight, elapsed time, rates, and temperature, and choose appropriate units for reporting various magnitudes.

Use cameras and tape recorders for capturing information. p. 294

12D Communication Skills

Locate information in reference books, back issues of newspapers and magazines, compact discs, and computer databases. p. 297

New York City Performance Standards

S7 Scientific Communication

The student demonstrates effective scientific communication by clearly describing aspects of the natural world using accurate data, graphs, or other appropriate media to convey depth of conceptual understanding in science; that is, the student:

S7a Represents data and results in multiple ways, such as numbers, tables, and graphs; drawings, diagrams, and artwork; and technical and creative writing.

S7b Argues from evidence, such as data produced through his or her own experimentation or by others.

S7c Critiques published materials.

S7d Explains a scientific concept or procedure to other students.

S7e Communicates in a form suited to the purpose and the audience, such as by writing instructions that others can follow; critiquing written and oral explanations; and using data to resolve disagreements.

Examples of activities through which students might demonstrate competence in scientific communication include:

▲ Earn the Drafting Merit Badge. (Boy Scouts of America) 7a, 4b, 5c, 6a

▲ Write an advertisement for a hair care product that explains the chemistry of how it works. 7b, 1a, 4b, 4c, 5d

▲ Analyze and give a speech about a ballot initiative on toxic chemicals. 7c, 1a, 2c, 3a, 4b, 5d, 6d

▲ Critique a USA Today article which reports that eating hot dogs in childhood causes adult leukemia. 7c, 2c, 4c, 5d

▲ Write a review of an episode of Beakman's World. 7c, 5d, 6d

▲ Make an animated video illustrating how white blood cells protect the body from infectious agents. 7d, 2a, 2c, 4c, 5c

New York State Learning Standards for Math, Science, & Technology

Standard 1 Analysis, Inquiry, and Design
Scientific Inquiry

3. The observations made while testing explanations, when analyzed using conventional and invented methods, provide new insights into phenomena.

Students:

design charts, tables, graphs, and other representations of observations in conventional and creative ways to help them address their research question or hypothesis. p. 5

National Documents which guided New York State and New York City

NRC National Science Education Standards

Standard A Science as Inquiry

Think critically and logically to make the relationships between evidence and explanations. p. 145

Communicate scientific procedures and explanations. p. 148

Project 2061, AAAS Benchmarks for Science Literacy

Chapter 9 The Mathematical World
9B Symbolic Relationships

Graphs can show a variety of possible relationships between two variables. p. 219

Chapter 12 Habits of Mind
12D Communication Skills

Organize information in simple tables and graphs and identify relationships they reveal. p. 297

12E Critical Response Skills

Question claims based on vague attributions (such as "Leading doctors say...") or on statements made by celebrities or others outside the area of their particular expertise.

Be skeptical of arguments based on very small samples of data, biased samples, or samples for which there was no control sample. p. 299

New York City Performance Standards

S8 Scientific Investigation

The student demonstrates scientific competence by completing projects drawn from the following kinds of investigations, including at least one full investigation each year and, over the course of middle school, investigations that integrate several aspects of Science Standards 1 to 7 and represent all four of the kinds of investigation:

S8a Controlled experiment.

S8b Fieldwork.

S8c Design.

S8d Secondary research, such as use of others' data.

A single project may draw on more than one type of investigation.

A full investigation includes:

• Questions that can be studied using the resources available.

• Procedures that are safe, humane, and ethical; and that respect privacy and property rights.

• Data that have been collected and recorded (see also Science Standard 6) in ways that others can verify, and analyzed using skills expected at this grade level (see also Mathematics Standard 4).

• Data and results that have been represented (see also Science Standard 7) in ways that fit the context.

• Recommendations, decisions, and conclusions based on evidence.

• Acknowledgment of references and contributions of others.

• Results that are communicated appropriately to audiences.

• Reflection and defense of conclusions and recommendations from other sources and peer review.

Examples of projects through which students might demonstrate competence in scientific investigation include:

▲ Analyze de-icers for relative effectiveness, cost, and environmental impact. 8a, 1a, 3d, 4d

▲ Study different methods for cooking chicken considering health and aesthetics. 8a, 8c, 4c

▲ Conduct a field study of monument degradation over time at a local cemetery. 8b, 1a, 3a

▲ Adopt a stream and use that location to study habitat and water quality over time. 8b, 2d, 3a

▲ Design a protective container for an uncooked egg using the concepts of force, motion, gravity, and acceleration and test the design by dropping the container (egg enclosed) from a one-story building. 8c, 1a, 1b

▲ Research local climate changes over the last century. 8d, 3a

New York State Learning Standards for Math, Science, & Technology

Standard 1 Analysis, Inquiry, and Design
Scientific Inquiry

1. The central purpose of scientific inquiry is to develop explanations of natural phenomena in a continuing, creative process.

2. Beyond the use of reasoning and consensus, scientific inquiry involves the testing of proposed explanations involving the use of conventional techniques and procedures and usually requiring considerable ingenuity. p. 4

3. The observations made while testing explanations, when analyzed using conventional and invented methods, provide new insights into phenomena. p. 5

Engineering Design

1. Engineering design is an iterative process involving modeling and optimization finding the best solution within given constraints which is used to develop technological solutions to problems within given constraints. p. 5

National Documents which guided New York State and New York City

NRC National Science Education Standards

Standard A Science as Inquiry

Design and conduct a scientific investigation. Students should develop general abilities, such as systematic observation, making accurate measurements, and identifying and controlling variables. They should also develop the ability to clarify their ideas that are influencing and guiding inquiry, and to understand how those ideas compare with current scientific knowledge. Students learn to formulate questions, design investigations, execute investigations, interpret data, use evidence to generate explanations, propose alternative explanations, and critique explanations and procedures. p. 145

Standard E Science and Technology

Identify a problem or design an opportunity.

Propose designs and choose between alternative solutions.

Implement a proposed solution.

Evaluate the solution and its consequences.

Communicate the problem, process, and solution. p. 192

Project 2061, AAAS Benchmarks for Science Literacy

Chapter 1 The Nature of Science
1B Scientific Inquiry

Scientists differ greatly in what phenomena they study and how they go about their work. Although there is no fixed set of steps that all scientists follow, scientific investigations usually involve the collection of relevant evidence, the use of logical reasoning, and the application of imagination in devising hypotheses and explanations to make sense of the collected evidence. p. 12

Chapter 3 The Nature of Technology
3B Design and Systems

Design usually requires taking constraints into account. Some constraints, such as gravity or the properties of materials to be used, are unavoidable. Other constraints, including economic, political, social, ethical, and aesthetic ones, limit choices. p. 51

Work Sample & Commentary: *Mechanical Nut*

Physical
Sciences
Concepts S1

Life
Sciences
Concepts

Earth and
Space Sciences
Concepts

Scientific
Connections and
Applications

Scientific
Thinking S5

Scientific Tools
and
Technologies

Scientific
Communication S7

Scientific
Investigation

The task

After a unit on motion and forces, students were asked to move a mechanical nut in a horizontal direction as far as possible without directly rolling, throwing, pushing, or sliding the nut itself. The students were given limited materials (cardboard tube, small plastic container with cap, 70 cm of ramp, cotton, small pebbles, and meter sticks) to accomplish the task. Additional "challenge" tasks were assigned, such as moving the nut exactly one meter. After recording observations and results of various experiments, the students were required to complete a written report including the following sections: title, purpose (hypothesis), materials, procedure, results, and conclusion.

For related work on Force and Motion, see "Come Back Can", page 36, and "The Challenger Disaster", page 153.

Circumstances of performance

This sample of student work was produced under the following conditions:

alone	√ in a group
√ in class	√ as homework
√ with teacher feedback	with peer feedback
timed	√ opportunity for revision

The quotations from the Science performance descriptions in this commentary are excerpted. The complete performance descriptions are shown on pages 68-84.

What the work shows

S1b Physical Sciences Concepts: The student produces evidence that demonstrates understanding of motions and forces, such as inertia and the net effects of balanced and unbalanced forces.

Ⓐ In the results, the students identify forces acting in this system, and describe the effects of those forces. The students correctly state that gravity pulls the mechanical nut down, affecting its motion. The students correctly identify how friction changes the motion of the nut.

This work sample illustrates a standard-setting performance for the following parts of the standards:

S1b **Physical Sciences Concepts: Motions and forces.**

S5b **Scientific Thinking: Use concepts from Science Standards 1 to 4.**

S5e **Scientific Thinking: Identify problems; propose and implement solutions; and evaluate the accuracy, design, and outcomes of investigations.**

S5f **Scientific Thinking: Work individually and in teams.**

S7e **Scientific Communication: Communicate in a form suited to the purpose and the audience.**

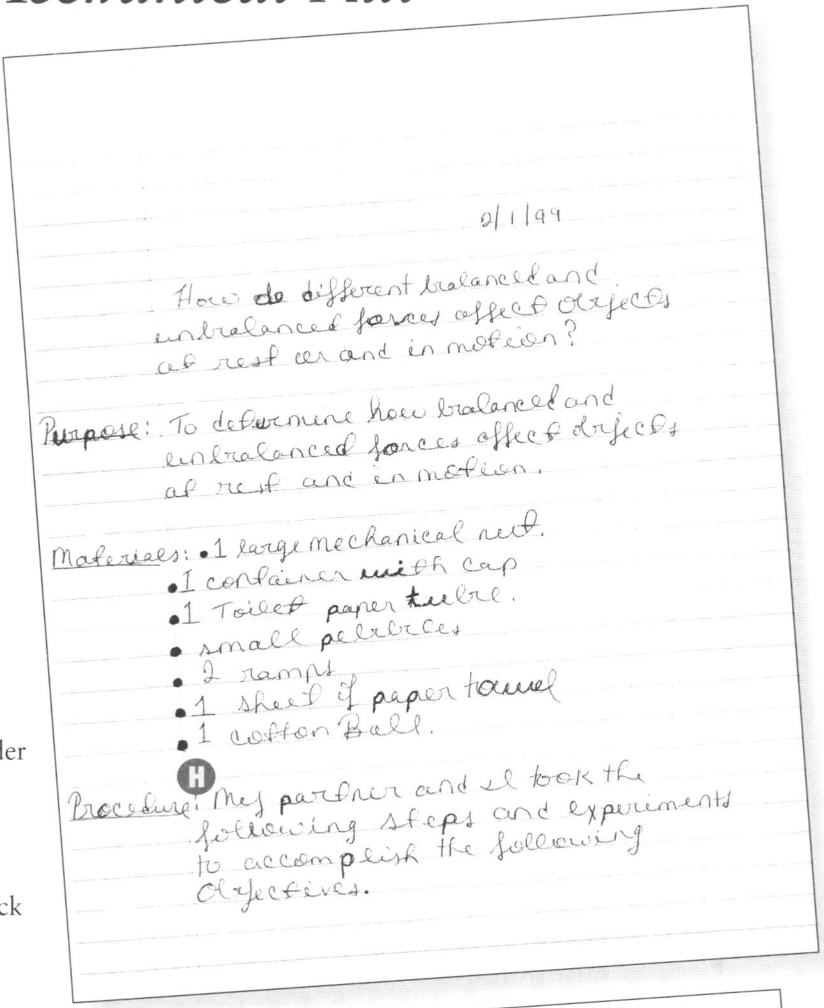

[Handwritten student work, page 1:]

2/1/99

How do different balanced and unbalanced forces affect objects at rest or and in motion?

Purpose: To determine how balanced and unbalanced forces affect objects at rest and in motion.

Materials:
• 1 large mechanical nut.
• 1 container with cap
• 1 Toilet paper tube.
• small pebbles
• 2 ramps
• 1 sheet of paper towel
• 1 cotton Ball.

Ⓗ Procedure: My partner and I took the following steps and experiments to accomplish the following Objectives.

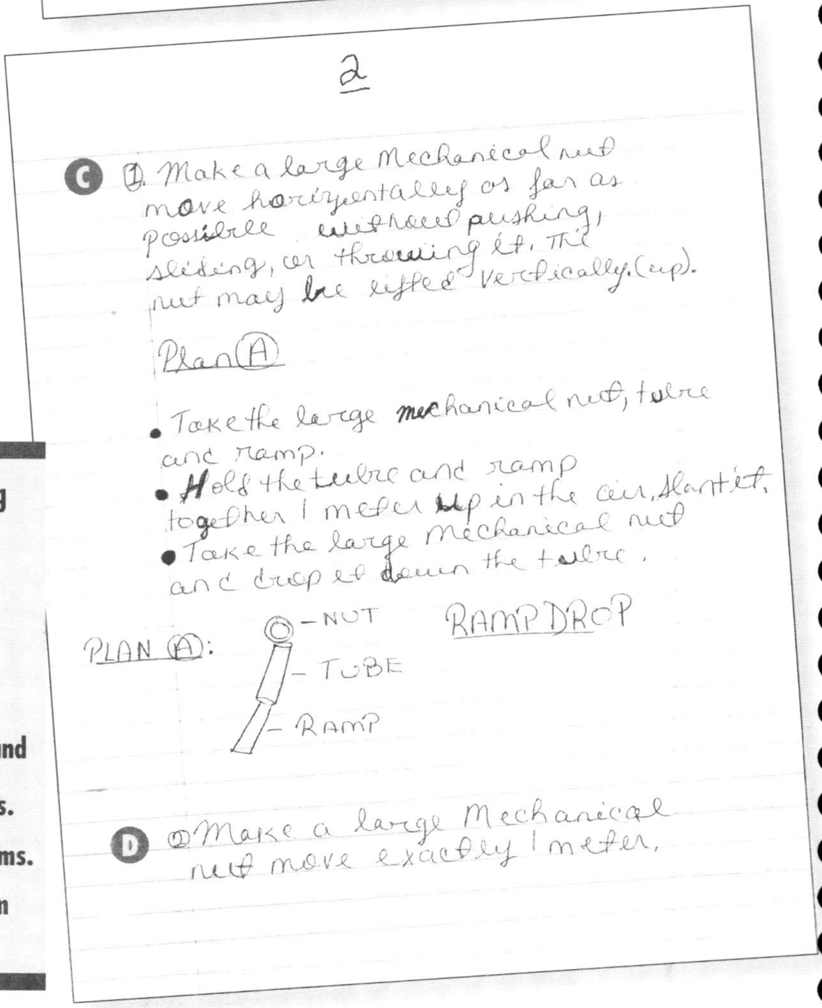

[Handwritten student work, page 2:]

2

Ⓒ ① Make a large Mechanical nut move horizentally as far as possible without pushing, sliding, or throwing it. The nut may be lifted vertically. (up).

Plan Ⓐ

• Take the large mechanical nut, tube and ramp.
• Hold the tube and ramp together 1 meter up in the air, slant it.
• Take the large mechanical nut and drop it down the tube.

PLAN Ⓐ: — NUT   RAMPDROP
            — TUBE
            — RAMP

Ⓓ ① Make a large Mechanical nut move exactly 1 meter.

Mechanical Nut

B The students' conclusion correctly describes how different forces affect the movement of the mechanical nut. The students describe how balanced and unbalanced forces act upon the nut in terms of changes in direction and/or speed.

S5 b Scientific Thinking: The student uses concepts from Science Standards 1 to 4 to explain a variety of observations and phenomena.

A The students correctly identify and describe the effects of friction on motion.

B The students correctly identify and describe the effects of gravity on the mechanical nut.

S5 e Scientific Thinking: The student identifies problems; proposes and implements solutions; and evaluates the accuracy, design, and outcomes of investigation.

A The students evaluate the successful outcomes of their procedural designs, and provide insight into the reasoning behind specific details of each procedure.

C D E F G The students identify five problems (numbered by the students themselves as A through E) and design and implement a procedure that solves each problem.

S5 f Scientific Thinking: The student works individually and in teams to collect and share information and ideas.

A In the results, the student who recorded for the team states overtly that the work was done as a team. Phrasing such as "My partner and I…" and "…we used…" makes it clear that the students worked cooperatively throughout the development of experiments and presentations.

H The student prefaces the activities with a statement that the procedure is being carried out in partnership with another student.

S7 e Scientific Communication: The student communicates in a form suited to the purpose and the audience, such as by writing instructions that others can follow….

C D E The students presented a written report that pairs each problem with a plan and a diagram of the set-up. Three plans are clear, concise and accurate representations of the procedures, and they meet the standard. (The remaining two pairs require some minor clarification for replication by other students.) The students created a report that demonstrates an organized structure appropriate to the purpose, audience and context, and excludes extraneous and inappropriate information.

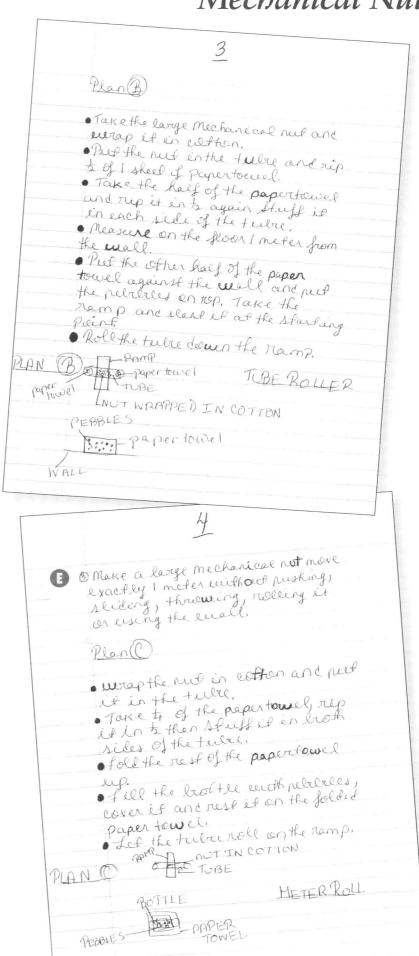

Physical Sciences Concepts

Life Sciences Concepts

Earth and Space Sciences Concepts

Scientific Connections and Applications

S5 Scientific Thinking

Scientific Tools and Technologies

S7 Scientific Communication

Scientific Investigation

Mechanical Nut

Physical
Sciences
Concepts · S1

Life
Sciences
Concepts

Earth and
Space Sciences
Concepts

Scientific
Connections and
Applications

Scientific
Thinking · S5

Scientific Tools
and
Technologies

Scientific
Communication · S7

Scientific
Investigation

5

F ④ Make a large mechanical nut move in one direction, stop and move in the other direction.

Plan ⓓ

- wrap the nut in cotton and stuff it in the bottle.
- Take the tube and the paper towel. Stuff the paper towel in one end of the tube.
- Take the other end of the paper towel in the ramp.
- Set up the ramp, paper towel and tube so that it is in front of the ramp and the bottle.
- Take the ramp, slant it and let the bottle go.

PLAN ⓓ NUT WRAPPED IN COTTON — RAMP — BOTTLE BOUNCE BACK

TUBE

RAMP PAPER TOWEL

6

G ⑤ Make a large mechanical nut move and return to the exact starting point.

Plan ⓔ

- wrap the nut in cotton and stuff it in the tube.
- Rip the paper towel in half and stuff it in each side of the tube.
- Measure one foot on the floor from the teachers desk.

PLAN ⓔ paper towel — RAMP — nut in cotton TUBE

TEACHERS DESK   EXACT BOUNCE

7

A

Results: Plans A through E were successful. For plan A, the nut drops down the tube because of gravity. In plan B, you may ask yourself why my partner and I put pebbles on the paper towel. The answer was to create friction, for a full and complete stop. The friction between the tube and the pebbles slowed the tube down. If the pebbles were not there, the tube would just bounce right back.

Plan C, the folded piece of paper towel was to act as a wall, or a stoppage.

In plan D, the soft paper towel in between the ramp and tube made the bottle bounce back.

For plan E, we used the teachers desk because it was hard and we needed more bounce than just the paper towel.

8

B

Conclusion: Gravity pulled down on the nut until something blocked it which was the floor. Gravity (a pull) affected this object in motion until it stopped. This is an example of balanced forces at work.

An example of how they affect forces and an object at rest and in motion, is in plan E. In plan E, when the tube rolls down the ramp, it hits the desk and bounces right back, → ← and stays still. The force pushed equally → ← on each side so when it bounces back it stays still.

In conclusion, balanced and unbalanced forces affect objects in motion or at rest.

Gravity can affect objects by pulling the object down or pushing it down. Friction can either keep an object in motion or at rest.

Work Sample & Commentary: *Acid Rain*

The task
Students designed and constructed a device to collect and measure rainwater. They recorded rainfall amounts and also tested samples of rain with pH paper over a three-month period, and compared their data with regional data collected by the National Weather Service.

Circumstances of performance
This sample of student work was produced under the following conditions:

alone	√ in a group
√ in class	√ as homework
√ with teacher feedback	with peer feedback
timed	√ opportunity for revision

What the work shows
S5c Scientific Thinking: The student uses evidence from reliable sources to develop explanations.

A B C D E F The students gathered data from classmates and web sites on the Internet. They compared their data and the class data to the experts data to verify their conclusions.

S5f Scientific Thinking: The student works in teams to collect and share information and ideas.

C D E G H I J K L M The students produced and compared charts of their own data, the class's data, and data from the Internet.

S6a Scientific Tools and Technologies: The student uses technology and tools to observe and measure objects organisms and phenomena directly, indirectly and remotely.

N Students designed a simple device to collect and measure rainfall. They used tools such as a ruler to measure rainfall in inches, and a graduated cylinder to measure sample volume in milliliters.

M O The students used indicators to test samples of rain. They observed that the pH of the samples caused chemical reactions that produced color changes in pH paper, and they correctly concluded that the rain samples were acidic.

S6d Scientific Tools and Technologies: The student acquires information from multiple sources such as the Internet and experimentation.

A D E M The students utilized the Internet as a data source. In addition, the students utilized the computer for word processing and spreadsheets.

This work sample illustrates a standard-setting performance for the following parts of the standards:

S5c **Scientific Thinking: Use evidence from reliable sources.**

S5f **Scientific Thinking: Work in teams.**

S6a **Scientific Tools and Technologies: Use technology and tools.**

S6d **Scientific Tools and Technologies: Acquire information from multiple sources.**

S7a **Scientific Communication: Represent data and results in multiple ways.**

S7b **Scientific Communication: Argue from evidence.**

S8b **Scientific Investigation: A systematic observation, such as a field study.**

For related work on Acids and Bases, see "Acid/Base", page 40, and "Buffer Lab", page 156.

The quotations from the Science performance descriptions in this commentary are excerpted. The complete performance descriptions are shown on pages 68-84.

Physical Sciences Concepts

Life Sciences Concepts

Earth and Space Sciences Concepts

Scientific Connections and Applications

S5 Scientific Thinking

S6 Scientific Tools and Technologies

S7 Scientific Communication

S8 Scientific Investigation

Acid Rain

S7a Scientific Communication: The student represents data and results in multiple ways such as numbers, tables and graphs.

C D E G H I J K The students organized and presented data in a series of tables and graphs. They attempted to maintain a degree of uniformity in the style of their graphic presentations.

S7b Scientific Communication: The student argues from evidence; such as data produced through his or her own experimentation by others.

P In the first paragraph of the conclusion, students argue for their hypothesis from the evidence of their own and others' data. They also correctly note the significance of the geographic difference between their own data and the data they accessed on the Internet.

S8b Scientific Investigation: The student demonstrates scientific competence by completing a controlled experiment, such as a field study.

G H N The students built their collecting apparatus and used it for a period of three months to collect data from natural phenomena that occurred outside the classroom.

Background:

A From our class discussions, the books that we read, and the information we got from the INTERNET, we learned about acids and bases, the water cycle, and acid rain.

What is the water cycle? It is the way we get our water. It's the way we use and reuse our water. The water cycle has three main stages: evaporation, condensation, and precipitation. Evaporation is when the water changes from a liquid to a gas and goes into the atmosphere. Condensation is when the water droplets form into clouds in the atmosphere. Precipitation is when all the water droplets come down in the forms of rain, hail, sleet, or snow.

An acid is a substance that can burn holes in your clothes. They have a sour taste. Some things that are acidic are vinegar and batteries. A neutral substance is harmless. A base is a substance that can burn the skin. It has a bitter taste. Some things that are basic are ammonia and lye.

A pH scale is a chart with the numbers 1-14 and different colors. It is used to tell us whether something is acidic, neutral, or basic. Hydrion paper is dipped into a substance and matched against the pH scale. A substance that is acidic will have a pH of 1-6. A substance that is neutral will have a pH of 7, which means it is neither an acid nor a base. A substance that is basic will have a pH of 8-14.

Acid rain is caused by pollution. Chemical pollution from the burning of coal, gasoline, and oil in buildings, cars, buses, factories, homes, and schools goes into the air. It remains in the air until it is washed out of the atmosphere and carried back to where we live, every time it rains. The rainwater comes down as acid rain. Acid rain is water that has been polluted. Acid rain can harm some plants and animals. It can destroy the food we eat. Acid rain can discolor the clothes we wear. Normal rainwater has a pH of about 6. Acid rain has a pH range of 2.5 to 5.7.

Problem: Do we have an acid rain problem where we live?

Hypothesis: We predict that we do have an acid rain problem where we live.

Materials:
* 100 ML graduated cylinder
* A wooden pole (121 cm)
* Hydrion pH paper
* A composition notebook
* Distilled water
* Masking tape
* Duct tape
* A rain gauge in CM and Inches

N **Procedure:**
1. We had to design and construct a device to collect rainwater at _____. We discussed what we had to make.
2. We discussed how we would attach the pole to the graduated cylinder and place it outside our classroom window.
3. We took a graduated cylinder and attached it to a pole that is 121 cm in length with masking tape. We found out that the masking tape did not work, so we used the duct tape instead to attach the pole to the graduated cylinder.
4. We decided to put the rainwater collecting device outside of a window that had the least blockage in room 307 at _____.
5. We discussed how we would collect and record our rainwater data using our collecting device. We decided to check the rainwater collecting device daily and record the date. If it rained, we would record the amount of rainfall in milliliters and inches.
O 6. We also decided that each time we collected rainwater, we would test the rainwater pH by taking one strip of hydrion paper and dipping it in the water and then taking it out comparing the color of the dipped hydrion paper to the pH color chart. We would match the color of the dipped paper to the pH color chart.
7. We would compare our group data with the class data.
B 8. We would compare the data collected at _____ with INTERNET acid rain data.

Acid Rain

G — Table 1

Title: Amount of Rainwater Collected by our Group During April, May & June 1998

	A Month	B Date	C Rainwater in Milliliters	D Total Monthly Rainfall in ml	E Inches	F Total Monthly Rainfall in Inches
1						
2						
3	April	4/2/98	30 m.l.		0.7 in	
4		4/20/98	90 m.l.	120 m.l.	2.5 in	3.2 in
5					1.8 in	
6	May	5/4/98	65 m.l.		0.7 in	
7		5/8/98	25 m.l.		0.7 in	
8		5/14/98	26 m.l.	116 m.l.	0.7 in	3.2 in
9	June	6/1/98	31 m.l.		0.8 in	
10		6/15/98	50 m.l.	81	1.3 in	2.1 in
11						

C — Table 2

Title: Amount of Rainfall Collected at _____ by Class _____ S.A.
During April, May & June of 1998

	A Month	B Date	C Amount of Rainfall in millimeters	D Total Monthly Rainfall in millimeters	E Inches	F Total Monthly Rainfall in Inches
1						
2					1.76 in	
3	April	4/1	54 ml		.80 in	
4		4/2	30 ml		1.86 in	
5		4/9	60 ml		.77 in	
6		4/17	26 ml		2.50 in	
7		4/20	90 ml		.82 in	8.53 in
8		4/23	28 ml	298 ml	1.60 in	
9	May	5/4	65 ml		.57 in	
10		5/5	22 ml		.60 in	
11		5/6	25 ml		.68 in	
12		5/11	26.5 ml		.70 in	
13		5/14	26 ml	178.5 ml	.42 in	4.77 in
14		5/25	14 ml		.80 in	
15	June	6/1	31 ml		1.29 in	
16		6/12	51 ml		1.30 in	
17		6/15	50 ml		.30 in	
18		6/17	12 ml		.79 in	4.48 in
19		6/30	27 ml	171 ml		
20						

D — Table 3

Title: Total Monthly Rainfall for New York State During April,
May & June 1998

	A Month	B Total Monthly Rainfall in Inches
1		
2	April	7.05 in
3	May	6.94 in
4	June	5.94 in
5		
6		
7	IINTERNET Site:	
8	http://www.nwsnoaa.gov/climatedata.html	

Title: pH Chart

pH 1 - red
pH 2 - brown red
pH 3 - orange brown
pH 4 - dark orange
pH 5 - light orange
pH 6 - yellow orange
pH 7 - greenish yellow
pH 8 - light green
pH 9 - green
pH 10 - dark green
pH 11 - greenish brown
pH 12 - brown
pH 13 - light purple
pH 14 - purple

H — Table 4

Title: p.H. of Rainwater Collected by our Group During April, May & June 1998

	A Month	B Date	C Starting Color of Hydrion Paper After Dipping It in Distilled Water	D Color of Hydrion Paper After Dipping in Rainwater	E Color of Hydrion Paper After Dipping in Rainwater	F p.H. Scale Reading	G Monthly Average p.H. Reading
1							
2							
3							
4							
5							
6	April	4/2	Yellow orange	Greenish Yellow	Yellow orange	6	
7		4/20	Yellow orange	Greenish Yellow	Yellow orange	6	
8	May	5/4	Yellow orange	Greenish Yellow	Light orange	5	5.5
9		5/6	Yellow orange	Greenish Yellow	Light orange	5	
10		5/14	Yellow orange	Greenish Yellow	Yellow orange	6	
11	June	6/1/98	Yellow orange	Greenish Yellow	Light orange	5	5.3
12		6/15/98	Yellow orange	Greenish Yellow	Light orange	5	5

I — Table 5

Title: p. H. of Rainwater Collected at _____ by Class _____ S.A During April, May & June 1998

	A Month	B Date	C Starting Color of Hydrion Paper	D Color of Hydrion Paper After Dipping in Distilled Water	E Color of Hydrion Paper After Dipping in Rainwater	F p.H. Reading on p.H. Scale	G Monthly Average p.H. Reading
1							
2							
3							
4							
5							
6							
7	April	4/1	Yellow orange	Greenish yellow	Light orange	5	
8		4/2	Yellow orange	Greenish yellow	Yellow orange	6	
9		4/9	Yellow orange	Greenish yellow	Light orange	5	
10		4/17	Yellow orange	Greenish yellow	Dark orange	4	
11		4/20	Yellow orange	Greenish yellow	Light orange	5	5.2
12		4/23	Yellow orange	Greenish yellow	Yellow orange	6	
13	May	5/4	Yellow orange	Greenish yellow	Light orange	5	
14		5/5	Yellow orange	Greenish yellow	Light orange	6	
15		5/6	Yellow orange	Greenish yellow	Yellow orange	5	
16		5/11	Yellow orange	Greenish yellow	Light orange	5	
17		5/14	Yellow orange	Greenish yellow	Light orange	6	5.3
18		5/25	Yellow orange	Greenish yellow	Light orange	5	
19	June	6/1	Yellow orange	Greenish yellow	Light orange	5	
20		6/12	Yellow orange	Greenish yellow	Light orange	5	
21		6/15	Yellow orange	Greenish yellow	Yellow orange	5	
22		6/17	Yellow orange	Greenish yellow	Yellow orange	6	5.4
23		6/30	Yellow orange	Greenish yellow			
24							

E — Table 6

p.H. of Rainfall for NY Region in April, May & June 1998

	A Month	B Average Precipiation p.H
1		
2	April	4.7
3	May	5.3
4	June	5.7
5		
6		
7		
8		
9		

WEb Sites:
http://www.madison K12.wi.us/stugeon/overallus.html
http://www.K12.hi.us/~cmark/AcidRainvacidrain7.html
http://h-20.usgs.gov/nwc/NWC/pH/html/NY.html

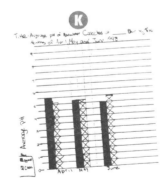

Title: Average pH of Rainwater Collected at _____ By _____ Fra terms of April May and June 1998

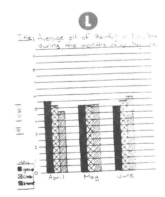

Title: Average pH of Rainfall in terms during the months of April May June

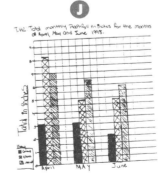

Title: Total monthly Rainfall in inches for the months of April, May and June 1998.

Physical Sciences Concepts

Life Sciences Concepts

Earth and Space Sciences Concepts

Scientific Connections and Applications

S5 Scientific Thinking

S6 Scientific Tools and Technologies

S7 Scientific Communication

S8 Scientific Investigation

Acid Rain

M

Conclusion:

P

In conclusion, our hypothesis is correct. We have an acid rain problem at _____. We looked at our group and class pH data that we collected during the months of April, May and June 1998, and found that we had pH readings of 5.5 and 5.2 for April, for May 5.3 and 5.3 and for June 5 and 5.4. We compared our group and class pH information to the average pH data for the New York State region on the INTERNET. We found out that our group data, class data and regional data were the same for the month of May with pH readings of 5.3, 5.3, and 5.3 but different in April (5.5, 5.2, 4.7) and in June (5, 5.4, 5.7). Because all group, class and INTERNET rainwater pH information collected was in the acid rain range of pH 2.5 - 5.7, we conclude that we have an acid rain problem at _____. Because the pH data on the INTERNET is for all of New York State and not just for New York City where we go to school, we think that our group and class pH data is better for _____ than the pH data on the INTERNET.

In April our group collected 3.2 inches of rain, the class collected 8.5, and the scientists collected a total of 7 inches of rain. Then in May our group collected 3.2 inches of rain , the class collected 4.7 inches and the scientists collected 6.9 inches. In June, our group collected 2.1 inches of rain, the class collected 4.4 and the scientists collected 5.9 inches. We found that our group, class and INTERNET data were very different. We think this is because in April the group only collected rainwater twice, the class collected 6 times. In May our group collected rainwater two times the class collected 7 times. In June our group collected rainwater 3 times the class collected five times. In April, May, and June scientists collected rainwater every time it rained. So we think that the scientists had the best rainfall data. So looking at their data we found out that there was less rain for the month of June (5.9 inches) than in April (7.0 inches) and May (6.9 inches).

Bibliography

1.   Baines, John. 1939. <u>Acid Rain</u>. Texas: Steck-Vaughn
2.   Grolier. 1998. <u>Multimedia Encyclopedia (CD-ROM)</u>. California: Grolier Interactive.
3.   Multimedia Curriculum Systems. 1998. <u>SciencePlus: Interactive Explorations, Level Red (CD-ROM)</u>. U.S.A.: Holt, Rinehart and Winston.
4.   http:// www. madison. k12.wl.us/stugeon/overallus.htm
5.   http:// www. k12.hi.us./ `cmark/Acid Rain/acid rain7.html
6.   http://h20.usqs.gov/nwc/NWC/pH/html/NY.html

Work Sample & Commentary: *Discovering Density*

The task

Following classroom discussion about the concept of density, students performed an extensive laboratory investigation. In the lab write up the students were asked to:

- discuss the definition of density;
- state a clear purpose for the investigation;
- give four clearly stated hypotheses;
- list all materials;
- clearly organize and label data;
- discuss any observed patterns;
- clearly explain laboratory procedures;
- summarize results;
- suggest ideas for future study.

Circumstances of performance

This sample of student work was produced under the following conditions:

alone	√ in a group
√ in class	as homework
√ with teacher feedback	√ with peer feedback
timed	√ opportunity for revision

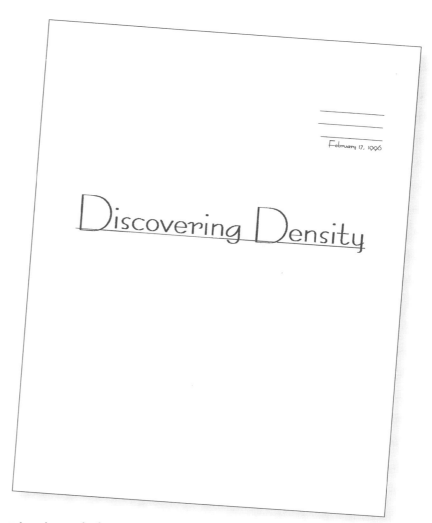

February 17, 1996

Discovering Density

Physical Sciences Concepts

Life Sciences Concepts

Earth and Space Sciences Concepts

S4 Scientific Connections and Applications

S5 Scientific Thinking

S6 Scientific Tools and Technologies

S7 Scientific Communication

Scientific Investigation

This work sample illustrates a standard-setting performance for the following parts of the standards:

S1 a **Physical Sciences Concepts: Properties and changes of properties in matter.**

S4 a **Scientific Connections and Applications: Big ideas and unifying concepts.**

S5 b **Scientific Thinking: Use concepts from Science Standards 1 to 4 to explain observations and phenomena.**

S5 c **Scientific Thinking: Use evidence from reliable sources.**

S5 e **Scientific Thinking: Evaluate the accuracy, design, and outcomes of investigations.**

S5 f **Scientific Thinking: Work individually and in teams.**

S6 a **Scientific Tools and Technologies: Use technology and tools to observe and measure.**

S7 a **Scientific Communication: Represent data and results in multiple ways.**

S7 e **Scientific Communication: Communicate in a form suited to the purpose and the audience.**

What the work shows

S1 a Physical Sciences Concepts: The student produces evidence that demonstrates understanding of properties and changes of properties in matter, such as density....

A B There is clear evidence here and throughout the work that the student understands how volume and mass relate to density.

C Although the student has a misconception (air does not have zero mass, and this should be corrected in a revision), the student does describe density in terms of volume and mass.

S4 a Scientific Connections and Applications: The student produces evidence that demonstrates understanding of big ideas and unifying concepts, such as order...; change and constancy; and cause and effect.

D E There are several places in this work where the student acknowledged that volume can remain constant and yet, if mass increases or decreases, the density is changed.

F The student provided evidence of understanding that if the density of an object is less than 1.0 g/ml the object will float in water.

For related work on Density, see "Flinkers", page 42, "Density of Sand", page 169, and "Density", page 173.

The quotations from the Science performance descriptions in this commentary are excerpted. The complete performance descriptions are shown on pages 68-84.

Discovering Density

Physical Sciences Concepts **S1**

Life Sciences Concepts

Earth and Space Sciences Concepts

Scientific Connections and Applications **S4**

Scientific Thinking **S5**

Scientific Tools and Technologies **S6**

Scientific Communication **S7**

Scientific Investigation

S5 b Scientific Thinking: The student uses concepts from Science Standards 1 to 4 to explain a variety of observations and phenomena.

E The conclusion ties together the concept of density and why objects in the experiment floated and why some sank. This shows that the student was able to use her conceptual understanding of density to predict whether an object would float or sink given information about the density of the medium into which the object is placed and the density of the object.

S5 c Scientific Thinking: The student uses evidence from reliable sources to develop descriptions, explanations, and models.

Throughout the work the student used information from reliable sources. One source was direct experimentation. However, the student took information, whether from the teacher or some other source, and explained some sophisticated concepts in her own voice.

Past History

Density is a measurement of how close atoms and/or molecules are together, or in other words how concentrated they are. For instance, 1,000 lbs. of feathers are less dense than an ounce of gold, because gold molecules are all much closer together than the feather molecules are. We need to know how dense things are, to see if they float or sink, to see if we can break through them, to see how sturdy a substance is, and for many other reasons.

Purpose

The purpose of this laboratory experiment is to examine and determine the relationships between mass, volume, and density.

Hypothesis

I believe that if the mass of an object goes up and the volume stays the same, the density will go up, because that means there are more molecules/atoms in the same amount of space. Accordingly, I think that if the volume of an object goes up and the mass stays the same, than then the density will go down, because there are the same amount of molecules/atoms in a larger amount of space. I think some objects float because there is space for air between molecules, and the molecules trap the are in the object so it floats. If the object is very dense, then there is no room for air in between the molecules, so it sinks. I think that a steel boat floats, because there are molecules that are not very dense, so air can go in the spaces between the molecules, and the sides of the boat add to that ability, because they constantly keep water from being on both the top and bottom of the molecules.

Materials

big block of wood	balance	square piece of foil	1000 ml beaker
20 steal BB's	tape measure3	rubber stoppers	balloon
3 unknown liquids	calculator	50 ml graduated cylinder	1 cork stopper
little block of wood	10 ml graduated cylinder	50 ml beaker	100 ml beaker

---

K

Station 1   SMALL BLOCK / LARGE BLOCK
1. Mass the block of wood.
2. Measure the length, height, and width of the block in centimeters.
3. Calculate the volume using the formula for a rectangular solid.
4. Calculate the density of the block.
5. Fill one of the large beakers 2/3 of the way with water.
6. Gently place each block of wood into water to determine if it floats.
7. Remove the block from water.
8. Repeat for the other block.

Station 2   STEEL BB'S
1. Fill the graduated cylinder with 5.0 ml of water.
2. Mass the graduated cylinder and water.
3. Gently roll 20 beads into graduated cylinder.
4. Mass the graduates cylinder, water, and beads.
5. Calculate mass of the 20 beads.
6. Record the volume of water and 20 beads.
7. Calculate volume of the 20 beads.
8. Calculate density of the 20 beads.
9. Record whether or not the steel beads float.
10. Pour water back into the beaker and replace the beads into a petri dish.

Station 3   UNKNOWN LIQUIDS
1. Mass the graduated cylinder.
2. Pour approximately 30 ml of Liquid into the graduated cylinder.
3. Mass the graduated cylinder and the Liquid.
4. Record the exact volume of the Liquid that was poured into graduated cylinder.
5. Calculate the density of the Liquid.
6. Repeat for other Liquids.

L

Station 4   BALLOON
1. Mass the balloon.
2. Use the tape measure to record the circumference if the balloon.
3. Calculate the radius of the balloon.
4. Using the following formula, calculate the volume of the balloon. $v = 4 * pi * r ^ 3/3$ **H**
5. Calculate the density of the balloon.
6. Verify whether or not the balloon floats.

Station 5   RUBBER STOPPERS
1. Mass the rubber stopper.
2. Pour approximately 40 ml into the graduated cylinder.
3. Record exact volume of water in graduated cylinder.
4. Gently place rubber stopper into graduated cylinder.
5. Be sure rubber stopper is completely covered with water and measure the volume of water and stopper.
6. Calculate volume of stopper.
7. Calculate density of stopper.
8. Repeat for other stoppers.

Station 6   CORKS
1. Mass the cork.
2. Pour approximately 40 ml into graduated cylinder.
3. Record exact volume of water in graduated cylinder.
4. Gently place cork into graduated cylinder.   **I**
5. Be sure cork is completely covered with water and measure volume of water and cork.
6. Calculate volume of cork.
7. Calculate density of cork.
8. Repeat for other corks.

Station 7   ALUMINUM FOIL BOAT/ALUMINUM BALL
1. Construct and aluminum boat following your instructor's instructions.
2. Mass the boat.
3. Measure the length, width, and height of the boat.
4. Calculate the volume of the boat.

Discovering Density

S5e Scientific Thinking: The student evaluates the accuracy, design, and outcomes of investigations.

G The student identified several reasonable sources of measurement error.

S5f Scientific Thinking: The student works individually and in teams to collect and share information and ideas.

S6a Scientific Tools and Technologies: The student uses technology and tools (such as traditional laboratory equipment…) to…measure objects…indirectly….

H The student determined the volume of the balloon by using the formula for a sphere.

I The student determined the volume of an irregularly shaped object by using water displacement.

S7a Scientific Communication: The student represents data and results in multiple ways, such as numbers, tables, and technical…writing.

J The student presented data in tabular form and analyzed the data in writing.

S7e Scientific Communication: The student communicates in a form suited to the purpose and the audience, such as by writing instructions that others can follow….

K **L** **M**

M
5. Calculate the density of the boat.
6. Determine whether the boat floats or sinks.
7. Squish the boat into a tight "cube" ball.
8. Record the mass of the ball.
9. Measure the length, width, and height of the aluminum ball to determine the volume of the ball.
10. Calculate the volume of the ball.
11. Calculate the density of the ball.
12. Determine if the boat floats or sinks.

Station 8   WATER
1. Mass the graduated cylinder.
2. Pour approximately 30 ml of water into the graduated cylinder.
3. Record the exact volume of the water in the graduated cylinder.
4. Mass the graduated cylinder and water.
5. Calculate the mass of the water in the graduated cylinder.
6. Calculate the density of the water.

Physical Sciences Concepts — S1
Life Sciences Concepts
Earth and Space Sciences Concepts
Scientific Connections and Applications — S4
Scientific Thinking — S5
Scientific Tools and Technologies — S6
Scientific Communication — S7
Scientific Investigation

Discussion **B**

The density of an object is most dependent on mass. This is because there are two factors concerning mass that contribute to the density of an object. At the atomic level each individual atom/molecule could weight a lot, thus effecting the mass which effects the density; or there could be a number of atoms/molecules squished up in a small area, which effects the mass and therefore effecting the volume. This is supported by all of the stations in this laboratory. In all of the stations, the mass and volume were taken, and in each case the individual weight of each atom/molecule and the weight of how ever many atoms/molecules there were affected the mass.

F Water's density is approximately 1.0 g/ml. You can see this in the Station 8 table of my data. With the data of all of the things that we testing whether they floated or sank it can be determined that things that float, have a density of less then 1.0 g/ml, and all of the things that sink have a density of greater than 1.0.

J

Floats	Density	Sinks	Density
Small Block	0.648 g/ml	Steel Beads	7 g/ml
Large Block	0.616 g/ml	Sm. Stopper	1.1 g/ml
Balloon	0.0052 g/ml	Med. Stopper	1.5 g/ml
Small Cork	0.15 g/ml	Lrg. Stopper	1.2 g/ml
Medium Cork	0.2 g/ml	Almn. Ball	1.2 g/ml
Large Cork	0.17 g/ml		
Almn. Boat	0.012 g/ml		

C The aluminum boat floated, because it's density was below 1.0 g/ml. Part of the reason, is because the empty space in the middle of the boat (which weighs nothing) is counted in the volume, then when you divide mass by volume the number drops greatly. With the ball you crammed alot of atoms/molecules into a small area, and the volume was so very small, when you divide the number stayed above 1.0 g/ml and it sinks.

D To find if what happens to the density of an object the mass of an object goes up, and the volume stays the same I looked in stations 5 and 6. and 3. If you look at the stoppers and corks that are the same volume, you will see that the mass of the stopper is larger. The density of the more massive object if higher in all three (small, medium, and large) cases. In the liquids station the volume always stayed the same, yet the more massive liquids always had a high density. So it can be concluded that if the mass of an object goes up and the volume stays the same, the density will go up.

To find what happens to the density of an object if the volume goes up and the mass stays the same I looked at station 7 backwards (if we had a aluminum ball first, then built it into a boat). When the aluminum

was in a ball, the density was high, and when it was a boat the density was low. This is because the space in the object was counted as part of the object. In conclusion, if the volume of an object goes up and the mass stays the same, the density will go down.

To find out why things float I looked at all of the stations, and the table I made on the previous page, those things with a density lower than the density of the liquid they are in will float, and those things with a density higher than the liquid they are in will sink.

A steel boat floats, because it has sides on it. If it were simply a steel panel, in would sink like a rock. The space in the middle of the boat, counts as part of a boat, therefore making the boat much less dense than the water.

G Some things that might have affected my data, and made it wrong, could have been, water left on the objects, so they had the added mass of the water when they were weighed; how you measured the circumference of the balloon, because it was not a perfect sphere; the holes in the bottom of the stoppers could have filled up with air, and given a false volume reading; the scales might not have always been zeroed correctly; measurements of water in the graduated cylinders might not have been totally accurate; and when measuring the volume of objects that floated using water displacement, the objects might not have been in the water all of the way, giving and inaccurate reading on the graduated cylinder.

Conclusion

E This lab, has made it very easy to understand the relationships between mass, volume, and density. After completing this lab, it is easy to conclude, that if the mass of an object goes up and the volume stays the same the density will go up; that if the volume of an object goes up and the mass stays the same the density will go down; that objects float because they are less dense then the substance that they are in; and that a steel boat floats because it has side. With this new knowledge and understanding I personally know a little bit more about how this world works. I will also know how to find the density of things if I ever need to know if something floats, like if I ever need to construct a boat, or something like that. Now that I know how to find the density of an object, it would be interesting to go into some physics, and find how much force you would have to apply to break through things with different density's. Knowing how to calculate this, and being able to calculate this might be good for a job in making durable synthetic materials, or finding sturdy materials to make something which must be very strong.

Work Sample & Commentary: *Paper Towels*

Physical Sciences Concepts

Life Sciences Concepts

Earth and Space Sciences Concepts

Scientific Connections and Applications ◀ **S4**

Scientific Thinking ◀ **S5**

Scientific Tools and Technologies

Scientific Communication ◀ **S7**

Scientific Investigation ◀ **S8**

The quotations from the Science performance descriptions in this commentary are excerpted. The complete performance descriptions are shown on pages 68-84.

The task

Students in a physical science class were asked to test the effectiveness of one of several different common products. The task required them to perform detailed and accurate testing and report results in a form for public presentation. Further, the students were asked to design and give a presentation promoting the most successful product.

Circumstances of performance

This sample of student work was produced under the following conditions:

alone   √ in a group

√ in class   as homework

√ with teacher feedback   √ with peer feedback

timed   √ opportunity for revision

Students had two weeks to complete the task which was part of a unit on scientific methodologies. While students videotaped a portion of their presentation, it is not included here.

Science required by the task

Paper towel testing is a common middle school activity, but many students select variables that are social in nature (e.g., cost, appearance) and are more easily measured than are strength or performance. This project tackled variables that required more imagination and effort to measure.

What the work shows

S4a Scientific Connections and Applications: The student produces evidence that demonstrates understanding of big ideas and unifying concepts, such as...form and function....

(A) The student related the thickness (form) of towels to the characteristic of strength (function).

This work sample illustrates a standard-setting performance for the following parts of the standards:

S4a **Scientific Connections and Applications: Big ideas and unifying concepts.**

S4b **Scientific Connections and Applications: The designed world.**

S5a **Scientific Thinking: Frame questions to distinguish cause and effect; identify or control variables in experimental or non-experimental research settings.**

S7a **Scientific Communication: Represent data and results in multiple ways.**

S8a **Scientific Investigation: Controlled experiment.**

(F) ➔

Test #1

<u>Problem</u>: Will the product, Brawny paper towels, be stronger than the other 3 brands of paper towels? Which brand is the strongest brand?

<u>Research</u>: Strength is a major part of this experiment. The word strong or strength doesn't necessarily have to deal with muscles. To be strong you must be powerful and able to resist attack. As well as being powerful, you must be well established, firm, solid, not easily broken, or steadfast. The word steadfast basically comes down to being firmly fixed, steady, and well built. The word strength has a similar meaning. To have strength it means to have the ability to endure, support, or force in numbers.
    Paper is a material made by pressing pulp of rags, straw, or wood into thin sheets.
    A towel can be cloth or paper. Based upon this experiment the towels being tested are made of paper. Drying is the major purpose for a paper towel, but sometimes they're used for scrubbing surfaces.

<u>Hypothesis</u>: Based from the research, I think our product, the Brawny paper towel will be stronger. Being that the towel is made of thin sheets of paper, there is the likely reason that it will rip when wet. But unlike the other brands Brawny is thicker. When we compare the characteristics of strength Brawny fits all the characteristics. It is well established, firm, solid (thick, in other words), and well built. In our test we will actually find out if it can handle "force in numbers."

<u>Set Up</u>: The paper towel will be laid over the rim of a plastic bowl, approximately 4 1/4 of an inch. The paper towel will be secured so that it is tight with a rubber band. The paper towel will be sprayed 20 times with a fine mist from a water bottle. Pennies (the weights) will be put on one at a time until the towel breaks. Then we'll count the pennies and record our data. The process will be repeated for the other brands as well.

A ➔

B ➔

S4b Scientific Connections and Applications: The student produces evidence that demonstrates understanding of the designed world, such as...the viability of technological designs.

(A) The student provided evidence of thinking through the design of paper towels and how well they would serve the intended purpose.

S5a Scientific Thinking: The student frames questions to distinguish cause and effect; and identifies or controls variables in experimental and non-experimental research settings.

S7a Scientific Communication: The student represents data and results in multiple ways, such as numbers, tables...drawings, diagrams, and artwork....

(D) (E) The results are communicated in tables, graphs, and words. The histogram is more effective than the pie chart. There is a reversal in the table for Test #2 (data for "Job Squad" and "Bounty"), but the multiple representations actually allow the reader to figure that out.

S8a Scientific Investigation: The student demonstrates scientific competence by completing a controlled experiment. A full investigation includes:

• Questions that can be studied using the resources available.

Paper Towels

Test #2

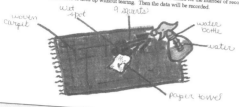

Problem: Will the product, Brawny paper towels be stronger than the other 3 brands of paper towels? Which brand is the strongest brand?

Research: Strength is a major part of this experiment. The word strong or strength doesn't necessarily have to deal with muscles. To be strong you must be powerful and able to resist attack. As well as being powerful, you must well established, firm, solid, not easily broken, or steadfast. The word steadfast basically comes down to being firmly fixed, steady, and well built. The word strength has a similar meaning. To have strength it means to have the ability to endure, support, or force in numbers.

Paper is a material made by pressing pulp of rags, straw, or wood into thin sheets.

A towel can be cloth or paper. Based upon this experiment the towels being tested are made of paper. Drying is the major purpose for a paper towel, but sometimes they're used for scrubbing surfaces.

Carpet is a woven or felted piece of material that covers floors. In many cases carpet must be cleaned. Usually they are cleaned with vacuums but sometimes when there is a spill a cleaning solution and a bundle of paper towels will do the job.

Hypothesis: Based from the research, I think our product, the Brawny paper towel will be stronger. Being that the towel is made of thin sheets of paper, there is the likely reason that it will rip if wet. But unlike the other brands Brawny is thicker. When we compare the characteristics of strength Brawny fits all of them. Brawny can resist attack. It is well establish, firm, solid, (thick in other words), and well built. In our second test we will actually find out if it can handle scrubbing a spill on a rough, woven piece of carpet.

Set Up: In this experiment the first step is to wet one area of the carpet by squirting it 9 times with the water bottle. The area will be squirted 9 times in the exact area for a single test. Then when the second brand is tested we'll move to a different area and squirt nine times (and so on). The wet surface will be scrubbed with one sheet of the paper towel. The carpet will be scrubbed over and over with the paper towel until the paper towel begins wearing away. With the first notice of "wear and tear" we'll stop rubbing. Each brand will be timed for the number of second or minutes it was able to hold up without tearing. Then the data will be recorded.

Brand of Paper Towel	# of Pennies (weights) it held
Bounty	196
High Dry	81
Job Squad	264
Brawny	256

Towels & Pennies

This graph gives you an idea of how much pennies filled the plastic bowl in our tests. The number of pennies the towel brand was able to hold is written across the pennies. In addition it tells out of the 797 pennies what percent of a certain brand was able to hold. In Brawny's case it held 32% of the pennies.

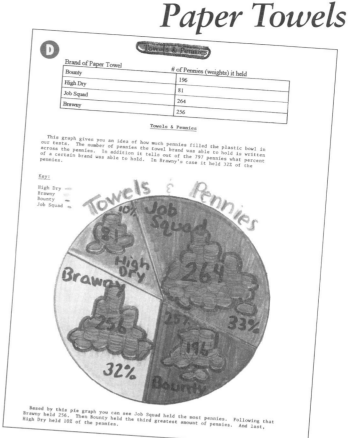

Based by this pie graph you can see Job Squad held the most pennies. Following that Brawny held 256. Then Bounty held the third greatest amount of pennies. And last, High Dry held 10% of the pennies.

Sidebar
- Physical Sciences Concepts
- Life Sciences Concepts
- Earth and Space Sciences Concepts
- **S4** Scientific Connections and Applications
- **S5** Scientific Thinking
- Scientific Tools and Technologies
- **S7** Scientific Communication
- **S8** Scientific Investigation

F

- Procedures that are safe, humane, and ethical; and respect privacy and property rights.
- Data that have been collected and recorded (see also Science Standard 6) in ways that others can verify, and analyzed using skills expected at this grade level (see also Mathematics Standard 4).

B C D E

- Data and results that have been represented (see also Science Standard 7) in ways that fit the context.

D E

- Recommendations, decisions, and conclusions based on evidence.

G

- Acknowledgement of references and ... of others.

Although the students did research, the sources of information were not acknowledged and should have been.

- Results that are communicated appropriately to audiences.
- Reflection and defense of conclusions and recommendations from other sources and peer review.

The student presented the work to others, though evidence of the presentation is not shown here.

E — Scrub Rug

Brand of Towel	Amount of Time before Wear & Tear
Brawny	30 seconds
Bounty	60 seconds (1 minute)
High Dry	12 seconds
Job Squad	16 seconds

Scrub & Rub

This bar graph shows which paper towel could stand up, and last the longest by rubbing it on a wet piece of carpet until it had a tear. The y-axis numbers by 5, with The x-axis names the brands of the 4 paper towels. This axis is the time axis. By looking at the graph a range of 0 to 62 seconds. None of the other you can see that Job Squad lasted for 60 seconds until ripping. None of the other towels were close to Job Squad's time.

Brawny took 30 seconds until it wore away. Bounty took 16 seconds before wear and tear. High Dry came in last, with only 12 seconds.

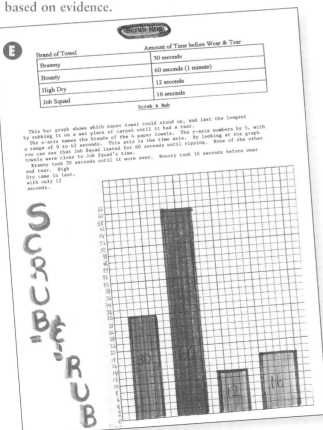

G — Conclusion

Conclusion:

Based from both tests and graphs, I compared my results and found that my hypothesis was incorrect. Job Squad turned out to be the stronger brand in both tests. Job Squad was able to hold 264 pennies before breaking, and was able to last 60 seconds without wear or tear. In the hypothesis I predicted that Brawny would be the strongest, but found that it was 8 pennies short of being tied with Job Squad. In the Scrub and Rub test their was a great difference in the results: Job Squad lasted for 60 seconds, while Brawny was only able to last for 30 seconds-a difference of 30 seconds.

When making my hypothesis I had trouble decided on which brand would be the strongest. Two of the four paper towels were rather thick, but Bounty seemed to be a bigger sheet. In my hypothesis I was partly right, Bounty was strong-but not the strongest.

Job Squad is the better and stronger brand. It can handle force in numbers, and obviously it was built very well, firm, steady, and it was not easily broken.

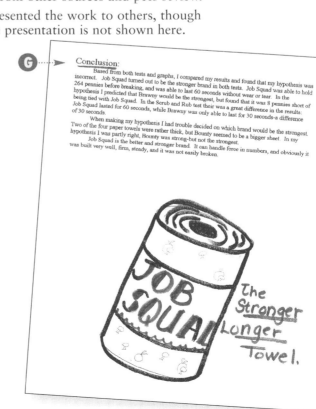

The Stronger Longer Towel.

Work Sample & Commentary: *Bio Box*

Physical
Sciences
Concepts

Life
Sciences
Concepts **S2**

Earth and
Space Sciences
Concepts

Scientific
Connections and **S4**
Applications

Scientific **S5**
Thinking

Scientific Tools
and
Technologies

Scientific
Communication

Scientific
Investigation

For related work on Interdependence, see "Biomes", page 52, "Owl Pellets", page 101, "Eagles", page 186, and "The Invincible Cockroach", page 188.

The task

After a study of the interactions that occur within ecosystems, students were asked to design a bio-box showing a pond ecosystem. Using pictures and models made from construction paper or clay, students were asked to depict both the living organisms and the non-living physical factors in a pond ecosystem. Students in groups of two to three met in a planning session to discuss a design for the ecosystem, using the diagram "Needs and Activities of Living Things" as a guide. Students gathered materials (e.g., glue, scissors, construction paper, tape, markers, colored pencils and a ruler) and made items to contribute to the bio-box which could be constructed in a shoe box, milk carton, or a 2L soda bottle cut lengthwise. In the second session, students constructed the bio-box. In the third session, students used the bio-box and their knowledge of interdependence to answer questions on the worksheet. Though the questions were answered by the entire group, the last section of the written component asked each student to list his or her individual contribution to the project, and the conclusions they drew about interactions in a pond ecosystem.

Circumstances of performance

This sample of student work was produced under the following conditions:

√ alone   √ in a group

√ in class   √ as homework

√ with teacher feedback   with peer feedback

     timed   √ opportunity for revision

The quotations from the Science performance descriptions in this commentary are excerpted. The complete performance descriptions are shown on pages 68-84.

THE LESSON

BUILD A BIO-BOX

"INTERDEPENDENCE IN A POND ECOSYSTEM"

Directions: Design a bio-box with items made from construction paper and clay, and magazine or drawn pictures of organisms that are found in a pond ecosystem. The box may be constructed from a shoe box, milk carton or a soda bottle (two-liter) cut lengthwise. Use the picture "Needs and Activities of Living Things" as a guide. Use the bio-box to answer the questions below about interdependence in a pond ecosystem.

1A. Look at the pond ecosystem and make a <u>list</u> of the living organisms.

The living organisms are: butterflies, spiders, lizard, frog, turtle, dragonfly, pond snake, tree, lilypads, insects and land strips, protozoans.

<u>LIVING ORGANISMS</u>

1B. Make a <u>list</u> of the nonliving, physical factors in the pond ecosystem.

<u>NONLIVING PHYSICAL FACTORS</u>

The non-living things are: air, water, sunlight, rocks, and earth.

2A. Using the bio-box as your guide, complete the chart below indicating which organisms are the producers, consumers and decomposers.

PRODUCERS	CONSUMERS	DECOMPOSERS
• plants	• frog	• bacteria
• trees	• turtle	• fungi
• pond lily	• snake	
	• lizard	
	• spider	
	• butterflies	

What the work shows

S2 d Life Sciences Concepts: The student produces evidence that demonstrates understanding of populations and ecosystems, such as the roles of producers, consumers, and decomposers in a food web; and the effects of resources and energy transfer on populations.

Ⓐ The students demonstrate one element of knowledge of the role of producer when they state "...carbon dioxide & water taken in [and] used by plants to make food." To meet this standard, students need to use the concept accurately to explain observations and make preditions and by representing the concept in other ways.

Ⓑ The students explain flow of resources within a system by explaining the dynamics of a food chain. Although their use of the term "food web" is erroneous, it is clear that they have a basic understanding of the functions of trophic levels.

This work sample illustrates a standard-setting performance for the following parts of the standards:

S2 d Life Sciences Concepts: Populations and ecosystems.

S4 a Scientific Connections and Applications: Big ideas and unifying concepts.

S5 b Scientific Thinking: Use concepts from Science Standards 1–4.

S5 f Scientific Thinking: Work individually and in teams.

Physical
Sciences
Concepts

S2 Life
Sciences
Concepts

Earth and
Space Sciences
Concepts

S4 Scientific
Connections and
Applications

S5 Scientific
Thinking

Scientific Tools
and
Technologies

Scientific
Communication

Scientific
Investigation

S4 a Scientific Connections and Applications: The student produces evidence that demonstrates understanding of big ideas and unifying concepts, such as order and organization;...change and constancy; and cause and effect.

B The students demonstrate an element of understanding of order and organization.

C D Some evidence of basic understanding of change and constancy is indicated in the students' statement concerning ecological balance.

E F The graphs showing the effect resources have on population size indicate some evidence of an understanding of cause and effect.

C D The students draw conclusions based on their knowledge of the roles of producers and consumers, and application of Science Standard **S2 d**.

G H The use of the plural "we" indicates that each student participated as a member of a team and contributed to the collective results.

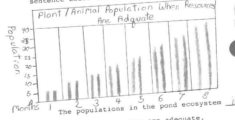

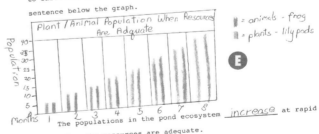

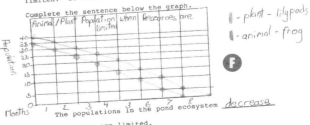

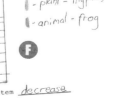

Bio Box

Physical
Sciences
Concepts

Life
Sciences **S2**
Concepts

Earth and
Space Sciences
Concepts

Scientific
Connections and **S4**
Applications

Scientific **S5**
Thinking

Scientific Tools
and
Technologies

Scientific
Communication

Scientific
Investigation

(4)

STUDENT ACCOUNTABILITY:

Each member of the team individually answers the questions below:

NAME: CLASS: DATE: January 13, 1928

1. What did you contribute to this project? In the space below, describe what you contributed to the design and building of the bio-box pond ecosystem, and the information that you contributed in answering the questions that were given to your team. If you need additional space, please feel free to write on the back of this page.

I brought in a shoe box, glue, scissors, markers, construction paper, scotch tape, pictures, leaves, and typing paper. I also went on the computer to do research on the pond ecosystem and I got a couple of pictures of animals that live in the pond ecosystem

C 2. What conclusions can you draw about the interactions in a pond ecosystem? I can conclude that a pond ecosystem has a food chain, and when the food chain is not balanced the animals and plants start dying.

G 3. List at least one (1) thing that you liked about doing this project, and at least one (1) thing that you disliked about doing this project. I liked this whole project because we got to learn how plants and animals interact in a pond ecosystem. The only bad part was that we did not have a lot of time to do this project

(4)

STUDENT ACCOUNTABILITY:

Each member of the team individually answers the questions below:

NAME: CLASS: DATE: Dec. 11, 1998

1. What did you contribute to this project? In the space below, describe what you contributed to the design and building of the bio-box pond ecosystem, and the information that you contributed in answering the questions that were given to your team. If you need additional space, please feel free to write on the back of this page.

What I contributed to the project was the shelled turtle, the pebbles, the glue, and the magic markers. I did not bring lots of supplies, but I took my share in the project and did most of the work, like measuring paper, drawing, and cutting alot of things out.

D 2. What conclusions can you draw about the interactions in a pond ecosystem? If the pond is not polluted, the animals and plants will have a good balance and live great. If the water is polluted, the plants will die, have no food for the insects, so the insects will die, and the frog will starve. Thats why the food web is needed.

H 3. List at least one (1) thing that you liked about doing this project, and at least one (1) thing that you disliked about doing this project. I loved the project, the whole intire thing. It was all exiting having to do something with the pond. The only thing I disliked was the time of work we had. It was so fun. I never wanted to take my hands off of it.

Work Sample & Commentary: *Owl Pellets*

The task

After a study of structure and function, students were asked to dissect owl pellets and to reconstruct the skeletal remains of animals contained within.

This activity is followed by a research report which includes the following information:

- Owls as predators,
- Conclusions about the diet and habits of the owl that made the pellet,
- How scientists determine the predatory structures and behaviors of dinosaurs, and
- A bibliography of books and internet sources used to compile the report.

After completing the dissection activity and the written component, students designed a labeled pictorial food web showing nutritional hierarchy based upon their analyses of their owl pellet.

Note: Commercially available owl pellets are sterilized and do not present a health or safety problem.

Circumstances of performance

This sample of student work was produced under the following conditions:

√ alone   √ in a group

√ in class   √ as homework

√ with teacher feedback   with peer feedback

   timed   √ opportunity for revision

What the work shows

A Based upon their analysis of owl pellets and follow-up research, students designed a labeled, pictorial food web showing a nutritional hierarchy.

This work sample illustrates a standard-setting performance for the following parts of the standards:

S2d Life Sciences Concepts: Populations and ecosystems.

S5b Scientific Thinking: Use concepts from Science Standards 1 to 4.

S5f Scientific Thinking: Work individually and in teams.

For related work on Interdependence, see "Biomes", page 52, "Bio Box", page 98, "Eagles", page 186, and "The Invincible Cockroach", page 188.

The quotations from the Science performance descriptions in this commentary are excerpted. The complete performance descriptions are shown on pages 68-84.

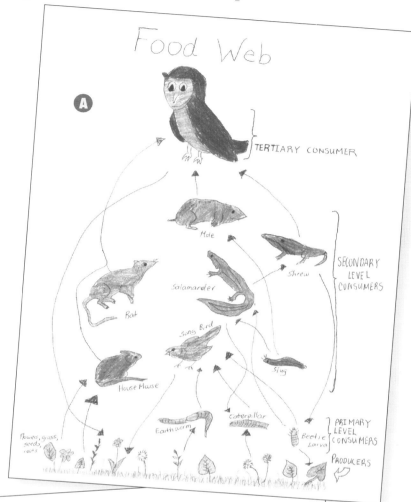

A Food Web

TERTIARY CONSUMER

SECONDARY LEVEL CONSUMERS

Mole   Shrew   Salamander   Rat   Song Bird   Slug   House Mouse

Caterpillar   Earthworm   Beetle Larva   PRIMARY LEVEL CONSUMERS

Flowers, grass, seeds, roots   PRODUCERS

B Analysis of Food Web
FOR OWL PELLET DISSECTION

<u>Producers</u>: producers are mainly plants such as flowers, grass, seeds, and roots. These organisms are the basis of the food web, and is the essential key to all life because they absorb the sun's energy. They make glucose, which is eaten by other organisms.

<u>Primary level/consumers</u>: consumers are herbivores such as gerbils, earthworms and a variety of insects. They feed on the plants. They are the main source of meat for the predators because they contain energy made by producers.

<u>Secondary level/consumers</u>: These consumers consists of carnivores and omnivores such as rodents, salamanders, and birds. They feed on the herbivores and occasionally some producers.

<u>Tertiary level/consumers</u>: These consumers are strictly carnivores and is represented as the owl in this food web. Their diet consists of animals from the primary and secondary levels.

Owl Pellets

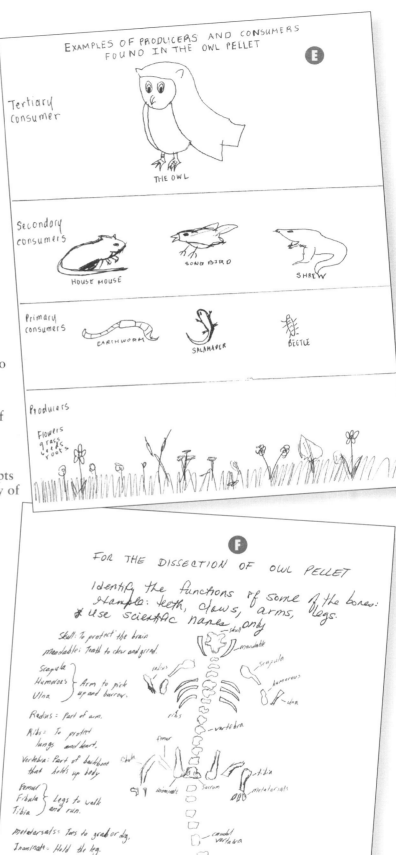

B The written "Analysis of Food Web" provides further evidence of understanding of structures and functions in an ecosystem.

The conclusion **D** about the diet of the owl that produced the pellet the student dissected is based on careful observations **C** and indicates an understanding of the predator/prey relationship between an owl and a shrew.

S2d Life Sciences Concepts: The student produces evidence that demonstrates understanding of populations and ecosystems, such as the roles of producers, consumers, and decomposers in a food web....

D The conclusion provides evidence of this understanding when it relates physical structure to predatory role.

E Additional evidence is provided by the table that organizes research into the ecological roles of organisms whose remains were found in the owl pellet.

S5b Scientific Thinking: The student uses concepts from Science Standards 1 to 4 to explain a variety of observations and phenomena.

D The conclusion accurately applies Science Standard **S2a**, especially as it relates jaw structure to diet.

E The table showing the organization of the food web accurately applies Science Standard **S2d**.

F Students successfully applied Science Standard **S2a** when they assembled the bones found in the pellet, and added the descriptive notes about physical structures to the left of the diagram.

S5f Scientific Thinking: The student works individually and in teams to collect and share information.

A B C D E F Throughout this investigation, students worked in groups to analyze the food web and to assemble the bone structure of the organisms that the owl ate. Use of the words "our" and "we" in **C** and **D** clearly indicate that this was a team effort.

Physical Sciences Concepts

Life Sciences Concepts **S2**

Earth and Space Sciences Concepts

Scientific Connections and Applications

Scientific Thinking **S5**

Scientific Tools and Technologies

Scientific Communication

Scientific Investigation

Owl Pellets

Owls

1. Owls as Predators

Owls are one of the best hunters in the world. Most owls are nocturnal, that means they sleep during the day, and are active during the night. There are however some owls that are active during the day. Owls hunt a variety of animals including mice, rats, moles, shrews, small birds, lemmings, and some types of insects and lizards. Although owls are often on top of the food chain, sometimes they feed on each other such as the Hawk and Great Horned owls would on the Spotted owl. Before launching an attack, owls spend from a few seconds to several hours watching and listening to their pray. When they strike, they attack from relatively short distances from their prey.

2. Conclusions Drawn from the Owl Pellets

a) What are owl pellets?

When an owl eats an animal it swallows it whole, without chewing. Once it reaches their intestines the meat and flesh of the animal gets digested, but the fur, bones, and other things that are too hard to digest are stored in another part of the owl's stomach. They form a small egg sized pellet which is later regurgitated by the owl. The skeletons of the animals eaten by the owl are kept well preserved in the pellets.

b) What did we find in our owl pellet?

After our group had dissected the owl's pellet we saw a lot of fur and hair. Using the instruments, we had our group members pick out the different bones that were in the pellet. We were able to form an almost perfect skeleton of a shrew. In addition to that we had found two more fractured skulls and some more bones. Using the chart we had in our class room we identified the bones to be bird bones.

c) Conclusions on the owl's diet

Knowing that this was a barn owl's pellet we can conclude that the barn owl is a carnivore who has the same inner functions as any other owl. We can also conclude that the barn owl feeds on small birds and shrews. By studying the jaw bones of those animals we see that they are also carnivores because they have strong sharp teeth.

d) What is the owls habitat like?

Most owls live in canopies, rocky cliffs, and in very old forests filled with different species of conifers. The climate there is basically mild, cold in the winter, and warm in the summer. There is one exception, and that is the snowy owl: it lives in arctic climates were it is always cold. In regions were most owls live the animals they hunt are mice, moles, rats, small birds, shrews, and some lizards and insects. These animals need a habitat which provides them with smaller animals such as snails, caterpillars, and voles to eat. Those animals need a habitat which provides them with flowers, grass, and roots to feed on. So the places listed above provide perfect habitats for owls because they feed on smaller animals. They provide a perfect habitat for smaller animals because they feed on even smaller animals, and they provide a perfect habitat for even smaller animals because they feed on plants.

3. Based on Finding Dinosaur Bones, How Can Scientists Determine the Story Line of Dinosaurs?

The bones of a dinosaur can tell you a lot about it. You could see how it was structured, and that would tell you it's diet and lifestyle. If you look at the teeth of the dinosaur you could tell if it was a herbivore or a carnivore because a carnivore would need strong, sharp teeth to pierce through the flesh of an animal, and a herbivore wouldn't. You could tell how old the dinosaur was by checking if it's bones were fully developed. You could also tell whether it had any special features to help it survive in it's environment. For example an animal would need strong legs if it chased it's prey for a long distance therefore, it's bones would have adapted to that need. Scientists have been observing and deriving information from dinosaur bones for many years, and that's why we know so much about them even though they died billions of years ago.

References: World Scope Encyclopedia
Internet Date: 12/4/98

Work Sample & Commentary: *Snails*

The task

Students were asked to design and conduct an experiment to determine how snails react to changes in their environment. The task included writing a report that describes the procedure, the outcome, and students' conclusions.

Circumstances of performance

This sample of student work was produced under the following conditions:

alone	√ in a group
√ in class	√ as homework
√ with teacher feedback	√ with peer feedback
timed	√ opportunity for revision

What the work shows

S2c Life Sciences Concepts: The student produces evidence that demonstrates understanding of regulation and behavior, such as senses and behavior, and response to environmental stimuli.

A B The student demonstrates an understanding of a response to an environmental stimulus by describing several observations of snail locomotion in response to a light source; and by making inferences based on those observations. While the inferences include some incorrect terminology (e.g., "tentacles"), it is clear that the student understands that the snail's actions were responses to the light.

S4a Scientific Connections and Applications: The student produces evidence that demonstrates understanding of big ideas and unifying concepts, such as…cause and effect.

C The conclusion uses the concept of cause and effect to explain why the snails in the experiment moved towards the light and away from the darkness.

This work sample illustrates a standard-setting performance for the following parts of the standards:

S2c Life Sciences Concepts: Regulation and behavior.

S4a Scientific Connections and Applications: Big ideas and unifying concepts.

S5f Scientific Thinking: Work individually and in teams.

S7e Scientific Communication: Communicate in a form suited to the purpose and audience.

Sidebar (left margin)

Physical Sciences Concepts

Life Sciences Concepts **S2**

Earth and Space Sciences Concepts

Scientific Connections and Applications **S4**

Scientific Thinking **S5**

Scientific Tools and Technologies

Scientific Communication **S7**

Scientific Investigation

For related work on Response to Environment, see "Bean Farmers", page 44, "Water Tolerance", page 50, "Toasted Bread", page 54, and "Endocrine Feedback", page 183.

The quotations from the Science performance descriptions in this commentary are excerpted. The complete performance descriptions are shown on pages 68-84.

Student work (right)

DO SNAILS PREFER LIGHT OR DARK?

Written by _____

Do Snails Prefer Light or Dark Better

Investigative question: Do snails prefer light better or dark better?

D **Hypothesis:** We think that the snails will prefer the dark better since the light may blind them.

Materials:

Box
Scissors
Marker
Ruler
Flashlight
Divider (Card Board)
Snail

Procedure:

E First get a regular sized box and divide it in half so that from a bird's view you can see two squares. Color one side white and one side black. Then carefully with a scissors cut out a two- inch square hole on the side of the box right in the middle of one of the squares. Then do the same to the one next to it. Next make another hole on the back of the box the same way except do it only to the black side. Carefully with a maker mark a spot (one centimeter from the corner of the box.) Do the same with the other side. Place the flashlight in rest position on the white hole in the back without any coverings, and turn it on. Put one snail on the marked spot on the white side with the light on and watch from the plastic window. Wait two minutes and then take it out and measure the amount it went. Do the same thing with the other side where there is no light on. Compare the difference and you'll see which they prefer better with the movement they took.

Snails

S5 f Scientific Thinking: The student works individually and in teams to collect and share information and ideas.

D Throughout the report, use of the plural "we" indicates that the student worked within a team to collect data and share information and ideas.

S7 e Scientific Communication: The student communicates in a form suited to the purpose and audience, such as by writing instructions that others can follow.

E The student's written procedure indicates the ability to communicate the experimental design in detail.

F The written procedure is supported by a diagram that clarifies the construction of the apparatus.

Observations-

LIGHT-
A When we first shinned the flashlight at the snail, the snail looked around stretching its four tentacles as wide as it could. Then as it got it adjusted to the light, and the snail began to move. Slowly the snail moved up coming almost out of his shell and then pulling the shell back into its body. We then thought, maybe if we moved the light away it would move faster, but instead the snail followed it and always went toward where the light would go. In total the snail's gooey trial in the light moved 6.3 inches.

DARK-
When we put the same snail into the dark side, we thought it would go a lot faster. Yet the results were totally different. When we lifted the box we saw that the snail went toward the side were there was more light and to our amazement the snail's trail only went 5.4 inches and seemed totally lost.

INFERENCE-
B We can infer that the snail prefers the light better because of the fact that the snail moved more quickly and followed the light. Also the distance of trail showed us that the snail prefer the light. We think this happened because the snail's eyes are similar to ours. If we were to turn off the lights and go some where we would walk a distance but seem confuse and likely we will go to a place where there is more light and then stay in the darkness. In the light we would walk much faster and move along the bright side. Snails like us have eyes too but their eyes are much smaller and are inside the tip of the two larger tentacles. Where the snail can distinguish between light, dark and feel their way around.

CONCLUSION-
C In conclusion the snails prefer the light better than the dark because the slimy trail left behind read 6.3inches for the light side and 5.4 inches for the dark side.

Physical Sciences Concepts

S2 Life Sciences Concepts

Earth and Space Sciences Concepts

S4 Scientific Connections and Applications

S5 Scientific Thinking

Scientific Tools and Technologies

S7 Scientific Communication

Scientific Investigation

Work Sample & Commentary: *It's All in the Genes*

For related work on Reproduction, see "Butterflies", page 47, "DNA Models", page 176, and "DNA Concept Map", page 179.

The task

Before working on this task the teacher engaged the whole class in a series of discussions about genotype, phenotype, and dominant and recessive traits. The teacher then instructed the students to create a three column chart with the following column headings—*Characteristic*, *Dominant*, *Appearance* or *Phenotype*. Students filled in the first column with a given list of twelve human characteristics; the second column with the dominant phenotype for each characteristic; and they left the third column blank. The teacher then broke the class into groups with each group member receiving a copy of the chart. Each student then filled in the third column, recording his or her own phenotype as determined by the other members of the group. The class then created a large graph to organize the data recorded by each student. On the X axis students listed the twelve dominant phenotypes. On the Y axis the class indicated the number of students expressing each dominant trait. The students were instructed to discuss a series of questions about their results and to compose individual responses.

Circumstances of performance

This sample of student work was produced under the following conditions:

alone	√ in a group
√ in class	as homework
√ with teacher feedback	√ with peer feedback
timed	√ opportunity for revision

The quotations from the Science performance descriptions in this commentary are excerpted. The complete performance descriptions are shown on pages 68-84.

What the work shows

S2b Life Sciences Concepts: The student produces evidence that demonstrates understanding of...the role of genes and environment on trait expression.

A The student observed, "Our traits are first determined by the genotype. We get this from our parents. The genes carry the traits. The mixture of genes partially determines what traits you get."

This work sample illustrates a standard-setting performance for the following parts of the standards:

S2b Life Sciences Concepts: The role of genes and environment.

S5f Scientific Thinking: Collect and share information and ideas.

S7a Scientific Communication. Represent data and results in multiple ways.

C

12/11/98

Science

The difference between phenotype and genotype is that you can see the phenotype and the genotype makes up the phenotype. Our traits are first determined by the **◄ A** genotype. We get this from our parents. The genes carry the traits. The mixture of genes partially determines what traits you get.

Tongue rolling, free earlobes and dark hair are the three most common traits in our class. Curly hair, dimples, and clockwise hair form are the least common. I think that the hair form wasn't tested correctly enough. One person out of 27 people had all of the dominant traits. One person out of 27 people had the least amount, with 3 out of 9 traits. We have different traits because we each have a different genetic make up.

I think the environment has an effect on our traits too. For example, freckles are affected by the environment. People who have freckles usually show them during the spring and summer. I think people with freckles live in environments where they have exposure to a lot of sun.

B ► I think that if people with the trait for freckles lived in a cold environment where it is cloudy and rains a lot, their freckles would not show as much. However, I think this type of environment would be more suitable for people with freckles, because they have spots of melanin in their skin instead of an even amount of melanin, which helps to protect the skin cells from damage due to exposure to the sun.

It's All in the Genes

	D	
Characteristic	**Dominant**	**Appearance** or **Phenotype**
Hair Whorl	Clockwise	Clockwise
Hair Form	Curly	Curly
Dimpled Cheeks	Dimpled Cheeks	Dimpled Cheeks
Tongue folding	Folder	Folder
Tongue Rolling	Roller	Roller
Long Eyelashes	Long Lashes	Short Lashes
Widow's Peak	Present	Absent
Free Earlobes	Free Lobes	Free Lobes
Hair Color	Dark	Dark
Normal Vision (Not Color Blind)	Normal	Normal
Eyesight	Normal	Normal
Freckles	Freckles	Absent

B The student correctly infers the role of the environment in the expression of a specific trait.

S5 f Scientific Thinking: The student works individually and in teams to collect and share information and ideas.

C Throughout this task students worked together gathering and representing data and sharing data and ideas. The production of the written work demonstrates the students ability to use the shared data and ideas to produce an individual piece of work.

D **E** The student worked with other team members in gathering data for the table of personal characteristics, and contributed to the bar graph that displays the whole class's characteristics.

S7 a Scientific Communication. The student represents data and results in multiple ways, such as numbers, tables, and graphs...and technical and creative writing.

C This evidence demonstrates the student's ability to explain results in narrative form.

D This evidence demonstrates the student's ability to represent data as a table.

E This evidence demonstrates the student's ability to represent data as a graph.

Physical Sciences Concepts

S2 Life Sciences Concepts

Earth and Space Sciences Concepts

Scientific Connections and Applications

S5 Scientific Thinking

Scientific Tools and Technologies

S7 Scientific Communication

Scientific Investigation

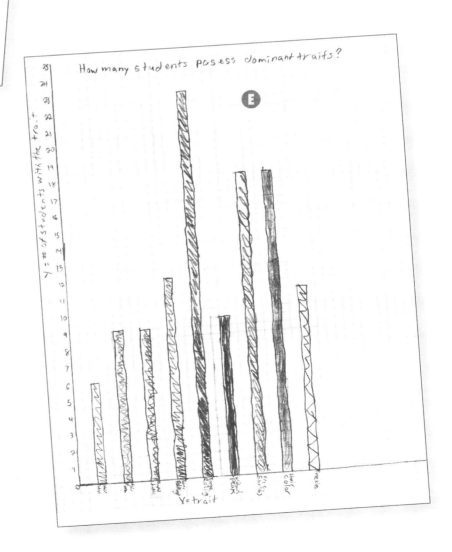

Work Sample & Commentary: *Diffusion*

The task

After a unit of study on cells, students were asked to demonstrate how diffusion occurs and write a report about their demonstrations.

Circumstances of performance

This sample of student work was produced under the following conditions:

alone	√ in a group
√ in class	as homework
√ with teacher feedback	with peer feedback
timed	opportunity for revision

The work was done in a group but written up individually.

What the work shows

S1a Physical Sciences Properties: The student produces evidence that demonstrates understanding of properties and changes of properties in matter....

A **B** The student accurately describes the meaning of "semipermeable."

The quotations from the Science performance descriptions in this commentary are excerpted. The complete performance descriptions are shown on pages 68-84.

Physical Sciences Concepts **S1**
Life Sciences Concepts **S2**
Earth and Space Sciences Concepts
Scientific Connections and Applications **S4**
Scientific Thinking **S5**
Scientific Tools and Technologies **S6**
Scientific Communication **S7**
Scientific Investigation

This work sample illustrates a standard-setting performance for the following parts of the standards:

S1a Physical Sciences Concepts: Properties and changes of properties in matter.

S2a Life Sciences Concepts: Structure and function of living systems.

S4a Scientific Connections and Applications: Big ideas and unifying concepts.

S5a Scientific Thinking: Frame questions; identify or control variables.

S5b Scientific Thinking: Use concepts from Science Standards 1 to 4.

S6a Scientific Tools and Technologies: Use technology and tools.

S7e Scientific Communication: Communicate in a form suited to the purpose and audience.

如何证明扩散作用?

工作: 我们如何证明扩散作用?
材料: 食物包素、烧杯、试管、lugol's液、澱粉、橡皮筋、金箔匠膜.

F 基础观识: 物质通过细胞膜的扩散作用对生物的功能很重要. 已说明消化了的食物和氧气如何进入细胞、废物如何离开细胞.

G 步骤: (A) 液体中的扩散作用
1. 把食物包素滴入烧杯中的水.
2. 食物包素很快沉向杯底並四散开来.
3. 整杯水未经搅拌, 全部变红.

H

(B) 液体通过薄膜的扩散作用(之一)
1. 用 lugol's 液装满半个试管.
2. 用橡皮筋把一片金箔匠膜扫住试管口.
3. 宫口朝下放入含澱粉悬液的烧杯.

- *2* -

Diffusion

S2a Life Sciences Concepts: The student produces evidence that demonstrates understanding of structure and function of living systems, such as the complementary nature of structure and function in cells....

A **C** The student demonstrates conceptual understanding of the structure and diffusive function of cell membranes.

S4a Scientific Connections and Applications: The student produces evidence that demonstrates understanding of big ideas and unifying concepts, such as...cause and effect.

D The student correctly identifies an example of diffusion, ruling out gravity as an alternative cause of the observed phenomena.

S5a Scientific Thinking: The student frames questions to distinguish cause and effect; and identifies or controls variables in experimental and non-experimental research settings.

B The student identifies pore size as a variable.

E The student frames her results as a series of questions and answers.

S5b Scientific Thinking: The student uses concepts from Science Standards 1 to 4 to explain a variety of observations and phenomena.

C **D** The student applies elements of **S1**a and **S2**a in her discussion of the property of semipermeability and the process of diffusion.

S6a Scientific Tools and Technologies: The student uses technology and tools (such as traditional laboratory apparatus...) to observe and measure...phenomena directly....

F **G** The list of materials and the four parts of the procedure indicate that the student used traditional laboratory apparatus to observe the process of diffusion directly.

H **I** **J** **K** The student provides photographs of the laboratory set-ups.

S7e Scientific Communication: The student communicates in a form suited to the purpose and audience, such as by writing instructions that others can follow....

G The student demonstrates effective scientific communication by clearly outlining a procedure that other students could follow.

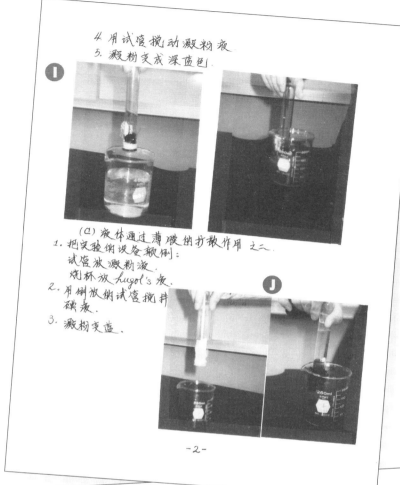

I 4. 用试管搅动澱粉液.
5. 澱粉变成深蓝色.

(a) 液体通过薄膜的扩散作用 之二.
1. 把实验设备颠倒:
   试管放澱粉液.
   烧杯放 lugol's 液.
2. 用倒放的试管搅拌碘液.
3. 澱粉变蓝.

J

-2-

K (b) 气体通过薄膜的扩散作用.
1. 用无色的酚酞装满半个试管.
2. 用橡皮痲把一片塑膠膜包在管口.
3. 管口朝下, 放在揃开的氨水瓶上. 4. 半小时後, 试管变成桃红.

E 讨论: (1)塑膠膜代表细胞的那一部分? 它是否半透性?
如果在实验B中? 何者可以透过?

A —— 塑膠膜代表细胞膜, 且是半透性的, 碘和氨可以通过.

(2)如果膜上的小孔容许有些物质通过, 它们大小如何?

B —— 膜上的孔比碘液和氨大, 比澱粉和酚酞小.

(3)从实验C中, 我们得到什么结论?

Diffusion

Physical Sciences Concepts — S1
Life Sciences Concepts — S2
Earth and Space Sciences Concepts
Scientific Connections and Applications — S4
Scientific Thinking — S5
Scientific Tools and Technologies — S6
Scientific Communication — S7
Scientific Investigation

D —— 实验 C 的 装置 刚好 和 B 相反，但 淀粉 们 然 变蓝. 证明 碘 分子 借 扩散 作用 通过 薄膜，而 不是 靠 地 心 引力.

(4) 这个 期质 从 高 浓度 到 低 浓度 的 过程 叫 什么？它 如何 在 消化 和 循环 作用 中 发挥 作用？

C —— 叫 扩散. 小肠 消化 了 的 食 物 则 借 扩散 作用 进入 血 流，又 经 血 流 进入 全 身 的 细 胞，细胞 产 生 的 废 物 则 借 扩散 作用 进入 血 流 运到 特定 器官 排出.

– 4 –

Translation

PROBLEM: How can we demonstrate diffusion?

BACKGROUND INFORMATION: Diffusion of substances through cell membranes is important to the functioning of living things. It explains how digested food and oxygen enter cells, and how wastes leave cells.

F MATERIALS: food coloring, beakers, test tubes, iodine solution, starch, rubber band, goldbeater membrane

G PROCEDURE:
(A) Diffusion in liquid
1. Add a drop of food coloring into the water in a beaker.
2. Allow the food coloring to settle to the bottom and then spread all over.
3. Wait until the whole beaker of water turns red without stirring.
(B) #1. Diffusion of molecules in liquid through a membrane
1. Fill a test tube half-full with Lugol's solution.
2. Use a rubber band to cover the mouth of the test tube with a piece of goldbeater membrane.
3. Place the test tube, mouth downward, into a beaker containing a suspension of starch and water.
4. Stir the starch mixture with the test tube.
5. Wait until the starch turns deep blue.
(C) #2. Diffusion of molecules in liquid through a membrane #2
1. Reverse the set-up in #1: Place starch in a test tube and Lugol's solution in a beaker.
2. Follow the same procedure as above.
3. Wait until the starch in the test tube turns blue.
(D) #3. Diffusion of molecules in gas through a membrane
1. Fill a test tube half-full with colorless phenophthalein
2. Use a rubber band to cover the mouth of the test tube with a piece of goldbeater membrane.
3. Place the test tube, mouth downward, on the mouth of a uncovered bottle of ammonia solution.
4. Wait until the phenophthalein solution in the test tube turns pink red.

E DISCUSSION:
1. Which part of an actual cell does the goldbeater membrane represent? Is it semi-permeable? Suppose in a situation specified in experiment #2, which substance would pass through the goldbeater membrane?
   A • The goldbeater membrane represents the cell membrane. It is semipermeable and therefore both iodine and ammonia can pass through it.
2. If certain materials can pass through the goldbeater membrance, what could you determine about the size of the cell of that substance?
   B • The pores in the goldbeater membrane are larger than iodine or ammonia, but smaller than starch or phenophthalein.
3. What conclusions can you draw in experiment #3?
   D • The set-up in experiment #3 is the reverse of that in #2. Nonetheless, the starch still turns blue. This symbolizes that the iodine molecules pass through the goldbeater membrane by way of diffusion, not as a result of the functioning of gravitational force.
4. What name is given to the process in which substances move from areas of high concentration to areas of low concentration? How does the process function in life activities, such as digestion, transport, and excretion?
   C • The process is called diffusion. The digested food in small intestine enters blood and then into body cells by diffusion. On the other hand, the wastes produced by the cells leave cells by entering blood and into excretory organs also by diffusion.

Work Sample & Commentary: *The Rock Cycle*

The task

Students were asked to develop graphic models of the rock cycle as the culmination of six weeks of study. During those six weeks, classroom lessons and laboratory experiences were conducted to study the three major rock groups; and the class went on two field trips to observe rock formations and collect rocks. In developing their graphic models, students were asked to include any forces and processes that cause rocks to change.

Circumstances of performance

This sample of student work was produced under the following conditions:

√ alone   in a group

√ in class   as homework

√ with teacher feedback   with peer feedback

    timed   √ opportunity for revision

What the work shows

S3a Earth Sciences Concepts: The student produces evidence that demonstrates understanding of structure of the Earth system, such as...rock cycles.

A The student shows a clear understanding of the cyclical relationship that exists between igneous, sedimentary and metamorphic rocks, and many of the forces that cause these changes.

S4a Scientific Connections and Applications: The student produces evidence that demonstrates understanding of big ideas and unifying concepts, such as...cause and effect.

B C D The student correctly shows that forces such as subduction, volcanic eruptions, etc. are cause agents for change in the rock cycle.

S5b Scientific Thinking: The student uses concepts from Science Standards 1-4 to explain a variety of observations and phenomena.

B C D The student uses the concept of Earth processes (Standard **S3**b) to explain how rocks change from one form to another. In a revision, the student should be asked to rethink the order of erosion and weathering in both places where these processes are noted.

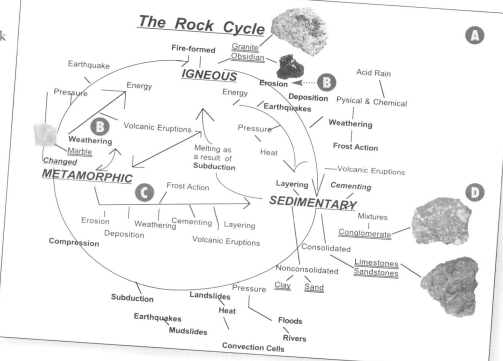

The Rock Cycle

S6d Scientific Tools and Technologies: The student acquires information from multiple sources, such as print, the Internet, computer data bases, and experimentation.

A Examples of the rocks were chosen by the student, using an internet web site: www.calvin.edu. The pictures were reduced on a photocopier to fit into the diagram.

S7a Scientific Communication: The student represents data and results in multiple ways, such as...tables...artwork.

A Student effectively blends a concept map and downloaded images to convey understanding of the rock cycle.

This work sample illustrates a standard-setting performance for the following parts of the standards:

S3a **Earth Sciences Concepts: Structure of the Earth system.**

S4a **Scientific Connections and Applications: Big ideas and unifying concepts.**

S5b **Scientific Thinking: Use concepts from Science Standards 1 to 4.**

S6d **Scientific Tools and Technologies: Acquire information from multiple sources.**

S7a **Scientific Communication: Represent data and results in multiple ways.**

The quotations from the Science performance descriptions in this commentary are excerpted. The complete performance descriptions are shown on pages 68-84.

Physical Sciences Concepts

Life Sciences Concepts

S3 Earth and Space Sciences Concepts

S4 Scientific Connections and Applications

S5 Scientific Thinking

S6 Scientific Tools and Technologies

S7 Scientific Communication

Scientific Investigation

Work Sample & Commentary: *River Cutters*

For related work on Erosion, see "Erosion", page 62.

The quotations from the Science performance descriptions in this commentary are excerpted. The complete performance descriptions are shown on pages 68-84.

The task

After extensive study on river formation, students conducted a stream-table activity generated from the GEMS guide *River Cutters*, revised edition. Each student team was asked to design a stream-table experiment that would model the production of various land features shaped by running water.

Circumstances of performance

This sample of student work was produced under the following conditions:

√ alone √ in a group
√ in class   as homework
√ with teacher feedback   with peer feedback
  timed √ opportunity for revision

What the work shows

S3 b Earth Sciences Concepts: The student produces evidence that demonstrates understanding of Earth's history, such as earth processes including erosion and...change over time....

A The "Observations" section clearly demonstrates that the student understands that running water causes landforms such as V-shaped valleys and oxbow lakes.

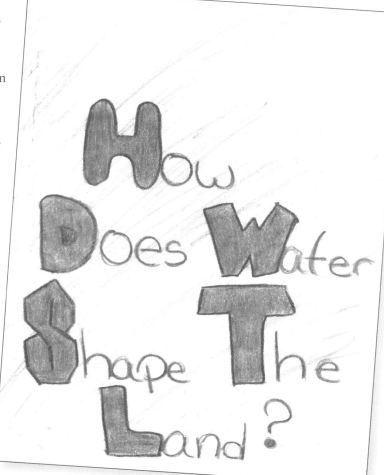

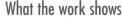

This work sample illustrates a standard-setting performance for the following parts of the standards:

S3 b Earth Sciences Concepts: Earth's history.

S4 a Scientific Connections and Applications: Big ideas and unifying concepts.

S5 b Scientific Thinking: Use concepts from Science Standards 1 to 4.

S5 f Scientific Thinking: Work individually and in teams.

S6 a Scientific Tools and Technologies: Use technology and tools.

S6 d Scientific Tools and Technologies: Acquire information from multiple sources.

S7 a Scientific Communication: Represent data and results in multiple ways.

S8 a Scientific Investigation: Controlled experiment.

B C D The three diagrams and their accompanying notes demonstrate that the student understands the progressive nature of landform-building. In D, the student notes, "This water session was a big success because the running time was longer. This happened because the longer water runs the greater the effect it can have on the earth."

E The student directly relates the formation of certain landforms to longer periods of time.

S4 a Scientific Connections and Applications: The student produces evidence that demonstrates understanding of big ideas and unifying concepts, such as...cause and effect.

A The entire "Observations" section presents implicit cause and effect relationships. At **F**, for example, the student relates the disappearance of the delta to the longer duration of water flow.

In the notes accompanying diagram **D**, the statement "...the longer water runs, the greater the effect it can have on the earth..." is evidence that the student understands cause and effect.

River Cutters

S5 b Scientific Thinking: The student uses concepts from Science Standards 1 to 4 to explain a variety of observations and phenomena.

G Throughout the conclusion, the student applies Science Standard **S3 b** in concluding that water flowing over land causes the formation of geographical features.

S5 f Scientific Thinking: The student works individually and in teams to collect and share information and ideas.

H The photographs show that the student worked as part of a team. The entire lab report, however, is an individual effort.

Physical Sciences Concepts

Life Sciences Concepts

S3 Earth and Space Sciences Concepts

S4 Scientific Connections and Applications

S5 Scientific Thinking

S6 Scientific Tools and Technologies

S7 Scientific Communication

S8 Scientific Investigation

February 23, 1999

Lab Report

Problem:

How does water shape the land?

Research:

It takes a long time for water to shape the land. If the water runs fast, it will take less time for the water to shape the land. While the water is shaping the land, it can form many different shapes.

Hypothesis:

I predict that the water will form a river or canal on the land.

I **Materials:**

1) Dripper System
2) River Model Tub
3) Coffee Can
4) Wooden Block
5) Sponge
6) Spray bottle
7) Newspaper

L **Procedure:**

– First, I got a river tub and carried it to my table where the desks were covered with newspaper.

– Next, I wet the earth in the river tub using the spray bottle.

– I set up the dripper system for 2 drops per second.

– I used the sponge to absorb the excess water and emptied it out into a bucket.

Procedure

– I put the coffee can on the side of the river tub and placed the Dripper System on top facing inside of the tub.

– I turned on the Dripper System for different time periods of two, five and ten minutes.

– I watched the river form and I wrote down what I observed for each time period.

– I drew a diagram for each period of time and studied the model some more.

River Cutters

S6a Scientific Tools and Technologies: The student uses technology and tools (such as traditional laboratory equipment...) to observe and measure objects, organisms, and phenomena, directly, indirectly, and remotely.

I The student used various tools to conduct the investigation.

S6d Scientific Tools and Technologies: The student acquires information from multiple sources, such as print...and experimentation.

A The observations are first-hand information the student acquired from experimentation.

J The bibliography demonstrates that the student acquired information from print sources.

Physical
Sciences
Concepts

Life
Sciences
Concepts

Earth and
Space Sciences **S3**
Concepts

Scientific
Connections and **S4**
Applications

Scientific **S5**
Thinking

Scientific Tools
and **S6**
Technologies

Scientific **S7**
Communication

Scientific **S8**
Investigation

A

Observation

- During the experiment, a river formed on the land. In my 9 minute river cutting session, two V-shaped valleys formed as well as a delta.

- During the 9-minute river cutting session, a straight river formed with a few meanders. The water also flooded the delta and it disappeared.

- During the 10 minute river cutting session, an Ox-bow lake formed and many meanders. The river got curvy. That's what I observed during my river cutting sessions.

- When I was observing the river, I took notes, drew diagrams with labels and photographs. You can see all of this in my report.

H

Photographs

B

pg7

Drip Time: 2 min
Actual Time: 2000 yrs.

In the 2-minute river cutting session the water shaped the land in a V-shape valley. The water was running so fast that it caused a meander and a delta. As you can see, the diagram shows all the things that I mentioned.

Land

Delta

Land

V-shaped Valley

Mouth

River Cutters

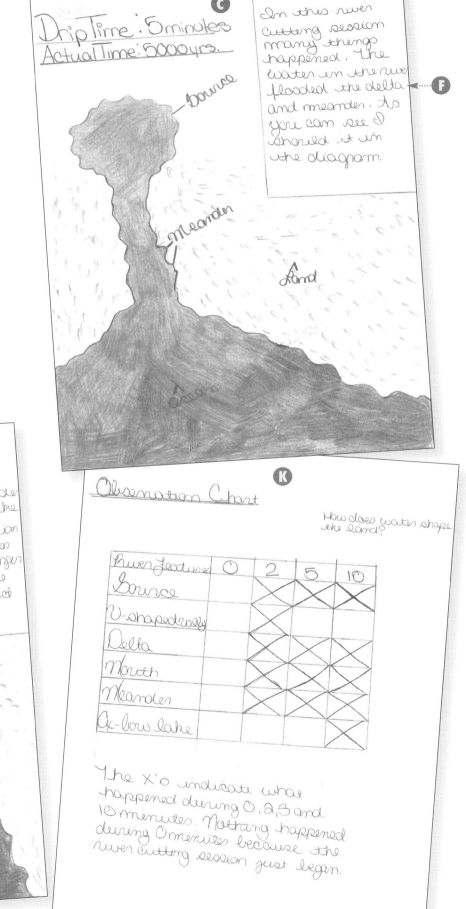

Drip Time: 5 minutes
Actual Time: 5000 yrs.

In this river cutting session many things happened. The water in the river flooded the delta and meander. As you can see I showed it in the diagram.

S7a Scientific Communication: The student represents data and results in multiple ways, such as numbers, tables, and graphs; drawings, diagrams, and artwork; and technical and creative writing.

B C D The student represents data in diagrams accompanied by narrative writing.

G The conclusion presents data in narrative form.

K The student also represents data in table form.

S8a Scientific Investigation: The student demonstrates scientific competence by completing [a] controlled experiment.

L The student's procedure indicates that all conditions remained the same except one variable: duration of time.

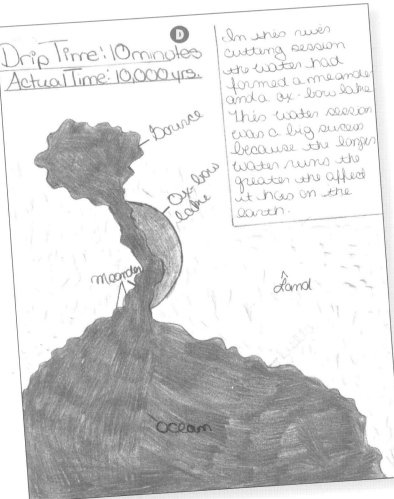

Drip Time: 10 minutes
Actual Time: 10,000 yrs.

In this river cutting session the water had formed a meander and a ox-bow lake. This water session was a big sucess because the longer water runs the greater the affect it has on the earth.

Observation Chart

How does water shape the land?

River Feature	0	2	5	10
Source		X	X	X
U-shaped valley				
Delta			X	X
Mouth			X	X
Meander			X	X
Ox-bow lake				X

The X's indicate what happened during 0, 2, 5 and 10 minutes. Nothing happened during 0 minutes because the river cutting session just began.

Physical Sciences Concepts

Life Sciences Concepts

S3 *Earth and Space Sciences Concepts*

S4 *Scientific Connections and Applications*

S5 *Scientific Thinking*

S6 *Scientific Tools and Technologies*

S7 *Scientific Communication*

S8 *Scientific Investigation*

River Cutters

G Conclusion:

In conclusion, my hypothesis was correct. The water cut through the land and made a river. The time periods represented two, five, and ten thousand years in the life of a river. The water first cut two V-shaped valleys and a delta. As the time increased, meanders and an ox-bow lake formed. **E**

I hope you like
my report
and I hope you
found it
interesting!

Definitions

1) Ox-bow river – A cresent-shaped lake formed from a curve or a meander of a river.

2) V-shaped valley – A valley with a "V" shaped profile, carved by a river.

3) Meander – A rounded or "s" shaped bend or loop usally seen in an "older" or "mature" river.

4) Delta – The deposit formed at the mouth of a stream or river as it enters another body of water, slows its flow rate, and drops its load of sediment.

5) Source – The beginning or origin of a stream or river.

6) Mouth – Part of a river where it flows into another body of water.

J Bibliography:

Earth Science, Snyder, Robert D.C.
Heath and Company, 1993. (pgs. 170-190).

World Book Encyclopedia, Volume W.
(pg. 53).

Work Sample & Commentary: *Where in the World Am I?*

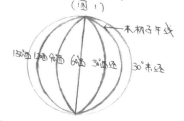

The task

Students were asked to imagine that they had stepped off a plane, only to realize that they had taken the wrong flight and landed in a strange country. They were asked to use their Earth Science to figure out where they were, then describe their situation in narrative form, explaining how they found their location by determining their longitude and latitude.

Circumstances of performance

This sample of student work was produced under the following conditions:

√ alone	√ in a group
√ in class	as homework
√ with teacher feedback	with peer feedback
timed	√ opportunity for revision

What the work shows

S3c Earth and Space Sciences Concepts: The student produces evidence that demonstrates understanding of Earth and the solar system, such as the predictable motions of planets, moons, and other objects in the solar system....

A The student states that the Earth rotates from west to east, indicating that the student understands that the Earth's motion is regular and predictable.

S4e Scientific Connections and Applications: The student produces evidence that demonstrates understanding of the impact of science, such as...interactions between science and society.

A B C The student bases the work on an application of science facts and process skills used to solve a real-world, albeit imaginary, problem.

This work sample illustrates a standard-setting performance for the following parts of the standards:

S3c Earth and Space Sciences Concepts: Earth and the solar system.

S4e Scientific Connections and Applications: Impact of science.

S5b Scientific Thinking: Use concepts from Science Standards 1 to 4.

S5e Scientific Thinking: Identify problems; propose and implement solutions; and evaluate the accuracy, design, and outcomes of investigations.

S7a Scientific Communication: Represent data and results in multiple ways.

The quotations from the Science performance descriptions in this commentary are excerpted. The complete performance descriptions are shown on pages 68-84.

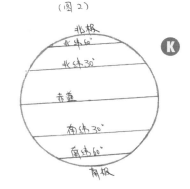

Sidebar

Physical Sciences Concepts
Life Sciences Concepts
S3 Earth and Space Sciences Concepts
S4 Scientific Connections and Applications
S5 Scientific Thinking
Scientific Tools and Technologies
S7 Scientific Communication
Scientific Investigation

Where in the World Am I?

S5b Scientific Thinking: The student uses concepts from Science Standards 1 to 4 to explain a variety of observations and phenomena.

A B The student uses concepts from **S3c** in describing a connection between the direction of Earth's rotation and time differences at different longitudes.

S5e Scientific Thinking: The student identifies problems; proposes and implements solutions; and evaluates the accuracy, design, and outcomes of investigations.

D The student identifies the problem.

E The student proposes a solution to the problem.

F The student considers a possible method for determining latitude, but knows that the method is not feasible.

G H The student describes how to use simple materials to build a device that can determine latitude.

I The student states that errors may occur during measuring, and that it would be necessary to repeat the procedure several times to obtain a more accurate mean measurement.

S7a Scientific Communication: The student represents data and results in multiple ways, such as…drawings, diagrams, and…technical and creative writing; and selects the most effective way to convey the scientific information.

H J K L M The student supports the narrative with diagrams and drawings.

N The narrative is essentially a work of creative writing that moves fluidly back and forth between the imaginary scenario and technical descriptions.

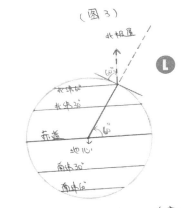

(图3)

北极星

L

北纬60°
北纬30°
赤道
地心
南纬30°
南纬60°

C 在北半球，北极星在水面上的高度等于观察北极星者的纬度。根据这一点，我就可以测量出我的纬度。测量所需的材料包括吸管、碗、及一个量角器。到了晚上，**G** 我将盛满水的碗放在空地上的一张桌子上。首先我先确定可以在空地上看见北极星，然后将吸管贴在碗边。从吸管的下方往上看，通过小孔来找北极星。慢慢移动吸管直到找到北极星。(见图4)我按住吸管不动，用量角器测量水面与吸管间的角度，那么来角的度数就是我的纬度。在测 **I** 量过程中，我们通常会有误差，所以我连续测量五次并取之平均值以减小误差。最后得到的度数约为75°。我的纬

度为北纬75°因为我可以看见北极星。

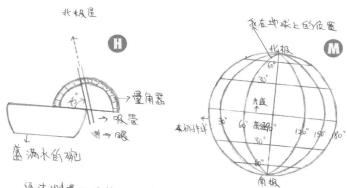

(图4)

北极星

H

量角器
吸管
眼
盛满水的碗

M 我在地球上的位置
北极
60°
30°
赤道
本初子午线 30° 60° 90° 120° 150° 180°
30°
60°
南极

经过测量与计算，我在地球上的位置为东经60°，北纬75°。跟据世界地图可以看见我在一个叫作 Novaya Zemlya 的地方。

N 我正得意在自己的成果时，听见有人唤我，一转身进入眼睛的是刺眼的灯光与母亲的面庞。原来刚才所有的一切只不过是一场梦。然而从中我学得历史、数学、科学等学校要求的必修课看似无用其实却有着一定的重要性。而且学习这些科目也让我们变得更聪明因为它让我们有了更多思考的空间与分析的能力。

Where in the World Am I?

Translation

1

How to Find Your Location on the Map

Getting off the plane, I found myself in London, the capital of England. I visited many famous places in London. While I was in Greenwich, I purchased a watch that had the time pre-set. After a couple of days of sightseeing, I was on the flight to my next destination. Upon arrival, I found myself in an unknown city. With no knowledge of the local language and no money in my pocket, I was in a desperate situation. However, I maintained my composure because I knew I could discover my whereabouts and could seek help from others.

A person's location can be found through the knowledge of longitude and latitude. Lines of longitude, called meridians, are imaginary lines on a globe that run from north to south. The Prime Meridian, 0 degrees longitude, passes through Greenwich, a suburb of London. The unit for longitude is degrees, and the maximum number of degrees is 180 in both the Eastern and Western Hemispheres. (See Figure 1.) I discovered that the local time was 9:00 A.M., while my watch from Greenwich said 5:00 A.M. Therefore, there was a time difference of four hours. Based on the knowledge from my Earth Science class, I knew that each hour of difference represented 15 degrees on the scale of longitude. Thus, my longitude was 60 degrees (15 degrees x 4 hours).

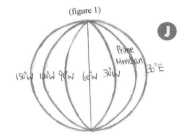

(figure 1)

2

Since the difference in time was four hours, and the earth rotates from west to east, I deduced that I must have been in the Eastern Hemisphere. However, the longitude by itself was insufficient to locate where I was. I was missing the latitude.

Latitudes are the axes that run east from west. Beginning at the equator (0°), the latitude goes up to 90° in both Northern and Southern Hemispheres. (See Figure 2.) The latitude of the North Pole is 90°N, while that of the South Pole is 90°S. There are various ways to measure latitude. For example, if a straight line could be drawn from the center of the earth to my location, the degree of the angle between the equator and my location would be the correlated latitude. (See Figure 3.) However, such a measurement was impossible. Therefore, the only method available to calculate latitude was to measure the angle of Polaris relative to Earth's horizon.

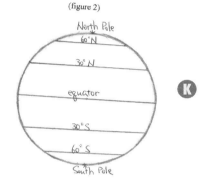

(figure 2)

3

(figure 3)

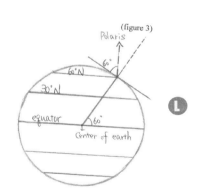

In the Northern Hemisphere, the location of a place is in direct correlation to the angle of relationship between Polaris and the horizon. Once I obtained the angle, I would be able to find my latitude. I managed to get a straw, a bowl, and a protractor, and proceeded to wait until the sky became dark. I placed the full bowl of water on a table in a spacious place and began my observations. First, I checked the sky to make sure that I could see Polaris. Then, I laid the straw across the bowl. Third, I tipped one end of straw down slowly until I could see Polaris through its hole. Finally, I held the straw and used the protractor to measure the angle between the straw and the water. This reading was my latitude.

In order to be accurate, I repeated the same procedure five times and calculated the mean. I used the mean as the final reading, which was approximately 75 degrees. Since I could see Polaris, I must have been somewhere in the Northern Hemisphere. Therefore, my latitude was 75 degrees north. I learned through the measurement and calculation that my location on the earth was 60 degrees longitude east and 75 degrees latitude north. Checking the world map, I realized that I was in Novaya Zemlya.

(figure 4)

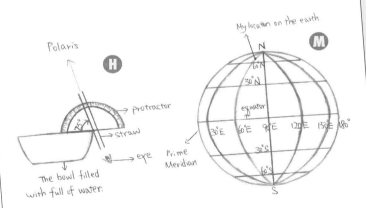

Just when I was feeling proud of my achievement, I heard someone calling my name. As I peered out of the darkness, I was confronted by a blinding light and the familiar face of my mother. What had occurred was just a dream, but I had increased my knowledge of social studies, mathematics, and science. Although I had thought that these subjects were useless, I realize that we need them. Most important, learning these subjects makes us smarter because they stimulate us to think more and analyze more, which results in expanding our intellectual abilities.

OVERVIEW OF THE PERFORMANCE STANDARDS

The high school standards are set at a level of performance approximately equivalent to the end of tenth grade. It is expected that some students might achieve this level earlier and others later than this grade. (See "Deciding what constitutes a standard-setting performance," page 9.)

S Science

S1 Physical Sciences Concepts

S1a Demonstrates an understanding of the structure of atoms.

S1b Demonstrates an understanding of structure and properties of matter.

S1c Demonstrates an understanding of chemical reactions.

S1d Demonstrates an understanding of motions and forces.

S1e Demonstrates an understanding of conservation of energy and increase in disorder.

S1f Demonstrates an understanding of interactions of energy and matter.

S2 Life Sciences Concepts

S2a Demonstrates an understanding of the cell.

S2b Demonstrates an understanding of biological evolution.

S2c Demonstrates an understanding of interdependence of organisms.

S2d Demonstrates an understanding of matter, energy, and organization in living systems.

S2e Demonstrates an understanding of evolution, diversity, and adaptation of organisms.

S2f Demonstrates an understanding of behavior of organisms.

S3 Earth and Space Sciences Concepts

S3a Demonstrates an understanding of energy in the Earth system.

S3b Demonstrates an understanding of geochemical cycles.

S3c Demonstrates an understanding of origin and evolution of the Earth system.

S3d Demonstrates an understanding of origin and evolution of the universe.

S3e Demonstrates an understanding of natural resource management.

S4 Scientific Connections and Applications

S4a Demonstrates an understanding of big ideas and unifying concepts.

S4b Demonstrates an understanding of the designed world.

S4c Demonstrates an understanding of health.

S4d Demonstrates an understanding of the impact of technology.

S4e Demonstrates an understanding of the impact of science.

S Science

S5 Scientific Thinking

S5a Frames questions to distinguish cause and effect; and identifies or controls variables.

S5b Uses concepts from Science Standards 1 to 4 to to explain a variety of observations and phenomena.

S5c Uses evidence from reliable sources to develop descriptions, explanations, and models ; and makes appropriate adjustments and improvements.

S5d Proposes, recognizes, analyzes, considers, and critiques alternative explanations; and distinguishes between fact and opinion.

S5e Identifies problems; proposes and implements solutions; and evaluates the accuracy, design, and outcomes of investigations.

S5f Works individually and in teams to collect and share information and ideas.

S6 Scientific Tools and Technologies

S6a Uses technology and tools to observe and measure objects, organisms, and phenomena, directly, indirectly, and remotely, with appropriate consideration of accuracy and precision.

S6b Records and stores data using a variety of formats.

S6c Collects and analyzes data using concepts and techniques in Mathematics Standard 4.

S6d Acquires information from multiple sources.

S6e Recognizes and limits sources of bias in data.

S7 Scientific Communication

S7a Represents data and results in multiple ways.

S7b Argues from evidence.

S7c Critiques published materials.

S7d Explains a scientific concept or procedure to other students.

S7e Communicates in a form suited to the purpose and the audience.

S8 Scientific Investigation

S8a Demonstrates scientific competence by completing a controlled experiment.

S8b Demonstrates scientific competence by completing fieldwork.

S8c Demonstrates scientific competence by completing a design.

S8d Demonstrates scientific competence by completing secondary research.

New York City Performance Standards

S1 Physical Sciences Concepts

The student demonstrates conceptual understanding by using a concept accurately to explain observations and make predictions and by representing the concept in multiple ways (through words, diagrams, graphs or charts, as appropriate). Both aspects of understanding—explaining and representing—are required to meet this standard.

S1 a The student produces evidence that demonstrates understanding of structure of atoms, such as atomic composition, nuclear forces, and radioactivity.

Examples of activities through which students might demonstrate conceptual understanding of physical sciences include:

▴ Debate the relative merits of harnessing nuclear fission and fusion as energy sources. 1a, 1b, 1c, E3b
▴ Predict the age of a hypothetical fossil based on the rate of radioactive decay of several radioactive isotopes. 1a, 2c, 3a, 3b, 3c, 3d
▴ Research the history of the periodic table; take and defend a position on the configuration that best illustrates properties of elements. 1a, 1b, 1c, 4e
▴ Explain why a local urban area has smog and what can be done about it. 1a, 1b, 1c, 1e, 4d

New York State Learning Standards for Math, Science, & Technology

Standard 4 Science
Physical Setting

3. Matter is made up of particles whose properties determine the observable characteristics of matter and its reactivity.

Students:

explain the uses and hazards of radioactivity. p. 34

National Documents which guided New York State and New York City

NRC National Science Education Standards

Standard B Physical Science
Structure of Atoms

Matter is made of minute particles, called atoms, and atoms are composed of even smaller components.

The atom's nucleus is composed of protons and neutrons, which are much more massive than electrons.

The nuclear forces that hold the nucleus of an atom together, at nuclear distances, are usually stronger than the electric forces that would make it fly apart.

Radioactive isotopes are unstable and undergo spontaneous nuclear reactions, emitting particles and/or wavelike radiation. p. 178

Project 2061, AAAS
Benchmarks for Science Literacy

Chapter 4 The Physical Setting
4D Structure of Matter

Atoms are made of a positive nucleus surrounded by negative electrons. An atom's electron configuration, particularly the outermost electrons, determines how the atom can interact with other atoms.

The nucleus, a tiny fraction of the volume of an atom, is composed of protons and neutrons, each almost two thousand times heavier than an electron. The number of positive protons in the nucleus determines what an atom's electron configuration can be and so defines the element. In a neutral atom, the number of electrons equals the number of protons. But an atom may acquire an unbalanced charge by gaining or losing electrons.

Although neutrons have little effect on how an atom interacts with others, they do affect the mass and stability of the nucleus.

The nucleus of radioactive isotopes is unstable and spontaneously decays, emitting particles and/or wavelike radiation. It cannot be predicted exactly when, if ever, an unstable nucleus will decay, but a large group of identical nuclei decay at a predictable rate. This predictability of decay rate allows radioactivity to be used for estimating the age of materials that contain radioactive substances. p. 80

New York City Performance Standards

S1 Physical Sciences Concepts

The student demonstrates conceptual understanding by using a concept accurately to explain observations and make predictions and by representing the concept in multiple ways (through words, diagrams, graphs or charts, as appropriate). Both aspects of understanding—explaining and representing—are required to meet this standard.

S1 b The student produces evidence that demonstrates understanding of structure and properties of matter, such as elements and compounds; bonding and molecular interaction; and characteristics of phase changes.

Examples of activities through which students might demonstrate conceptual understanding of physical sciences include:

▲ Debate the relative merits of harnessing nuclear fission and fusion as energy sources. 1a, 1b, 1c, E3b

▲ Research the history of the periodic table; take and defend a position on the configuration that best illustrates properties of elements. 1a, 1b, 1c, 4e

▲ Explain why a local urban area has smog and what can be done about it. 1a, 1b, 1c, 1e, 4d

New York State Learning Standards for Math, Science, & Technology

Standard 4 Science
Physical Setting

3. Matter is made up of particles whose properties determine the observable characteristics of matter and its reactivity.

Students:

explain the properties of materials in terms of the arrangement and properties of the atoms that compose them. p. 34

National Documents which guided New York State and New York City

NRC National Science Education Standards

Standard B Physical Science
Structure and Properties of Matter

Atoms interact with one another by transferring or sharing electrons that are furthest from the nucleus.

An element is composed of a single type of atom.

Bonds between atoms are created when electrons are paired up by being transferred or shared.

The physical properties of compounds reflect the nature of the interactions among its molecules.

Solids, liquids, and gases differ in the distances and angles between molecules or atoms and therefore the energy that binds them together.

Carbon atoms can bond to one another in chains, rings, and branching networks to form a variety of structures. pp. 178-180

Project 2061, AAAS Benchmarks for Science Literacy

Chapter 4 The Physical Setting
4D Structure of Matter

Atoms often join with one another in various combinations in distinct molecules or in repeating three-dimensional crystal patterns. An enormous variety of biological, chemical, and physical phenomena can be explained by changes in the arrangement and motion of atoms and molecules.

The configuration of atoms in a molecule determines the molecule's properties. Shapes are particularly important in how large molecules interact with others. p. 80

New York City Performance Standards

S1 Physical Sciences Concepts

The student demonstrates conceptual understanding by using a concept accurately to explain observations and make predictions and by representing the concept in multiple ways (through words, diagrams, graphs or charts, as appropriate). Both aspects of understanding—explaining and representing—are required to meet this standard.

S1 c The student produces evidence that demonstrates understanding of chemical reactions, such as everyday examples of chemical reactions; electrons, protons, and energy transfer; and factors that affect reaction rates such as catalysts.

Examples of activities through which students might demonstrate conceptual understanding of physical sciences include:

▲ Debate the relative merits of harnessing nuclear fission and fusion as energy sources. 1a, 1b, 1c, E3b
▲ Research the history of the periodic table; take and defend a position on the configuration that best illustrates properties of elements. 1a, 1b, 1c, 4e
▲ Determine the characteristics for a dinner table candle that will keep the candle burning longer. 1c, 1e
▲ Explain why a local urban area has smog and what can be done about it. 1a, 1b, 1c, 1e, 4d
▲ Explain how electric motors and generators illustrate the relationship between electricity and magnetism. 1c, 1d, 1e, 4a, 4b

New York State Learning Standards for Math, Science, & Technology

Standard 4 Science
Physical Setting

3. Matter is made up of particles whose properties determine the observable characteristics of matter and its reactivity.

Students:

use atomic and molecular models to explain common chemical reactions.

apply the principle of conservation of mass to chemical reactions.

use kinetic molecular theory to explain rates of reactions and the relationships among temperature, pressure, and volume of a substance.

5. Energy and matter interact through forces that result in changes in motion.

Students:

explain chemical bonding in terms of the motion of electrons. p. 34

National Documents which guided New York State and New York City

NRC National Science Education Standards

Standard B Physical Science
Chemical Reactions

Chemical reactions occur all around us, for example in health care, cooking, cosmetics, and automobiles.

Chemical reactions may release or consume energy.

A large number of important reactions involve the transfer of either electrons (oxidation/reduction reactions) or hydrogen ions (acid/base reactions) between reacting ions, molecules, or atoms.

Chemical reactions can take place in time periods ranging from a few femtoseconds ($10\text{-}15$ seconds) required for an atom to move a fraction of a chemical bond distance to geologic time scales of billions of years.

Catalysts, such as metal surfaces, accelerate chemical reactions. p. 179

Project 2061, AAAS
Benchmarks for Science Literacy

Chapter 4 The Physical Setting
4D Structure of Matter

The rate of reactions among atoms and molecules depends on how often they encounter one another, which is affected by the concentration, pressure, and temperature of the reacting materials. Some atoms and molecules are highly effective in encouraging the interaction. p. 80

4E Energy Transformation

Different energy levels are associated with different configurations of atoms and molecules. Some changes of configuration require an input of energy whereas others release energy. p. 86

New York City Performance Standards

S1 Physical Sciences Concepts

The student demonstrates conceptual understanding by using a concept accurately to explain observations and make predictions and by representing the concept in multiple ways (through words, diagrams, graphs or charts, as appropriate). Both aspects of understanding—explaining and representing—are required to meet this standard.

S1 d The student produces evidence that demonstrates understanding of motions and forces, such as gravitational and electrical; net forces and magnetism.

Examples of activities through which students might demonstrate conceptual understanding of physical sciences include:
▲ Make an informational videotape describing how an understanding of acceleration and velocity can make one a better driver. 1d, 1e, 7d
▲ Explain how electric motors and generators illustrate the relationship between electricity and magnetism. 1c, 1d, 1e, 4a, 4b

New York State Learning Standards for Math, Science, & Technology

Standard 4 Science
Physical Setting

5. Energy and matter interact through forces that result in changes in motion.

Students:

explain and predict different patterns of motion of objects (e.g., linear and angular motion, velocity and acceleration, momentum and inertia). p. 34

National Documents which guided New York State and New York City

NRC National Science Education Standards

Standard B Physical Science
Motions and Forces

Objects change their motion only when a net force is applied.

Gravitation is a universal force that each mass exerts on any other mass.

The electric force is a universal force that exists between any two charged objects.

Between any two charged particles, electric force is vastly greater than the gravitational force.

Electricity and magnetism are two aspects of a single electromagnetic force. pp. 179-180

Project 2061, AAAS
Benchmarks for Science Literacy

Chapter 4 The Physical Setting
4G Forces of Nature

Gravitational force is an attraction between masses. The strength of the force is proportional to the masses and distance between them.

Electromagnetic forces acting within and between atoms are involved in all chemical reactions.

There are two kinds of changes - positive and negative. A small excess or deficit of negative charges in a material produces electric forces.

Different kinds of material respond differently to electric forces.

Moving electric charges produce magnetic forces and moving magnets produce electric forces.

Forces that hold the nucleus of an atom together are much stronger than the electromagnetic force. pp. 96-97

New York City Performance Standards

S1 Physical Sciences Concepts

The student demonstrates conceptual understanding by using a concept accurately to explain observations and make predictions and by representing the concept in multiple ways (through words, diagrams, graphs or charts, as appropriate). Both aspects of understanding—explaining and representing—are required to meet this standard.

S1 e The student produces evidence that demonstrates understanding of conservation of energy and increase in disorder, such as kinetic and potential energy; energy conduction, convection, and radiation; random motion; and effects of heat and pressure.

Examples of activities through which students might demonstrate conceptual understanding of physical sciences include:

▲ Determine the characteristics for a dinner table candle that will keep the candle burning longer. 1c, 1e

▲ Explain why a local urban area has smog and what can be done about it. 1a, 1b, 1c, 1e, 4d

▲ Make an informational videotape describing how an understanding of acceleration and velocity can make one a better driver. 1d, 1e, 7d

▲ Explain how electric motors and generators illustrate the relationship between electricity and magnetism. 1c, 1d, 1e, 4a, 4b

▲ Explain to a younger student the difference between temperature and heat. 1e, 7d

▲ Compare the efficiency and energy consumption of several different methods of generating electricity that could be used locally. 1e, 1f, 4b, 4d

New York State Learning Standards for Math, Science, & Technology

Standard 4 Science
Physical Setting

4. Energy exists in many forms and when these forms change energy is conserved.

   Students:

   observe and describe transmissions of various forms of energy.

   explain heat in terms of kinetic molecular theory. p. 34

National Documents which guided New York State and New York City

NRC National Science Education Standards

Standard B Physical Science
Conservation of Energy and the Increase in Disorder

The total energy of the universe is constant.

All energy can be considered to be either kinetic energy, which is the energy of motion; potential energy, which depends on relative position; or energy contained by a field, such as electromagnetic waves.

Heat consists of random motion and the vibration of atoms, molecules, and ions.

Everything tends to become less organized and less orderly over time. p. 180

Project 2061, AAAS
Benchmarks for Science Literacy

Chapter 4 The Physical Setting
4E Energy Transformations

Whenever the amount of energy in one place or form diminishes, the amount in the other places or forms increases by same amount.

Heat energy in a material consists of the disordered motion of its atoms or molecules.

Different energy levels are associated with different configurations of atoms and molecules. Some changes require an input of energy whereas others release energy.

When energy of an isolated atom or molecule changes, it does so in a definite jump from one value to another, with no possible values in between.

Energy is released whenever the nucleus of very heavy atoms split. p. 88

New York City Performance Standards

S1 Physical Sciences Concepts

The student demonstrates conceptual understanding by using a concept accurately to explain observations and make predictions and by representing the concept in multiple ways (through words, diagrams, graphs or charts, as appropriate). Both aspects of understanding—explaining and representing—are required to meet this standard.

S1 f The student produces evidence that demonstrates understanding of interactions of energy and matter, such as waves, absorption and emission of light, and conductivity.

Examples of activities through which students might demonstrate conceptual understanding of physical sciences include:

▲ Compare the efficiency and energy consumption of several different methods of generating electricity that could be used locally. 1e, 1f, 4b, 4d

▲ Earn the Energy Merit Badge (Boy Scouts of America) and explain how it helped you to understand the interactions of matter and energy. 1f, 4b, 4d

▲ Trace the transformations of energy from the electric current that enters a CD player or boombox to a sound that can be heard as music. 1f, 4b

New York State Learning Standards for Math, Science, & Technology

Standard 4 Science
Physical Setting

4. Energy exists in many forms and when these forms change, energy is conserved.

   Students

   explain variations in wavelength and frequency in terms of the source of the vibrations that produce them e.g. molecules, electrons, and nuclear particles. p. 34

National Documents which guided New York State and New York City

NRC National Science Education Standards

Standard B Physical Science
Interactions of Energy and Matter

Waves, including sound and seismic waves, waves on water, and light waves, have energy and can transfer energy when they interact with matter.

Electromagnetic waves result when a charged object is accelerated or decelerated.

Each kind of atom or molecule can gain or lose energy only in particular discrete amounts and thus can absorb and emit light only at wavelengths corresponding to these amounts.

In some materials, such as metals, electrons flow easily, whereas in insulating materials such as glass they can hardly flow at all. pp. 180-181

Project 2061, AAAS
Benchmarks for Science Literacy

Chapter 4 The Physical Setting
4E Energy Transformations

The change in energy of an atom occurs when radiation is absorbed or emitted, so the radiation also has distinct energy values. p. 86

4F Motion

The observed wavelength of a wave depends upon the relative motion of the source and the observer.

Waves can superpose on one another, bend around corners, reflect off surfaces, be absorbed by materials they enter and change direction when entering a new material. p. 92

4G Forces of Nature

Different kinds of materials respond differently to electric forces. p. 97

S2 Life Sciences Concepts

The student demonstrates conceptual understanding by using a concept accurately to explain observations and make predictions and by representing the concept in multiple ways (through words, diagrams, graphs or charts, as appropriate). Both aspects of understanding—explaining and representing—are required to meet this standard.

S2 a The student produces evidence that demonstrates understanding of the cell, such as cell structure and function relationships; regulation and biochemistry; and energy and photosynthesis.

Examples of activities through which students might demonstrate conceptual understanding of life sciences include:

▲ Create a picture book to explain how a producer converts solar energy to chemical energy through an ecosystem. 2a, 1c, 3a
▲ Explain how cell functions are regulated to allow organisms to respond to the environment and to control and coordinate growth and differentiation. 2a, 2b, 2c, 2f, 1c
▲ Predict how long a plant will live planted in a closed glass jar located by a window; and explain what additional information regarding the plant and the surrounding environment would be needed to improve the prediction. 2a, 1a, 3a, 3b

New York State Learning Standards for Math, Science, & Technology

Standard 4 Science
The Living Environment

1. Living things are both similar to and different from each other and non-living things.

   Students

   describe and explain the structures and functions of the human body at different organizational levels (e.g., systems, tissues, cells, organelles).

   explain how a one-celled organism is able to function despite lacking the levels of organization present in more complex organisms. p. 35

National Documents which guided New York State and New York City

NRC National Science Education Standards

Standard C Life Science
The Cell

Cells have particular structures that underlie their functions. Every cell is surrounded by a membrane....

Most cell functions involve chemical reactions.

Cells store and use information to guide their functions. The genetic information stored in DNA....

Cell functions are regulated. Regulation occurs....

Plant cells contain chloroplasts, the site of photosynthesis. Plants and many microorganisms.... p. 184

Matter, Energy, and Organization in Living Systems

All matter tends toward more disorganized states. Living systems require a continuous input of energy....

The energy for life primarily derives from the sun. Plants capture energy by....

The chemical bonds of food molecules contain energy. Energy is released when....

The complexity and organization of organisms accommodates the need for obtaining, transforming,.... p. 186

Project 2061, AAAS
Benchmarks for Science Literacy

Chapter 5 The Living Environment
5C Cells

Every cell is covered by a membrane that controls what can enter and leave the cell.

Within every cell are specialized parts for the transport of materials, energy transfer, protein building, waste disposal, information feedback, and even movement.

The work of the cell is carried out by the many different types of molecules it assembles, mostly proteins.

Most cells function best within a narrow range of temperature and acidity.

A living cell is composed of a small number of chemical elements mainly carbon, hydrogen, nitrogen, oxygen, phosphorous, and sulfur. pp. 113-114

5F Evolution of Life

Life on earth is thought to have begun as simple, one-celled organisms about 4 billion years ago. p. 125

Chapter 6 The Human Organism
6C Basic Functions

The immune system is designed to protect against microscopic organisms and foreign substances that enter from outside the body and against some cancer cells that arise within.

The nervous system works by electrochemical signals in the nerves and from one nerve to the next.

Communication between cells is required to coordinate their diverse activities. p. 138

6E Physical Health

Some allergic reactions are caused by the body's immune responses to usually harmless environmental substances.

Some viral diseases, such as AIDS, destroy critical cells of the immune system, leaving the body unable to deal with multiple infection agents and cancerous cells. p. 146

New York City Performance Standards

S2 Life Sciences Concepts

The student demonstrates conceptual understanding by using a concept accurately to explain observations and make predictions and by representing the concept in multiple ways (through words, diagrams, graphs or charts, as appropriate). Both aspects of understanding—explaining and representing—are required to meet this standard.

S2 b The student produces evidence that demonstrates understanding of molecular basis of heredity, such as DNA, genes, chromosomes, and mutations.

Examples of activities through which students might demonstrate conceptual understanding of life sciences include:

▲ Explain how cell functions are regulated to allow organisms to respond to the environment and to control and coordinate growth and differentiation. 2a, 2b, 2c, 2f, 1c
▲ Create a working model to show how the instructions for specifying an organism's characteristics are carried in DNA and its subunits. 2b, 2c, 5c
▲ Make a storyboard and give a presentation to younger students explaining the increasing prevalence of dark forms of moths 150 years ago and the more recent return to light forms. 2b, 2c, 2d, 7d, E3c

New York State Learning Standards for Math, Science, & Technology

Standard 4 Science
The Living Environment

2. Organisms inherit genetic information in a variety of ways that result in continuity of structure and function between parents and offspring.

Students:

explain how the structure and replication of genetic material result in offspring that resemble their parents.

explain how the technology of genetic engineering allows humans to alter the genetic makeup of organisms.

4. The continuity of life is sustained through reproduction and development.

Students:

explain how organisms, including humans reproduce their own kind. p. 35

National Documents which guided New York State and New York City

NRC National Science Education Standards

Standard C Life Science
The Molecular Basis of Heredity

In all organisms, the instructions for specifying the characteristics of the organisms are carried in DNA, a large....

Most of the cells in human contain two copies of each of 22 different chromosomes. In addition, there is....

Changes in DNA (mutations) occur spontaneously at low rates. Some of these changes.... p. 185

Project 2061, AAAS
Benchmarks for Science Literacy

Chapter 5 The Living Environment
5A Diversity of Life

The degree of kinship between organisms or species can be estimated from the similarity of their DNA. p. 105

5B Heredity

The sorting and recombination of genes in sexual reproduction results in a great variety of combinations from the offspring of any two parents.

The information passed from parents to offspring is coded in DNA molecules.

Genes are segments of DNA molecules.

The many body cells in an individual can be very different from one another, even though they are all descended from a single cell and thus have essentially identical genetic instructions. p. 109

5C Cells

The genetic information encoded in DNA molecules provides instructions for assembling protein molecules.

Gene mutation in a cell can result in uncontrolled cell division, called cancer. p. 114

5F Evolution of Life

Heritable characteristics can be observed at molecular and whole-organism levels—in structure, chemistry, or behavior. p. 125

New heritable characteristics can result from new combinations of existing genes or from mutations of genes in reproductive cells. Changes in other cells of an organism cannot be passed on to the next generation. p. 125

Chapter 6 The Human Organism
6A Human Identity

The similarity of human DNA sequences and the resulting similarity in cell chemistry and anatomy identify human beings as a single species. p. 130

New York City Performance Standards

S2 Life Sciences Concepts

The student demonstrates conceptual understanding by using a concept accurately to explain observations and make predictions and by representing the concept in multiple ways (through words, diagrams, graphs or charts, as appropriate). Both aspects of understanding—explaining and representing—are required to meet this standard.

S2c The student produces evidence that demonstrates understanding of biological evolution, such as speciation, biodiversity, natural selection, and biological classification.

Examples of activities through which students might demonstrate conceptual understanding of life sciences include:

▪ Explain how cell functions are regulated to allow organisms to respond to the environment and to control and coordinate growth and differentiation. 2a, 2b, 2c, 2f, 1c

▪ Create a working model to show how the instructions for specifying an organism's characteristics are carried in DNA and its subunits. 2b, 2c, 5c

▪ Make a videotape debating the possible explanations for the extinction of dinosaurs. 2c, 2d, 7d

▪ Make a storyboard and give a presentation to younger students explaining the increasing prevalence of dark forms of moths 150 years ago and the more recent return to light forms. 2b, 2c, 2d, 7d, E3c

▪ Develop a recycling outreach program as part of a community service project to illustrate the limited availability of matter and energy in the ecosystem. 2c, 2d, 1c, 4b

▪ Research the development of, and recent advances in the theory of, evolutionary psychology. 2c, 2f, 4e

New York State Learning Standards for Math, Science, & Technology

Standard 4 Science
The Living Environment

3. Individual organisms and species change over time.
   Students:
   explain the mechanisms and patterns for evolution. p. 35

National Documents which guided New York State and New York City

NRC National Science Education Standards

Standard C Life Science
Biological Evolution

Species evolve over time. Evolution is the consequence....

The great diversity of organisms is the result of more than 3.5 million years of evolution that has filled every available niche with life forms.

Natural selection and its evolutionary consequences provide a scientific explanation for the fossil record of ancient life forms, as well as for the striking molecular similarities observed among the diverse species of living organisms.

The millions of different species of plants, animals, and microorganisms that live on earth are today related by descent from common ancestors.

Biological classifications are based on how organisms are related. Organisms are classified into a hierarchy of.... p. 185

The Behavior of Organisms

Like other aspects of an organism's biology, behaviors have evolved through natural selection. Behaviors often have an adaptive logic when viewed in terms of evolutionary principles.

Behavioral biology has implications for humans, as it provides links to psychology, sociology and anthropology. p. 187

Project 2061, AAAS
Benchmarks for Science Literacy

Chapter 5 The Living Environment
5F Evolution of Life

The basic idea of biological evolution is that the earth's present-day species developed from earlier, distinctly different species.

Molecular evidence substantiates the anatomical evidence for evolution and provides additional detail about the sequence in which various lines of descent branched off from one another.

Natural selection provides the following mechanism for evolution: Some variation in heritable characteristics exists within....

Heritable characteristics can be observed at molecular and whole-organism levels—in structure, chemistry, or behavior. These....

New heritable characteristics can result from new combinations of existing genes or from mutations of genes in reproductive cells. Changes in other cells of an organism cannot be passed on to the next generation.

Natural selection leads to organisms that are well suited for survival in particular environments. Chance alone can result in....

The theory of natural selection provides a scientific explanation for the history of life on earth as depicted in the fossil record and in the similarities evident within the diversity of organisms.

Life on earth is thought to have begun about 4 billion years ago as a simple, one-celled organism. Over time complex multicellular organisms evolved.

Evolution builds on what already exists, so the more variety there is, the more there can be in the future. But evolution does not.... p. 125

Chapter 6 The Human Organism
6A Human Identity

The similarity of human DNA sequences and the resulting similarity in cell chemistry and anatomy identify human beings as a single species.

Written records and photographic and electronic devices enable human beings to share, compile, use, and misuse great amounts of information and misinformation. p. 130

New York City Performance Standards

S2 Life Sciences Concepts

The student demonstrates conceptual understanding by using a concept accurately to explain observations and make predictions and by representing the concept in multiple ways (through words, diagrams, graphs or charts, as appropriate). Both aspects of understanding—explaining and representing—are required to meet this standard.

S2 d The student produces evidence that demonstrates understanding of interdependence of organisms, such as conservation of matter; cooperation and competition among organisms in ecosystems; and human effects on the environment.

Examples of activities through which students might demonstrate conceptual understanding of life sciences include:

▲ Make a videotape debating the possible explanations for the extinction of dinosaurs. 2c, 2d, 7d

▲ Make a storyboard and give a presentation to younger students explaining the increasing prevalence of dark forms of moths 150 years ago and the more recent return to light forms. 2b, 2c, 2d, 7d, E3c

▲ Earn the Ecology Merit Badge (Girl Scouts of the U.S.A.) or the Environmental Science Merit Badge (Boy Scouts of America) and explain how it helped you to understand the interdependence of organisms. 2d, 2e

▲ Develop a recycling outreach program as part of a community service project to illustrate the limited availability of matter and energy in the ecosystem. 2c, 2d, 1c, 4b

New York State Learning Standards for Math, Science, & Technology

Standard 4 Science
The Living Environment

6. Plants and animals depend on each other and their physical environment.

   Students:

   explain the importance of preserving diversity of species and habitats.

   explain how the living and nonliving environments change over time and respond to disturbances.

7. Human decisions and activities have had a profound impact on the physical and living environment.

   Students:

   describe the range of interrelationships of humans with the living and nonliving environment.

   explain the impact of technological development and growth in the human population on the living and nonliving environment.

   explain how individual choices and societal actions can contribute to improving the environment. p. 35

National Documents which guided New York State and New York City

NRC National Science Education Standards

Standard C Life Science
The Interdependence of Organisms

The atoms and molecules on the earth cycle among the living and nonliving components of the biosphere.

Energy flows through ecosystems in one direction, from photosynthetic organisms to herbivores to carnivores and decomposers.

Human beings live within the world's ecosystems. p. 186

Population Growth

Populations grow or decline through the combined effects of....

Various factors influence birth rates and fertility rates.

Populations can reach limits to growth. p. 198

Natural Resources

Human populations use resources in the environment.

The earth does not have the infinite resources.

Humans use many natural systems as resources. p. 198

Environmental Quality

Materials from human societies affect both physical and chemical cycles of the earth.

Many factors influence environmental quality. p. 198

Science and Technology in Local, National, and Global Changes

Progress in science and technology can be affected by social issues and challenges. Funding priorities for specific health problems serve as examples of ways that social issues influence science and technology.

Individuals and society must decide on proposals involving new research and the introduction of new technologies into society.

Humans have a major effect on other species. p. 199

Project 2061, AAAS Benchmarks for Science Literacy

Chapter 5 The Living Environment
5A Diversity of Life

The variation of organisms within a species increases the likelihood that at least some members of the species will survive under changed environmental conditions, and a great diversity of species increases the chance that at least some living things will survive in the face of large changes in the environment. p. 105

5D Interdependence of Life

Ecosystems can be reasonably stable over hundreds or thousands of years. As any population of organisms grows, it is held in check by one or more environmental factors: depletion of food or nesting sites, increased loss to increased numbers of predators, or parasites. If a disaster such as a flood or fire occurs, the damaged ecosystem is likely to recover in stages that eventually result in a system similar to the original one.

Like many complex systems, ecosystems tend to have cyclic fluctuations around a state of rough equilibrium. In the long run, however, ecosystems always change when climate changes or when one or more new species appear as a result of migration or local evolution.

Human beings are part of the earth's ecosystems. Human activities can, deliberately or inadvertently, alter the equilibrium in ecosystems. p. 117

New York City Performance Standards

S2 Life Sciences Concepts

The student demonstrates conceptual understanding by using a concept accurately to explain observations and make predictions and by representing the concept in multiple ways (through words, diagrams, graphs or charts, as appropriate). Both aspects of understanding—explaining and representing—are required to meet this standard.

S2 e The student produces evidence that demonstrates understanding of matter, energy, and organization in living systems, such as matter and energy flow through different levels of organization; and environmental constraints.

Examples of activities through which students might demonstrate conceptual understanding of life sciences include:

▲ Make a humorous travel brochure describing the pathway of a carbon dioxide molecule and an oxygen molecule through the living and non-living components of the biosphere. 2e, 1b

▲ Earn the Ecology Merit Badge (Girl Scouts of the U.S.A.) or the Environmental Science Merit Badge (Boy Scouts of America) and explain how it helped you to understand the interdependence of organisms. 2d, 2e

▲ Trace a candy bar from the time it is purchased to the time it is completely expended. 2e

New York State Learning Standards for Math, Science, & Technology

Standard 4 Science
The Living Environment

6. Plants and animals depend on each other and their physical environment.

   Students:

   explain factors that limit growth of individuals and populations. p. 35

National Documents which guided New York State and New York City

NRC National Science Education Standards

Standard C Life Science
Matter, Energy, and Organization in Living Systems

As matter and energy flows through different levels of organization of living systems—cells, organs. organisms. communities—and between living systems and the physical environment, chemical elements are recombined in different ways. Each recombination results in storage and dissipation of energy into the environment as heat. Matter and energy are conserved in each change.

The distribution and abundance of organisms and populations in ecosystems are limited by the availability of matter and energy and the ability of the ecosystem to recycle materials. p. 186

Project 2061, AAAS
Benchmarks for Science Literacy

Chapter 5 The Living Environment
5E Flow of Matter and Energy

At times, environmental conditions are such that plants and marine organisms grow faster than decomposers can recycle them back to the environment. Layers of energy-rich organic material have been gradually turned into great coal beds and oil pools by the pressure of the overlying earth. By burning these fossil fuels, people are passing most of the stored energy back into the environment as heat and releasing large amounts of carbon dioxide.

The amount of life any environment can support is limited by the available energy, water, oxygen, and minerals, and by the ability of ecosystems to recycle the residue of dead organic materials. Human activities and technology can change the flow and reduce the fertility of the land.

The chemical elements that make up the molecules of living things pass through food webs and are combined and recombined in different ways. At each link in a food web, some energy is stored in newly made structures but much is dissipated into the environment as heat. Continual input of energy from sunlight keeps the process going. p. 121

New York City Performance Standards

S2 Life Sciences Concepts

The student demonstrates conceptual understanding by using a concept accurately to explain observations and make predictions and by representing the concept in multiple ways (through words, diagrams, graphs or charts, as appropriate). Both aspects of understanding—explaining and representing—are required to meet this standard.

S2 f   The student produces evidence that demonstrates understanding of behavior of organisms, such as nervous system regulation; behavioral responses; and connections with anthropology, sociology, and psychology.

Examples of activities through which students might demonstrate conceptual understanding of life sciences include:
▲ Explain how cell functions are regulated to allow organisms to respond to the environment and to control and coordinate growth and differentiation. 2a, 2b, 2c, 2f, 1c
▲ Conduct an investigation to determine how different kinds of plants respond to various environmental stimuli. 2f
▲ Research the development of, and recent advances in the theory of, evolutionary psychology. 2c, 2f, 4e

New York State Learning Standards for Math, Science, & Technology

Standard 4 Science
The Living Environment

5. Organisms maintaining dynamic equilibrium that sustains life.

   Students:

   explain the basic biochemical processes in living organisms and their importance in maintaining a dynamic equilibrium.

   explain disease as a failure of homeostasis.

   relate processes at the system level to the cellular level in order to explain dynamic equilibrium in multicelled organisms. p. 35

National Documents which guided New York State and New York City

NRC National Science Education Standards

Standard C Life Science
The Behavior of Organisms

Multicellular animals have nervous systems that generate behavior. Nervous systems are formed from specialized cells....

Organisms have behavioral responses to internal changes....

Behavioral biology has implications for humans, as it provides links to psychology, sociology and anthropology.
p. 187

Project 2061, AAAS
Benchmarks for Science Literacy

Chapter 6 The Human Organism
6D Learning

Differences in the behavior of individuals arise from the interaction of heredity and experience....

The expectations, moods, and prior experiences of human beings can affect how they interpret new perceptions or ideas.

Human thinking involves the interaction of ideas, and ideas about ideas. People can produce many associations internally.... p. 142

6E Physical Health

Some allergic reactions are caused by the body's immune responses to usually harmless environmental substances.

Faulty genes can cause body parts or systems to work poorly. Some genetic diseases appear only when an individual has inherited a certain faulty gene from both parents.

New medical techniques, efficient health care delivery systems, improved sanitation, and a fuller understanding of the nature of disease....

Some viral diseases such as AIDS, destroy critical cells of the immune system, leaving the body unable to deal with multiple infection agents and cancerous cells. p. 146

6F Mental Health

Stresses are especially difficult for children to deal with and may have long-lasting effects.

Biological abnormalities, such as brain injuries or chemical imbalances, can cause or increase susceptibility to psychological....

Reactions of other people to an individual's emotional disturbance may increase its effects.

Human beings differ greatly in how they cope with emotions and may therefore puzzle one another.

Ideas about what constitutes good mental health and proper treatment for abnormal mental states vary from one time period to another.... p. 149

New York City Performance Standards

S3 Earth and Space Sciences Concepts

The student demonstrates conceptual understanding by using a concept accurately to explain observations and make predictions and by representing the concept in multiple ways (through words, diagrams, graphs or charts, as appropriate). Both aspects of understanding—explaining and representing—are required to meet this standard.

S3 a The student produces evidence that demonstrates understanding of energy in the Earth system, such as radioactive decay, gravity, the Sun's energy, convection, and changes in global climate.

Examples of activities through which students might demonstrate conceptual understanding of Earth and space sciences include:

- Make a brochure providing an orientation to the climate of the local region to a newcomer; and explain the likely weather in that context. 3a
- Explain the relationship between gravity and energy. 3a, 1d
- Analyze the risk of natural disasters in the local region and make recommendations for actions that can be taken to mitigate the damage. 3a, 3b, 4b
- Germinate seeds on a rotating platform and explain the observed growth pattern. 3a, 1d, 2e

New York State Learning Standards for Math, Science, & Technology

Standard 4 Science
Physical Setting

1. The Earth and celestial phenomena can be described by principles of relative motion and perspective.

   Students:

   explain complex phenomena, such as tides, variations in day length, solar insolation, apparent motion of the planets, and annual traverse of the consellations.

2. Many of the phenomena that we observe on Earth involve interactions among components of air, water, and land.

   Students:

   use the concepts of density and heat energy to explain observations of weather patterns, seasonal changes, and the movements of the Earth's plates.

   explain how incoming solar radiations, ocean currents, and land masses affect weather and climate. p. 34

National Documents which guided New York State and New York City

NRC National Science Education Standards

Standard D Earth and Space Sciences
Energy in the Earth System

Earth systems have internal and external sources of energy, both of which create heat.

The outward transfer of earth's internal heat drives convection circulation in the mantle that propels the plates comprising earth's surface across the face of the globe.

Heating of earth's surface and atmosphere by the sun drives convection within the atmosphere and oceans, producing winds and ocean currents.

Global climate is determined by energy transfer from the sun at and near the earth's surface. p. 189

Project 2061, AAAS Benchmarks for Science Literacy

Chapter 4 The Physical Setting
4B The Earth

Weather (in the short run) and climate (in the long run) involve the transfer of energy in and out of the atmosphere. p. 70

4C Processes that Shape the Earth

The slow movement of material within the earth results from heat flowing out from the deep interior and the action of gravitational forces on regions of different density.

Earthquakes often occur along the boundaries between colliding plates, and molten rock from below creates pressure that is released by volcanic eruptions, helping to build up mountains. p. 74

Chapter 8 The Designed World
8C Energy Sources and Use

Energy from the sun (and the wind and water energy derived from it) is available indefinitely. p. 194

New York City Performance Standards

S3 Earth and Space Sciences Concepts

The student demonstrates conceptual understanding by using a concept accurately to explain observations and make predictions and by representing the concept in multiple ways (through words, diagrams, graphs or charts, as appropriate). Both aspects of understanding—explaining and representing—are required to meet this standard.

S3b The student produces evidence that demonstrates understanding of geochemical cycles, such as conservation of matter; chemical resources and movement of matter between chemical reservoirs.

Examples of activities through which students might demonstrate conceptual understanding of Earth and space sciences include:
▲ Analyze the risk of natural disasters in the local region and make recommendations for actions that can be taken to mitigate the damage. 3a, 3b, 4b
▲ Conduct a study of the geology of an area near the school; and describe the likely history of the region, using observations and reference materials. 3b, 3c

New York State Learning Standards for Math, Science, & Technology

No comparable standard.

National Documents which guided New York State and New York City

NRC National Science Education Standards

Standard D Earth and Space Science
Geochemical Cycles

The earth is a system containing essentially a fixed amount of each stable chemical atom or element. Each element can exist in several different chemical reservoirs. Each element on earth moves among reservoirs in the solid earth, oceans, atmosphere, and organisms as part of geochemical cycles.

Movement of matter between reservoirs is driven by the earth's internal and external sources of energy. p. 189

Project 2061, AAAS
Benchmarks for Science Literacy

Chapter 5 The Living Environment
5E Flow of Matter and Energy

At times, environmental conditions are such that plants and marine organisms grow faster than decomposers can recycle them back to the environment. Layers of energy-rich organic material have been gradually turned into great coal beds and oil pools by the pressure of the overlying earth. By burning these fossil fuels, people are passing most of the stored energy back into the environment as heat and releasing large amounts of carbon dioxide.

The chemical elements that make up the molecules of living things pass through food webs and are combined and recombined in different ways. At each link in a food web, some energy is stored in newly made structures but much is dissipated into the environment as heat. Continual input of energy from sunlight keeps the process going. p. 121

New York City Performance Standards

S3 Earth and Space Sciences Concepts

The student demonstrates conceptual understanding by using a concept accurately to explain observations and make predictions and by representing the concept in multiple ways (through words, diagrams, graphs or charts, as appropriate). Both aspects of understanding—explaining and representing—are required to meet this standard.

S3c The student produces evidence that demonstrates understanding of origin and evolution of the Earth system, such as geologic time and the age of life forms; origin of life; and evolution of the Solar System.

Examples of activities through which students might demonstrate conceptual understanding of Earth and space sciences include:

▲ Conduct a study of the geology of an area near the school; and describe the likely history of the region, using observations and reference materials. 3b, 3c
▲ Diagram the birth, development, and death of a human; contrast with the geologic time frame of the origin and evolution of the Earth system or the universe. 3c, 3d, 2c
▲ Work with other students to become an "expert panel" to describe the historical events leading to the development of the "big bang" theory. 3c, 3d, 5f

New York State Learning Standards for Math, Science, & Technology

Standard 4 Science
Physical Setting

1. The Earth and celestial phenomena can be described by principles of relative motion and perspective.

   Students:

   Describe current theories about the origin of the universe and solar system. p. 34

National Documents which guided New York State and New York City

NRC National Science Education Standards

Standard D Earth and Space Science
Origin and Evolution of the Earth System

The sun, the earth, and the rest of the solar system formed from a nebular cloud of dust and gas 4.6 billion years ago.

Geologic time can be estimated by observing rock sequences and using fossils to correlate the sequences at various locations.

Interactions among the solid earth, the oceans, the atmosphere, and organisms have resulted in the ongoing evolution of the earth system.

Evidence for one-celled forms of life—the bacteria—extends back more than 3.5 billion years. The evolution of life caused dramatic changes in the composition of the earth's atmosphere, which did not originally contain oxygen. pp. 189-190

Project 2061, AAAS
Benchmarks for Science Literacy

Chapter 10 Historical Perspectives
10D Extending Time

Scientific evidence implies that some rock near the earth's surface is several billion years old.

The idea that the earth might be vastly older than most people believed made little headway in science until the publication of *Principles of Geology* by an English scientist, Charles Lyell, early in the 19th century.

In formulating and presenting his theory of biological evolution, Charles Darwin adopted Lyell's belief about the age of the earth and his style of buttressing his argument with vast amounts of evidence. p. 246

10H Explaining the Diversity of Life

The scientific problem that led to the theory of natural selection was how to explain similarities within the great diversity of existing and fossil organisms.

Darwin argued that only biologically inherited characteristics could be passed on to offspring.

After the publication of *Origin of Species*, biological evolution was supported by the rediscovery of the genetics experiments of an Austrian monk, Gregor Mendel, by the identification of genes and how they are sorted in reproduction, and by the discovery that the genetic code found in DNA is the same for almost all organisms. pp. 254-255

New York City Performance Standards

S3 Earth and Space Sciences Concepts

The student demonstrates conceptual understanding by using a concept accurately to explain observations and make predictions and by representing the concept in multiple ways (through words, diagrams, graphs or charts, as appropriate). Both aspects of understanding—explaining and representing—are required to meet this standard.

S3 d The student produces evidence that demonstrates understanding of origin and evolution of the universe, such as the "big bang" theory; formation of stars and elements; and nuclear reactions.

Examples of activities through which students might demonstrate conceptual understanding of Earth and space sciences include:
▲ Diagram the birth, development, and death of a human; contrast with the geologic time frame of the origin and evolution of the Earth system or the universe. 3c, 3d, 2c
▲ Work with other students to become an "expert panel" to describe the historical events leading to the development of the "big bang" theory. 3c, 3d, 5f
▲ Write a research paper to explain how stars produce energy from nuclear reactions and how these processes led to the formation of other elements. 3d, 1a, 1b, 1c, 1f, E2a

New York State Learning Standards for Math, Science, & Technology

Standard 4 Science
Physical Setting

1. The Earth and celestial phenomena can be described by principles of relative motion and perspective.

   Students:

   Describe current theories about the origin of the universe and solar system. p. 34

National Documents which guided New York State and New York City

NRC National Science Education Standards

Standard D Earth and Space Sciences
The Origin and Evolution of the Universe

The origin of the universe remains one of the greatest questions in science. The "big bang" theory places the origin between 10 and 20 billion years ago, when the universe began in a hot dense state; according to this theory, the universe has been expanding ever since.

Early in the history of the universe, matter, primarily the light atoms hydrogen and helium, clumped together by gravitational attraction to form countless trillions of stars. Billions of galaxies, each of which is a gravitationally bound cluster of billions of stars, now form most of the visible mass in the universe.

Stars produce energy from nuclear reactions, primarily the fusion of hydrogen to form helium. These and other processes in stars have led to the formation of all the other elements. p. 190

Project 2061, AAAS
Benchmarks for Science Literacy

Chapter 4 The Physical Setting
4A The Universe

On the basis of scientific evidence, the universe is estimated to be over ten billion years old. The current theory is that its entire contents expanded explosively from a hot, dense, chaotic mass. Stars condensed by gravity out of clouds of molecules of the lightest elements until nuclear fusion of the light elements into heavier ones began to occur. Fusion released great amounts of energy over millions of years. Eventually, some stars exploded, producing clouds of heavy elements from which other stars and planets could later condense. The process of star formation and destruction continues.

Increasingly sophisticated technology is used to learn about the universe. Visual, radio, and x-ray telescopes collect information from across the entire spectrum of electromagnetic waves; computers handle an avalanche of data and increasingly complicated computations to interpret them; space probes send back data and materials from the remote part of the solar system; and accelerators give subatomic particles energies that simulate conditions in the stars and in the early history of the universe before stars formed. p. 65

New York City Performance Standards

S3 Earth and Space Sciences Concepts

The student demonstrates conceptual understanding by using a concept accurately to explain observations and make predictions and by representing the concept in multiple ways (through words, diagrams, graphs or charts, as appropriate). Both aspects of understanding—explaining and representing—are required to meet this standard.

S3 e The student produces evidence that demonstrates understanding of natural resource management.

Examples of activities through which students might demonstrate conceptual understanding of Earth and space sciences include:

▴ Identify a place that is subject to periodic flooding, evaluate its positive and negative effects, and study different ways of maintaining, reducing, or eliminating the likelihood of flooding. 3e

---

New York State Learning Standards for Math, Science, & Technology

No comparable standard.

National Documents which guided New York State and New York City

NRC National Science Education Standards

Standard F Science in Personal and Social Perspectives Natural Resources

Human populations use resources in the environment in order to maintain and improve their existence.

The earth does not have infinite resources; increasing human consumption places severe stress on the natural processes that renew some resources, and it depletes those resources that cannot be renewed.

Humans use many natural systems as resources. p. 198

Environmental Quality

Natural ecosystems provide an array of basic processes that affect humans

Materials from human societies affect both physical and chemical cycles of the earth.

Many factors influence environmental quality. Factors that students might investigate include population growth, resource use, population distribution, overconsumption, the capacity of technology to solve problems, poverty, the role of economic, political, and religious views, and different ways humans view the earth. p. 198

Project 2061, AAAS Benchmarks for Science Literacy

Chapter 7 Human Society
7E Political and Economic Systems

In the free-market model, the control of production and consumption is mainly in private hands.

In the central-planning model, production and consumption are controlled by the government.

The countries of the world use elements of both systems and are neither purely free-market nor entirely centrally controlled. p. 170

7G Global Interdependence.

The wealth of a country depends partly on the effort and skills of its workers, its natural resources, and the capital and technology available to it.

Because of increasing international trade, the domestic products of any country may be made up in part by parts made in other countries.

The growing interdependence of world social, economic, and ecological systems does not always bring greater worldwide stability and often increases the costs of conflict. p. 178

New York City Performance Standards

S4 Scientific Connections and Applications

The student demonstrates conceptual understanding by using the concept to explain observations and make predictions and by representing the concept in multiple ways (through words, diagrams, graphs or charts, as appropriate). Both aspects of understanding—explaining and representing—are required to meet this standard.

The student produces evidence that demonstrates understanding of:

S4a Big ideas and unifying concepts, such as order and organization; models, form and function; change and constancy; and cause and effect.

S4b The designed world, such as the reciprocal relationship between science and technology; the development of agricultural techniques; and the reasonableness of technological designs.

S4c Health, such as nutrition and exercise; disease and epidemiology; personal and environmental safety; and resources, environmental stress, and population growth.

S4d Impact of technology such as constraints and trade-offs; feedback; benefits and risks; and problems and solutions.

S4e Impact of science, such as historical and contemporary contributions; and interactions between science and society.

Examples of activities through which students might demonstrate conceptual understanding of scientific connections and applications include:

▲ Construct a computer-controlled robot arm that mimics the form and function of a human hand and forearm. 4a, 4b, 4c, 2a

▲ Work with other students to give a presentation based on scientific principles arguing for a systemic solution to an environmental problem that concerns the school or community. 4a, 4b, 4c, 4d, 1a, 2d, 2e, A1b

▲ Propose modifications to improve skateboards, in-line skates, bicycles, or similar objects to make them safer, faster, or less expensive. 4b, 4c, 1a, A1b

▲ Conduct a study of the school cafeteria including: food storage and preparation, nutrition, and student preferences; and make recommendations for improvement. 4c, 4d

▲ Debate the positive and negative consequences of a recently developed technological innovation. 4b, 4d, 4e, E3b

▲ Earn the Food, Fibers, and Farming Merit Badge (Girl Scouts of the U.S.A.) and make a poster that shows understanding of agriculture or technology. 4b, 4c, 4d, 4e

New York State Learning Standards for Math, Science, & Technology

Standard 6 Interconnectedness: Common Themes

Students will understand the relationships and common themes that connect mathematics, science, and technology and apply the themes to these and other areas of learning.

Systems Thinking

1. Through systems thinking, people can recognize the commonalities that exist among all systems and how parts of a system interrelate and combine to perform specific functions.

Models

2. Models are simplified representations of objects, structures, or systems used in analysis, explanation, interpretation, or design. p. 56

Magnitude and Scale

3. The grouping of magnitudes of size, time, frequency, and pressures or other units of measurement into a series of relative order provides a useful way to deal with the immense range and the changes in scale that affect the behavior and design of systems.

Equilibrium and Stability

4. Equilibrium is a state of stability due either to a lack of changes (static equilibrium) or a balance between opposing forces (dynamic equilibrium). p. 57

Patterns of Change

5. Identifying patterns of change is necessary for making predictions about future behavior and conditions.

Optimization

6. In order to arrive at the best solution that meets criteria within constraints, it is often necessary to make trade-offs. p.58

National Documents which guided New York State and New York City

NRC National Science Education Standards

Unifying Concepts and Processes

Systems, order, and organization
Evidence, models, and explanation
Constancy, change, and measurement
Evolution and equilibrium
Form and function pp. 115-119

Standard E Science and Technology pp. 190-193

Standard F Science in Personal and Social Perspectives

Personal Health
Characteristics and Changes in Populations
Types of Resources
Changes in Environments
Science and Technology in Local Challenges pp. 193-199

Standard G History and Nature of Science pp. 200-204

Project 2061, AAAS Benchmarks for Science Literacy

Chapter 3 The Nature of Technology pp. 41-57

Chapter 6 The Human Organism pp. 127-149

Chapter 8 The Designed World pp. 181-207

Chapter 10 Historical Perspectives pp. 237-259

Chapter 11 Common Themes
11A Systems
11B Models
11C Constancy and Change
11D Scale pp. 261-279

New York City Performance Standards

S5 Scientific Thinking

The student demonstrates skill in scientific inquiry and problem solving by using thoughtful questioning and reasoning strategies, common sense and diverse conceptual understanding, and appropriate ideas and methods to investigate science; that is, the student:

S5a Frames questions to distinguish cause and effect; and identifies or controls variables in experimental and non-experimental research settings.

S5b Uses concepts from Science Standards 1 to 4 to explain a variety of observations and phenomena.

S5c Uses evidence from reliable sources to develop descriptions, explanations, and models; and makes appropriate adjustments and improvements based on additional data or logical arguments.

S5d Proposes, recognizes, analyzes, considers, and critiques alternative explanations; and distinguishes between fact and opinion.

S5e Identifies problems; proposes and implements solutions; and evaluates the accuracy, design, and outcomes of investigations.

S5f Works individually and in teams to collect and share information and ideas.

Examples of activities through which students might demonstrate skill in scientific thinking include:

▲ Evaluate the claims and potential benefits and risks of steroid use and apply the scientific evidence to a reported "case study" of an athlete. 5a, 5b, 5c, 5d

▲ Predict how long a plant will live, planted in moist soil in a closed glass jar located by a window; explain what additional information would be needed to make a better prediction. 5a, 5b, 5c

▲ Compare and contrast the nutritional value of several common brands of cereals. 5b, 5c, 5d

▲ Compare and contrast lines of evidence for theories of dinosaur extinction. 5b, 5c, 5d, 2c, 2d

▲ Explain the chain of inference in DNA testing and debate both positions regarding its inclusion as evidence in a capital trial. 5c, 5d, 1b, 1c, 2a, 2b, 4d

New York State Learning Standards for Math, Science, & Technology

Standard 1 Analysis, Inquiry, and Design
Scientific Inquiry

1. The central purpose of scientific inquiry is to develop explanations of natural phenomena in a continuing, creative process.

2. Beyond the use of reasoning and consensus, scientific inquiry involves the testing of proposed explanations involving the use of conventional techniques and procedures and usually requiring considerable ingenuity. p. 6

3. The observations made while testing explanations, when analyzed using conventional and invented methods, provide new insights into phenomena. p. 7

National Documents which guided New York State and New York City

NRC National Science Education Standards

Standard A Science as Inquiry

Identify questions and concepts that guide scientific investigations....

Formulate and revise scientific explanations and models using logic and evidence....

Recognize and analyze alternative explanations and models.... p. 175

Project 2061, AAAS Benchmarks for Science Literacy

Chapter 1 The Nature of Science
1B Scientific Inquiry

Hypotheses are widely used in science for choosing what data to pay attention to and what additional data to seek, and for guiding the interpretation of the data (both new and previously available).

Sometimes, scientists can control conditions in order to obtain evidence. When that is not possible for practical or ethical reasons, they try to observe as wide a range of natural occurrences as possible to be able to discern patterns.

In the short run, new ideas that do not mesh well with mainstream ideas in science often encounter vigorous criticism. In the long run, theories are judged by how they fit with other theories, the range of observations they explain, how well they explain observations, and how effective they are in predicting new findings. p. 13

Chapter 12 Habits of Mind
12D Communication Skills

Participate in group discussions on scientific topics by restating or summarizing accurately what others have said, asking for clarification or elaboration, and expressing alternative positions. p. 297

Suggest alternative ways of explaining data and criticize arguments in which data, explanations, or conclusions are represented as the only ones worth consideration, with no mention of other possibilities. p. 300

New York City Performance Standards

S6 Scientific Tools and Technologies

The student demonstrates competence with the tools and technologies of science by using them to collect data, make observations, analyze results, and accomplish tasks effectively; that is, the student:

S6a Uses technology and tools (such as traditional laboratory equipment, video, and computer aids) to observe and measure objects, organisms, and phenomena, directly, indirectly, and remotely, with appropriate consideration of accuracy and precision.

S6b Records and stores data using a variety of formats, such as data bases, audiotapes, and videotapes.

S6c Collects and analyzes data using concepts and techniques in Mathematics Standard 4, such as mean, median, and mode; outcome probability and reliability; and appropriate data displays.

S6d Acquires information from multiple sources, such as print, the Internet, computer data bases, and experimentation.

S6e Recognizes and limits sources of bias in data, such as observer and sample biases.

Examples of activities through which students might demonstrate competence in the tools and technologies of science include:

▲ Work with other students to repeat a historical series of experiments, such as those leading to the current understanding of photosynthesis, and write an essay comparing and contrasting the differences in available tools and technologies. 6d, 2a, 4d, 4e, 5c, 7b

▲ Evaluate the accuracy and timeliness of information reported during the "life" of a hurricane or tropical storm. 6d, 3a, 4a, 5c

▲ Use the Internet to get current information on a rapidly changing scientific topic. 6d

▲ Use a computer interface to measure the velocity of objects. 6d, 1d, 5c

▲ Use telecommunications to compare data on similar investigations with students in another state. 6d

▲ Earn the Orienteering Merit Badge (Boy Scouts of America) and teach another student what to do if he or she gets lost. 6d, 3a, 5c, 7d

New York State Learning Standards for Math, Science, & Technology

Standard 2 Information Systems

1. Information technology is used to retrieve, process, and communicate information and as a tool to enhance learning.

   Students:

   access, select, collate, and analyze information obtained from a wide range of sources such as research databases, foundations, organizations, national libraries, and electronic communication networks, including the Internet. p. 12

Standard 3 Mathematics Modeling/Multiple Representation

4. Students use mathematical modeling/multiple representation to provide a means of presenting, interpreting, communicating, and connecting mathematical information and relationships. p. 23

Measurement

5. Students use measurement in both metric and English measure to provide a major link between the abstractions of mathematics and the real world in order to describe and compare objects and data. p. 24

National Documents which guided New York State and New York City

NRC National Science Education Standards

Standard A Science as Inquiry

Use technology and mathematics to improve investigations and communications. p. 175

Project 2061, AAAS Benchmarks for Science Literacy

Chapter 1 The Nature of Science
1B Scientific Inquiry

Scientists in any one research group tend to see things alike, so even groups of scientists may have trouble being entirely objective about their methods and findings. For that reason, scientific teams are expected to seek out he possible sources of bias in the design of their investigations and in their data analysis. Checking each other's results and explanations helps, but that is no guarantee against bias. p 13

Chapter 12 Habits of Mind
12B Computation and Estimation

Use computer spreadsheet, graphing, and database programs to assist in quantitative analysis. p. 291

12C Manipulation and Observation

Use computers for producing tables and graphs and for making spreadsheet calculations. p. 294

12D Communication Skills

Choose appropriate summary statistics to describe group differences, always indicating the spread of the data as well as the data's central tendencies. p. 297

New York City Performance Standards

S7 Scientific Communication

The student demonstrates effective scientific communication by clearly describing aspects of the natural world using accurate data, graphs, or other appropriate media to convey depth of conceptual understanding in science; that is, the student:

S7a Represents data and results in multiple ways, such as numbers, tables, and graphs; drawings, diagrams, and artwork; technical and creative writing; and selects the most effective way to convey the scientific information.

S7b Argues from evidence, such as data produced through his or her own experimentation or data produced by others.

S7c Critiques published materials, such as popular magazines and academic journals.

S7d Explains a scientific concept or procedure to other students.

S7e Communicates in a form suited to the purpose and the audience, such as by writing instructions that others can follow; critiquing written and oral explanations; and using data to resolve disagreements.

Examples of activities through which students might demonstrate competence in scientific communication include:
- Analyze a ballot initiative on a local endangered species. 7a, 7b, 2c, 4d, 5a
- Critique a Time article which reports on something you have studied. 7c
- Make a "claymation" video illustrating in simple terms how a virus attacks the human body. 7c, 2d, 4c, 5c
- Give an oral report describing the change over time in local air quality. 7d, 2d, 3e, 4d, E3c
- Earn the Model Design and Building Merit Badge (Boy Scouts of America) and explain what constitutes an effective model. 7d, 4b, 5c
- Write an advertisement for a cold relief product that explains how it works. 7e, 4c, 5c, 5d, 6d

New York State Learning Standards for Math, Science, & Technology

Standard 1 Analysis, Inquiry, and Design
Scientific Inquiry

3. The observations made while testing proposed explanations, when analyzed using conventional and invented methods, provide new insights into phenomena.

   Students:

   use various means of representing and organizing observations (e.g., diagrams, tables, charts, graphs, equations, matrices) and insightfully interpret the organized data. p. 7

National Documents which guided New York State and New York City

NRC National Science Education Standards

Standard A Science as Inquiry

Communicate and defend a scientific argument. p. 176

Project 2061, AAAS Benchmarks for Science Literacy

Chapter 1 The Nature of Science
1B Scientific Inquiry

There are different traditions in science about what is investigated and how, but they all have in common certain basic beliefs about the value of evidence, logic, and good arguments. And there is agreement that progress in all fields of science depends on intelligence, hard work, imagination, and even chance. p. 13

Chapter 9 The Mathematical World
9B Symbolic Relationships

Tables, graphs, and symbols are alternative ways of representing data and relationships that can be translated from one to the other. p. 221

9D Uncertainty

The way data are displayed can make a big difference in how they are interpreted. p. 230

Chapter 12 Habits of Mind
12D Communication Skills

Write clear, step-by-step instructions for conducting investigations, operating something, or following a procedure.

Participate in group discussions on scientific topics by restating or summarizing accurately what others have said, asking for clarification or elaboration, and expressing alternative positions. p. 297

New York City Performance Standards

S8 Scientific Investigation

The student demonstrates scientific competence by completing projects drawn from the following kinds of investigation, including at least one full investigation each year and, over the course of high school, investigations that integrate several aspects of Science Standards 1 to 7 and represent all four of the kinds of investigation:

S8a Controlled experiment.

S8b Fieldwork

S8c Design

S8d Explains a scientific concept or procedure to other students.

S8e Secondary research.

A single project may draw on more than one type of investigation.

A full investigation includes:

• Questions that can be studied using the resources available.

• Procedures that are safe, humane, and ethical; and that respect privacy and property rights.

• Data that have been collected and recorded (see also Science Standard 6) in ways that others can verify, and analyzed using skills expected at this grade level (see also Mathematics Standard 4).

• Data and results that have been represented (see also Science Standard 7) in ways that fit the context.

• Recommendations, decisions, and conclusions based on evidence.

• Acknowledgment of references and contributions of others.

• Results that are communicated appropriately to audiences.

• Reflection and defense of conclusions and recommendations from other sources and peer review.

Examples of projects through which students might demonstrate competence in scientific investigation include:

▲ Investigate the effectiveness of common household cleaners on bacterial growth. 8a, 1c, 2a, 4c

▲ Conduct research to determine if the incidence of asthma is related to weather. 8b, 3a, 4c

▲ Conduct a study of the geology of an area near the school and describe the likely history of the region, using observations and reference materials. 8b, 8d, 3c, 6d

▲ Compare and contrast the designs of different sports shoes and evaluate the designs considering the varying demands of different sports. 8c

▲ Conduct an investigation to determine if the shape of a stereo speaker container affects sound quality. 8c, 1f

▲ Study the distribution of a species in the region or state and discuss the likelihood of it becoming endangered. 8d, 2c, 5c, 6c

New York State Learning Standards for Math, Science, & Technology

Standard 1 Analysis, Inquiry, and Design
Scientific Inquiry

1. The central purpose of scientific inquiry is to develop explanations of natural phenomena in a continuing, creative process.

2. Beyond the use of reasoning and consensus, scientific inquiry involves the testing of proposed explanations involving the use of conventional techniques and procedures and usually requiring considerable ingenuity. p. 6

3. The observations made while testing explanations, when analyzed using conventional and invented methods, provide new insights into phenomena. p. 7

Engineering Design

1. Engineering design is an iterative process involving modeling and optimization finding the best solution within given constraints which is used to develop technological solutions to problems within given constraints. p. 7

National Documents which guided New York State and New York City

NRC National Science Education Standards

Standard A Science as Inquiry

Design and conduct scientific investigations. Designing and conducting a scientific investigation requires introduction to the major concepts in the area being investigated, proper equipment, safety precautions, assistance with methodological problems, recommendations for the use of technologies, clarification of ideas that guide the inquiry, and scientific knowledge obtained from sources other than the actual investigation. The investigation may also require student clarification of the question, method, controls, and variables; student organization and display of data; student revision of methods and explanations; and a public presentation of the results with critical response from peers. Regardless of the scientific investigation performed, students must use evidence, apply logic, and construct an argument for their proposed explanations. p. 175

Standard E Science and Technology

Identify a problem or design opportunity.

Propose designs and choose between alternate solutions.

Implement a proposed solution.

Evaluate the solution and its consequences.

Communicate the problem, processes, and solution. p. 192

Project 2061, AAAS Benchmarks for Science Literacy

Chapter 1 The Nature of Science
1B Scientific Inquiry

Sometimes, scientists can control conditions in order to obtain evidence. When it is not possible for practical or ethical reasons, they may try to observe as wide a range of natural occurrences as possible to be able to discern patterns.

There are different traditions in science about what is investigated and how, but they all have in common certain basic beliefs about the value of evidence, logic, and good arguments. And there is agreement that progress in all fields of science depends on intelligence, hard work, imagination, and even chance. p. 13

Chapter 3 The Nature of Technology
3B Design and Systems

In designing a device or process, thought should be given to how it will be manufactured, replaced, and disposed of and who will sell, operate, and take care of it. The costs associated with these functions may introduce yet more constraints on the design. p. 52

Work Sample & Commentary: *Pendulum Experiment*

The task

The task was an investigation in which students analyzed an archeological artifact—a pendulum—discovered by the fictional Morgan International Research Institute during an expedition in Mali, West Africa. The students were asked to decide what function the artifact might have served, and to investigate the variables that affect the period of a pendulum's oscillation.

For related work on Pendula, see "Pendulum", page 38.

Circumstances of performance

These samples of student work were produced under the following conditions:

√ alone   √ in a group

√ in class   √ as homework

√ with teacher feedback   with peer feedback

    timed   opportunity for revision

Physical Sciences Concepts S1

Life Sciences Concepts

Earth and Space Sciences Concepts

Scientific Connections and Applications S4

Scientific Thinking S5

Scientific Tools and Technologies S6

Scientific Communication S7

Scientific Investigation S8

The quotations from the Science performance descriptions in this commentary are excerpted. The complete performance descriptions are shown on pages 122-143.

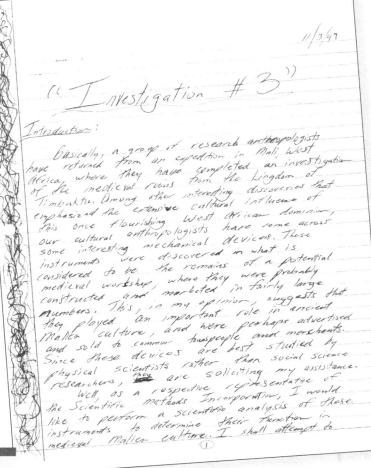

Student 1

11/3/97

"Investigation # 3"

Introduction:

Basically, a group of research anthropologists have returned from an expedition in Mali, West Africa, where they have completed an investigation of the medieval ruins from the Kingdom of Timbuktu. Among other interesting discoveries that emphasized the extensive cultural influence of this once flourishing West African dominion, our cultural anthropologists have come across some interesting mechanical devices. These instruments were discovered in what is considered to be the remains of a potential medieval workshop, where they were probably constructed and marketed in fairly large numbers. This, in my opinion, suggests that they played an important role in ancient Malian culture, and were perhaps advertised and sold to common townspeople and merchants. Since these devices are best studied by physical scientists rather than social science researchers, they are soliciting my assistance.

Well, as a respective representative of the Scientific methods Incorporation, I would like to perform a scientific analysis of these instruments to determine their function in medieval Malian culture. I shall attempt to

①

These work samples illustrates standard-setting performances for the following parts of the standards:

S1d **Physical Sciences Concepts: Motions and forces.**

S4e **Scientific Connections and Applications: Impact of science.**

S5a **Scientific Thinking: Frame questions to distinguish cause and effect.**

S5b **Scientific Thinking: Use concepts from Science Standards 1 to 4.**

S5e **Scientific Thinking: Identify problems.**

S5f **Scientific Thinking: Work individually and in teams.**

S6a **Scientific Tools and Technologies: Use technology and tools.**

S7a **Scientific Communication: Represent data and results in multiple ways.**

S7b **Scientific Communication: Argue from evidence.**

S7e **Scientific Communication: Communicate in a form suited to the purpose and the audience.**

S8a **Scientific Investigation: Demonstrate scientific competence by completing a controlled experiment.**

What the work shows

S1d Physical Sciences Concepts: The student provides evidence that demonstrates understanding of motions and forces, such as gravitational....

A B The student correctly states that the pendulum's motion is due to the influence of gravity, and notes differences in gravity related to geographical location.

C D The hypothesis and the narrative comparison of the data tables demonstrate understanding of concepts related to motion and force.

Pendulum Experiment

Student 1

S4e Scientific Connections and Applications: The student produces evidence that demonstrates understanding of the impact of science, such as historical and contemporary contributions....

E The student incorporates into the report several references to Galileo's work with pendulums.

S5a Scientific Thinking: The student frames questions to distinguish cause and effect; and identifies or controls variables in experimental and non-experimental research settings.

F The student frames the question appropriately.

G **H** **I** The student identified and controlled each variable in designing her experiment, and in recording data in the tables and graphs.

J The "Explanation," clearly demonstrates the student's understanding of variables. This section of the report describes the efforts made to control variables and the limitations of those efforts.

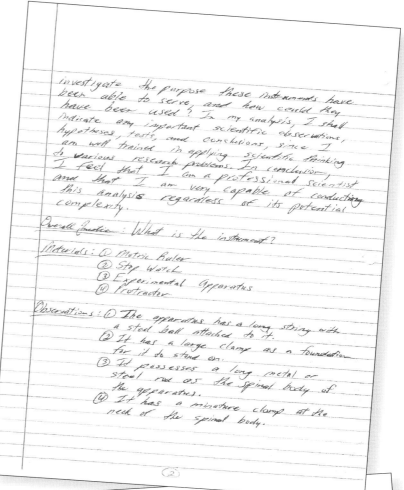

investigate the purpose these instruments have been able to serve, and how could they have been used? In my analysis, I shall indicate any important scientific observations, hypothesis, tests, and conclusions, since I am well trained in applying scientific thinking to various research problems. In conclusion, I feel that I am a professional scientist and that I am very capable of conducting this analysis regardless of its potential complexity.

Overall Question: What is the instrument?

Materials: ① Metric Ruler
② Stop Watch
③ Experimental Apparatus
④ Protractor

Observations: ① The apparatus has a long string with a steel ball attached to it.
② It has a large clamp as a foundation for it to stand on.
③ It possesses a long metal or steel rod as the spinal body of the apparatus.
④ It has a miniature clamp at the neck of the spinal body.

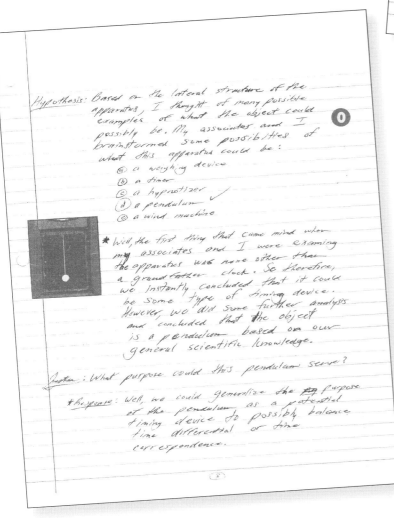

Hypothesis: Based on the lateral structure of the apparatus, I thought of many possible examples of what the object could possibly be. My associates and I brainstormed some possibilities of what this apparatus could be:
ⓐ a weighing device
ⓑ a timer
ⓒ a hypnotizer ✓
ⓓ a pendulum ✓
ⓔ a wind machine

O

* Well, the first thing that came mind when my associates and I were examining the apparatus was none other than a grandfather clock. So therefore, we instantly concluded that it could be some type of timing device. However, we did some further analysis and concluded that the object is a pendulum based on our general scientific knowledge.

Question: What purpose could this pendulum serve?

*Response: Well, we could generalize the purpose of the pendulum as a potential timing device to possibly balance time differential or time correspondence.

Pendulum Experiment

S5 b   Scientific Thinking: The student uses concepts from Science Standards 1 to 4 to explain a variety of observations and phenomena.

K L M N Throughout the "Interpretations" section and in the conclusion, the student applies concepts related to Science Standard **S1** d.

S5 e   Scientific Thinking: The student identifies problems; proposes and implements solutions; and evaluates the accuracy, design, and outcomes of investigations.

J In the "Explanation" the student identifies limitations of the procedure and comments on the resulting level of accuracy of the data collected.

S5 f   Scientific Thinking: The student works individually and in teams to collect and share information and ideas.

G J O Both students mention working with team members. (The reports, however, are individual efforts.)

Student 1

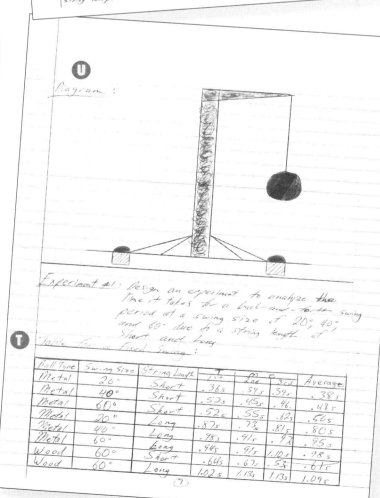

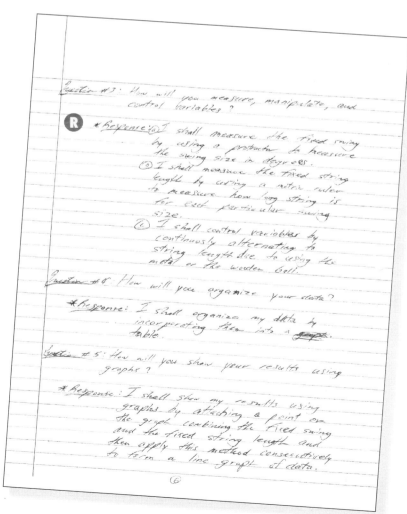

Ball Type	Swing Size	String Length	1st	2nd	3rd	Average
Metal	20°	Short				
Metal	40°	Short	.36s	.34s	.34s	.38s
Metal	60°	Short	.52s	.45s	.46	.48s
Metal	20°	Long	.80s	.73s	.81s	.56s
Metal	40°	Long				.80s
Metal	60°	Long	.98s	.91s	.97	.95s
Wood	60°	Short	.94s	.91s	1.10s	.98s
Wood	60°	Long	.64s	.62	.53s	.61s
			1.02s	1.13s	1.13s	1.09s

Student 1 ## Pendulum Experiment

S6a Scientific Tools and Technologies: The student uses technology and tools (such as traditional laboratory equipment, video, and computer aids) to observe and measure objects, organisms, and phenomena, directly, indirectly, and remotely, with appropriate consideration of accuracy and precision.

P Q R S G The material lists, responses to the investigation questions, and procedure section make it clear that scientific tools were used during the investigation.

H I T The data in the tables and graphs demonstrate that the student repeated experiments to achieve an appropriate degree of precision.

J The student comments on the accuracy and precision of the procedure and data.

S7a Scientific Communication: The student represents data and results in multiple ways, such as numbers, tables, and graphs; diagrams; technical and creative writing; and selects the most effective way to convey the scientific information.

D J The student's narrative writing is clear and concise.

Experiment #2 : Design an experiment to analyze the time it takes for a back-and-forth swing period at a string length of 20 cm, 40 cm, 60 cm due to swing size of Big or Small

Table for a fixed String Length :

Ball Type	String Length	Swing Size	Time			
			1st	2nd	3rd	Average
Metal	20 cm	small	.75s	.62s	.5s	.64s
Metal	40 cm	small	.86s	.92s	.91s	.90s
Metal	60 cm	small	.94s	.96s	.88s	.94s
Metal	20 cm	Big	.72s	.73s	.68s	.71s
Metal	40 cm	Big	1.10s	1.15s	1.20s	1.15s
Metal	60 cm	Big	1.24s	1.29s	1.31s	1.28s
Wood	60 cm	small	1.10s	1.10s	1.16s	1.12s
Wood	60cm	Big	1.49s	1.52s	1.50s	1.50s

Experiment #3 - Design an experiment to analyze the time it takes for a back-and-forth swing period at a fixed string length and swing size.

Table for a fixed String Length combined with a fixed Swing size :

Ball Type	String Length	Swing Size	Time Period			
			1st	2nd	3rd	Average
Metal	20 cm	20°	.63s	.71s	.68s	.67
Metal	20 cm	40°	.63s	.73s	.67s	.68s
Metal	20 cm	60°	.63s	.72.	.64s	.66s
Metal	40 cm	20°	.89s	.80s	.82s	.84s
Metal	40 cm	40°	.90s	1.15s	.95s	1.00s
Metal	40 cm	60°	.89s	1.16s	.98s	1.01s
Metal	60 cm	20°	.96s	1.28s	.80s	1.01s
Metal	60 cm	40°	.96s	.95s	.96s	.96s
Metal	60 cm	60°	.96s	.98s	.97s	.97s
Wood	60 cm	60°	1.12s	1.50s	1.09s	1.24s

Interpretations :

① Graph for a fixed Swing:

K In this graph, when the pendulum has a short string length, there is a more immediate interval of time for a back-and-forth swing period due to a consecutive increase in swing size. However, when the pendulum has a long string length, there is a more delayed interval of time for a back-and forth swing period due to a consecutive increase in swing size.

② Graph for a fixed String Length:

L In this graph, when the pendulum has a small swing size, there is a slight jump during the interval of time for a back-and-forth swing period due to a consecutive increase in string length. However, when the pendulum has a big swing size, there is a sharp increase in time differential for a back-and-forth swing period due to a consecutive increase in string length.

③ Graph for a fixed Swing size and a fixed String Length:

M In this graph, when the pendulum has a fixed swing size and a fixed string length, there is a more upward and downward yet steady interval of time for a back-and-forth swing period due to a consecutive in swing size for category of 20 cm, 40 cm, and 60 cm.

E Q R Throughout the report, the narrative text adds to the flow of information. This is especially true at points such as **Q** and **R**, where the narrative is entirely original. The student also successfully incorporates book research into the report, as at **E**.

H I The student uses tables and graphs to collect and represent the data. Each data table and graph deals with changes in one variable.

T The student presents data from experiment 1 in three tables. However, data for only one manipulated variable should be presented in each table. It should also be pointed out that the student's use of the term 'fixed' when referring to variables being 'manipulated' is incorrect.

Pendulum Experiment

Student 1

Background Information if the Pendulum

(A) A pendulum is a device consisting of an object suspended from a fixed point that swings back and forth under the influence of gravity. Pendulums are used in several kinds of mechanical devices.

The most basic type of pendulum is the simple pendulum. In a simple pendulum, which oscillates back and forth in a single plane, all the mass of the device can be considered to reside entirely in the suspended object. The motion of pendulums such as those in clocks closely approximates the motion of a simple pendulum.

(E) The principle of the pendulum was discovered by Italian physicist and astronomer Galileo, who established that the period for the back-and-forth oscillation of a pendulum of a given length (11)

(B) remains the same, no matter how large its arc, or amplitude. This phenomenon is called isochronism, and Galileo noted its possible applications in timekeeping. Because of the role played by gravity, however, the period of a pendulum is related to geographical location, because the strength of gravity varies as a function of latitude and elevation. For example, the period will be greater on a mountain than at sea level. Thus, the pendulum can be used to determine accurately the local acceleration of gravity.

(12)

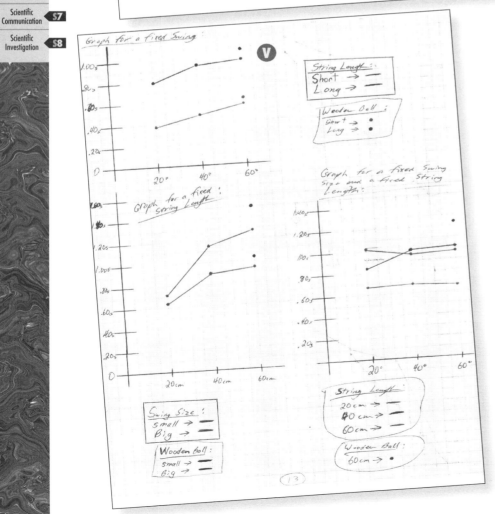

Graph for a Fixed Swing:

(V)

String Length:
Short →
Long →

Wooden Ball:
Short →
Long →

Graph for a Fixed Swing Size and a Fixed String Length:

Graph for a Fixed Swing Length:

Swing Size:
Small →
Big →

Wooden Ball:
Small →
Big →

String Length:
20cm →
40cm →
60cm →

Wooden Ball:
60cm →

(13)

Conclusion: (W)

Well, all in all, this investigation that the Morgan Institute required to accomplish was an extremely difficult task of analysis. Nevertheless, I believe I have successfully derived at the overall solution to the question all the respective researchers of the Morgan Institute have been pondering.

* Which variable of the pendulum has had the most influencial impact on its change of time duration due to a fixed swing size?

(N)

* Well, due to my data in the first table, which is the table for a fixed swing, when the string is either long or short there seem to be a wide differential in seconds of time duration. I discovered that there is a more immediate interval of time for a back-and-forth swing period due to a consecutive increase in swing size. However, when there is a long string length, there is a more delayed interval of time for a back-and-forth swing period due to a consecutive increase in swing size. So I conclude that the most influencial variable is the string length.

(13)

Pendulum Experiment

Student 2

U The student uses a diagram to clarify his written description.

V The student represents data and results in graphs. Again, the student attempts to incorporate too much information in one graph. (The original graphs were in color; this distinction is lost in reproduction.)

S7b Scientific Communication: The student argues from evidence, such as data produced through his or her own experimentation or data produced by others.

W In the "Conclusions" section, the student argues from the experimental data that "...the most influential variable is the string length."

D The student uses graphic representations of the data to argue that the largest changes in the pendulum's period of time occurred when the string length was changed.

X Based on the graphed data, the student concludes that the largest change in the pendulum 's period of time occurred when the length of the pendulum changed.

S1 Physical Sciences Concepts

Life Sciences Concepts

Earth and Space Sciences Concepts

S4 Scientific Connections and Applications

S5 Scientific Thinking

S6 Scientific Tools and Technologies

S7 Scientific Communication

S8 Scientific Investigation

10/17/97

Investigation #3 - The Pendulum

F Question #1 - what variable changes the period (time for a back-and-forth swing) of the pendulum the most?

C Hypothesis - The period changes the most by changing the length of the pendulum.

S Materials
1. the clamp and metal cylinder that hold the pendulum to the desk.
2. The smaller clamp that goes at the top of the metal cylinder and holds the pendulum's string so that it can swing back-and-forth freely.
3. 2 pendulums; one with a metal ball at the end of the string and the other one with a wooden ball at the end of the string.
4. a stop watch for timing.

2

5. a protractor for measuring the swing angle.
6. a ruler for measuring length.

Observations
The metal ball of the first pendulum is heavier than the wooden ball of the second pendulum.

G Procedures
1. First we set up the pendulum stand.
2. Then we tested the first variable which is the size of the swing.
3. We used the protractor to measure the angle of the swing.
4. We held the string at 70° on the protractor, and let it swing back-and-forth once while timing it, and recorded our observations.
5. We did the same thing with the string held at 50° and then let go and with string held at 30° and then let go. For each one we recorded the time it took for one swing.

3

6. We then tested the second variable which was the mass of the ball at the end of the two pendulums.
7. First we weighed each ball and recorded the data.
8. Then we used one length of the string, and one angle and we tested the variable.
9. We first let the metal ball swing back and forth once and timed it.
10. Then we let the wooden ball swing back-and-forth keeping the length of the string and the angle the same as the metal ball while timing it.
11. We recorded our observations.
12. Then the third variable was tested which was the length of the string.
13. We tested three lengths of string and with each test we used the metal pendulum and an 80° angle.
14. With each length we recorded the

Pendulum Experiment

Student 2

S7e Scientific Communication: The student communicates in a form suited to the purpose and the audience, such as by writing instructions that others can follow [and] critiquing written and oral explanations....

D **X** The student determines which variable contributed most in determining a pendulum's period, and clearly communicates the results in written form.

G **J** The student provides a clearly written procedure for others to follow in repeating the experiment, and notes limitations of the procedure.

S8a Scientific Investigation: The student demonstrates scientific competence by completing a controlled experiment.

T **V** The tables and graphs showed that the student performed a series of steps that tested for specific variables. However, data for only one variable should be presented in each table and graph.

W The student uses data from the investigation to reach a correct conclusion.

G The student clearly outlines the experiment and states how each variable can be evaluated in a controlled way.

4

time it took for one back-and-forth swing.

X Conclusion: After we tested all the variables and recorded our observations we graphed the results. As shown through the graphs our hypothesis was right, the period changes the most by changing the length of the pendulum. In the graph of the swing size the biggest difference of seconds between 2 angles of swings was .03 seconds. In the graph of the ball mass the difference in time between the 2 masses was .07 seconds. Finally, in the graph of the string lengths, the biggest difference in seconds between 2 lengths was .68 seconds. This being the biggest difference of all 3 graphs shows that it is the variable that changes the "period" of the pendulum the most.

H Evidence:

Variable #1: Size of swing
String length - 25 cm, Used-metal ball- 66.2 grams

Size of swing	1st trial	2nd trial	3rd trial	Average
70°	.88s	.84s	.75s	.82s
50°	.81s	.84s	.84s	.83s
30°	.82s	.75s	.82s	.80s

Variable #2: Mass of ball
String length - 15 cm, angle of swing - 60°

Mass of ball	1st trial	2nd trial	3rd trial	Average
Wood (5.9 grams)	.62s	.56s	.59s	.59s
metal (66.2 grams)	.75s	.63s	.59s	.66s

Variable #3: length of string
angle of swing - 80°, Used - metal ball - 66.2 grams

Length of string	1st trial	2nd trial	3rd trial	Average
15 cm	.54s	.59s	.56s	.56s
30 cm	1.06s	1.12s	1.03s	1.07s
45 cm	1.25s	1.18s	1.28s	1.24s

Pendulum Experiment

① Graphs
Size of Swing

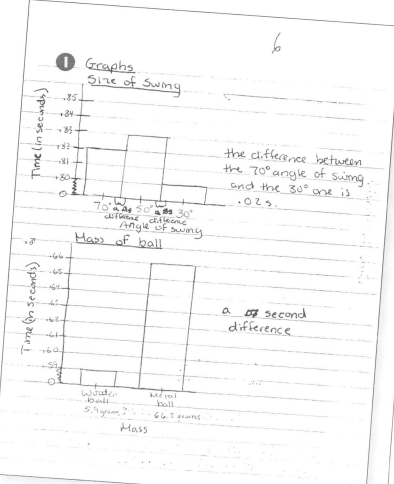

the difference between the 70° angle of swing and the 30° one is .02s.

Mass of ball

a 07 second difference

Wooden ball 5.9 grams   Metal ball 66.2 grams

Mass

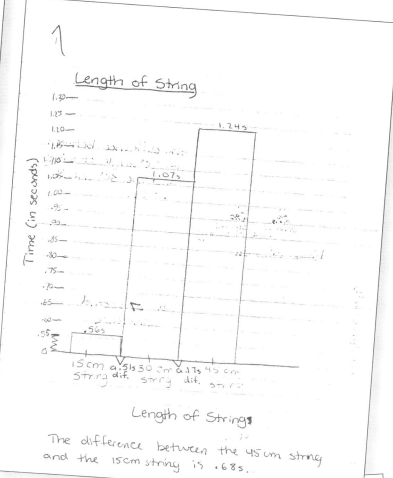

Length of String

Length of String

The difference between the 45 cm string and the 15 cm string is .68s.

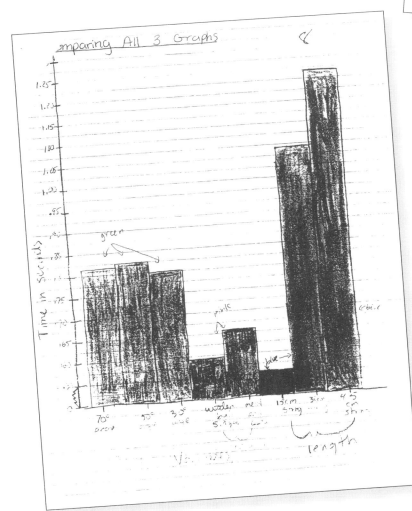

comparing All 3 Graphs

D In comparing all 3 graphs on the same scale I found that it was easier to see what variable affected the period of the pendulum the most. As you can see in the green bars, or the bars showing the variable of angle swing, the difference in time is very little. In the pink bars or the bars comparing the wooden ball period with the metal ball period there is also a slight difference, a little bit bigger than with the green bars. Then in the last bars, the blue bars, which compare the period changes with the string length the difference is definitely the largest. There we can see how much the period changed from having the 15 cm string and then to the 30 cm string and again to the 45 cm string. These three blue bars show the biggest difference

Pendulum Experiment

Student 2

10

Category #3
Scientific Inquiry II

J Explanation:
There were a few limitations
of the data used in this experiment.
The factor that created the most
unreliability was accuracy. Unfortunately,
humans can not be very precise
on reflexes alone. In this particular
investigation we had to time the
swing of a pendulum. Since we
didn't have a machine that could
be perfect, we had to try to be
as quick with the stop watch as
possible. This reduced our accuracy
by a certain percentage. We also
had to measure the string length of
the pendulum a few times to get
a so-called "best-value". We also
had to let the pendulum fall
from different angles and had to
let ~~them~~ if fall from the same
angle a few times to get a "best-
value." We did all of this by
hand with a stop watch, a ruler, and
a protractor. We weren't extremely
precise and this could have led to
error in all sorts of measurements
we did. A few angles could have

11

been wrong and even a couple of
the timings.

Summary:
I picked this investigation because
I worked so hard on all the graphs
and tables I drew. Graphs are
a very organized way of putting
together data. It is also a lot
easier to compare variables through
graphs. Interpreting data can
be difficult without them. Making
the graphs and tables helped me
understand the data better and improve
my investigation as a whole.

Work Sample & Commentary: *The Challenger Disaster*

The task

The task was in the form of an investigation in which students were asked to test the hypothesis that the unusually cold temperatures at the time of the Space Shuttle Challenger launch might have reduced the ability of O-Rings to expand and seal the Solid Fuel Booster Rocket Field Joints. Students designed and performed experiments in research teams. The students then prepared individual reports of their findings to the Challenger Commission as a homework assignment.

Circumstances of performance

This sample of student work was produced under the following conditions:

√ alone   in a group

in class   √ as homework

√ with teacher feedback   with peer feedback

timed   √ opportunity for revision

The Challenger Disaster

Introduction

The space shuttle Challenger exploded and was destroyed during its launch killing all aboard. Many factors contributed to this disaster. One engineer tried to delay the launch. He believed the temperature had been too cold overnight. There was frost on the ground and on the shuttle earlier in the morning. The project managers were not convinced that the risk overshadowed the economic and public relations costs of delaying the launch.

Everything went on as planned and they launched the rocket. A few seconds later, the color of the flame changed. The main hydrogen tank had ruptured. The hydrogen was now fueling in the flame. This intense flame caused the strut to completely separate. The booster could now pivot freely. The aft dome of the hydrogen tank failed and dropped away. The remaining hydrogen was suddenly released producing a thrust that drove the remains of the hydrogen tank into the oxygen tank. At the same time the solid booster swung around and collided with the bottom of the oxygen tank rupturing it and releasing the contained gas. The explosion that followed was massive.

(A) My prediction about the outcome of our experiment is that the O-rings when frozen or cold will react different. I feel they won't stretch properly and may of caused this Challenger disaster.

Materials

Rubber bands (3)	String (1 ft)
Container (with ice)	Plastic cup
Paper clips	Ruler
Marbles (30)	

(E) Procedures

The materials above is what we used for our experiment. What we did was punch two holes on the side of the cup (opposite each side). Then we inserted a paper clip in each hole. We connected each paper clip on both side to make a handle. The third paper clip was taped on the top side of the container. We then attached the rubber band to the paper clip and tied the string around the rubber band. With the other end of the string we tied it to the paper clip that were on the cup. So now the cup is hanging from the container.

(B) We then proceeded to add five marbles to the cup at a time.. Each time we dropped five marbles into the cup we measured the length of the rubber band. We did this six times, because we had thirty marbles. We did the whole experiment three times to see if there was any difference any time. After this we averaged out measurements and got a precise average. We also calculated the % change in length since the rubber bands started at different lengths. **(F)**

(C) The next day we did the same exact experiment with one change. The plastic bowl this time didn't have ice. We did this to see if there was a difference in the measurements which would allow us to predict what went wrong on the Challenger.

(G) Then I graphed our length and % change in length data.

Standards sidebar:

S1 Physical Sciences Concepts

Life Sciences Concepts

Earth and Space Sciences Concepts

S4 Scientific Connections and Applications

S5 Scientific Thinking

S6 Scientific Tools and Technologies

S7 Scientific Communication

S8 Scientific Investigation

This work sample illustrates a standard-setting performance for the following parts of the standards:

S1b Physical Sciences Concepts: Structure and properties of matter.

S1d Physical Sciences Concepts: Motions and forces.

S4a Scientific Connections and Applications: Big ideas and unifying concepts.

S5a Scientific Thinking: Identify and control variables.

S5e Scientific Thinking: Identify problems.

S5f Scientific Thinking: Work individually and in teams.

S6c Scientific Tools and Technologies: Collect and analyze data.

S7a Scientific Communication: Represent data in multiple ways.

S7b Scientific Communication: Argue from evidence.

S7e Scientific Communication: Communicate in a form suited to the purpose and the audience.

S8a Scientific Investigation: Controlled experiment.

What the work shows

S1b Physical Sciences Concepts: The student produces evidence that demonstrates understanding of structure and properties of matter....

(A) The student states that "...O-Rings when frozen or cold will react different. I feel they won't stretch properly..." indicating an understanding of how environmental conditions may affect the physical properties of materials.

S1d Physical Sciences Concepts: The student produces evidence that demonstrates understanding of motion and forces,....

(B) The student designed an experiment in which increasing force was applied to the rubber band. The student measured the change in length resulting from the increase in applied force.

For related work on Force and Motion, see "Come Back Can", page 36, and "Mechanical Nut", page 86.

The quotations from the Science performance descriptions in this commentary are excerpted. The complete performance descriptions are shown on pages 122-143.

The Challenger Disaster

S4a Scientific Connections and Applications: The student produces evidence that demonstrates understanding of big ideas and unifying concepts, such as…cause and effect.

A The student links the temperature effects on rubber elasticity with the failure of the O-Rings to perform properly during the Challenger launch.

S5a Scientific Thinking: The student identifies and controls variables in experimental…research.

B The student altered the independent variable (marble mass) in a systematic manner and evaluated the dependent variable (rubber band length). "We then proceeded to add five marbles at a time. …we measured the stretch of the rubber band."

C "The next day, we did the exact experiment with one change. The plastic bowl this time didn't have ice." This clearly indicates understanding of the importance of altering only one condition at a time.

S5e Scientific Thinking: The student identifies problems…evaluates the accuracy, design, and outcomes of investigations.

D The student raises the duration of exposure to freezing temperatures as a possible variable, and suggests extending the exposure time to determine if this has a significant effect on elasticity.

S5f Scientific Thinking: The student works individually and in teams to collect and share information and ideas.

E The student indicates in the Procedure section that experiments were designed and performed as a team, but the data analysis, graphing and report writing were done individually.

S6c Scientific Tools and Technologies: The student collects and analyzes data….

F The student indicates that experiments were repeated three times, and the results averaged to obtain a more precise measurement.

G The student calculated a percent change in length to analyze the experimental results.

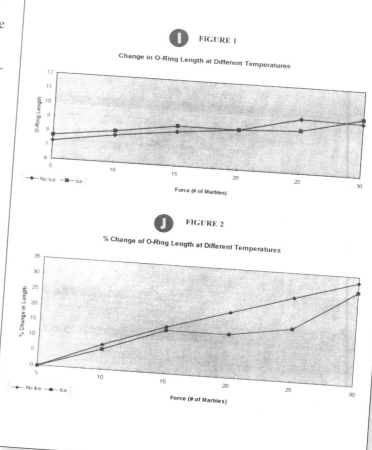

Discussion

L As you can see in our report and data charts there was a slight change in measurements between the experiment with the ice and the experiment without ice. The experiment with ice, the rubber band stretched less. So I'm figuring that on the space shuttle Challenger disaster, the O-rings might of stretched less than usual and might of caused this disaster.

D Another way to investigate this problem is leaving the rubberband over night over the bowl of ice. Since the Challenger in the morning was found frozen, so this could of happened in the night. In our experiment we didn't leave the rubber bands long enough on the ice to see if there's a real big difference. If we do this there might be a greater change in our measurements.

This project on the Challenger Disaster was a great learning experience and it was fun while I learned. The challenger disaster was a horrible accident that maybe can be avoided. I'm thankful my classmates and I can be helpful.

H TABLE 1. Rubber Band Stretch Without Ice

# of Marbles	First Test	Second Test	Third Test	Average	Percent Change
				7.3 cm	0%
5	7.2 cm	7.4 cm	7.4 cm	7.9	8
10	8.0	7.8	7.8	8.4	15
15	8.5	8.2	8.4	8.8	21
20	8.8	8.5	9.0	9.4	27
25	9.8	9.0	9.3	9.7	33
30	10.0	9.5	9.6		

TABLE 2. Rubber Band Stretch With Ice

# of Marbles	First Test	Second Test	Third Test	Average	Percent Change
				7.7 cm	0%
5	7.5 cm	7.5 cm	8.0 cm	8.2	6.5
10	8.5	8.0	8.0	8.8	14
15	9.0	9.0	8.5	8.8	14
20	9.0	9.0	9.0	9.0	17
25	9.0	9.0	10.0	10.0	30
30	10.5	9.5			

I FIGURE 1

Change in O-Ring Length at Different Temperatures

J FIGURE 2

% Change of O-Ring Length at Different Temperatures

The Challenger Disaster

S7a Scientific Communication: The student represents data and results in multiple ways, such as numbers, tables and graphs....

H The student presented the raw, averaged and percent change in length data in table forms.

I The student graphed the averaged data for the two experimental conditions (with and without ice).

J The student graphed the percent change in length data for the two experimental conditions.

K The student provided a drawing of the experimental setup to supplement her written description of the equipment used.

S7b Scientific Communication: The student argues from evidence....

L The student notes the change in elasticity as a result of cooling demonstrated by her data and argues that this is consistent with her hypothesis that the Challenger O-Rings were unable to perform properly on the day of the accident.

S7e Scientific Communication: The student demonstrates effective scientific communication, that is the student communicates in a form suited to the purpose and the audience....

The student work contains Introduction, Materials, Procedure, Results, and Discussion sections, typical of a formal scientific report. This is appropriate to the assigned task of reporting results to a Presidential Commission.

S8a Scientific Investigation: The student demonstrates scientific competence by completing a controlled experiment.

C The experiment described in this procedure is properly designed to evaluate the effect of temperature on elasticity. The same procedure was used for experiments at room and ice temperatures.

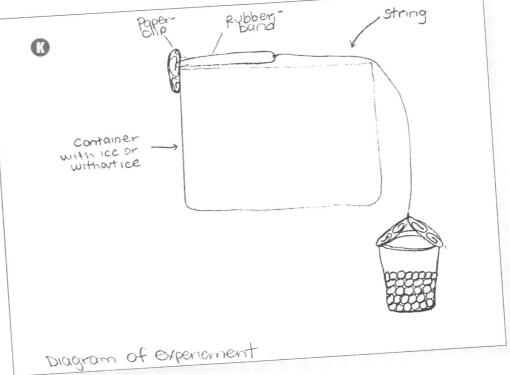

Diagram of experiment

S1 Physical Sciences Concepts

Life Sciences Concepts

Earth and Space Sciences Concepts

S4 Scientific Connections and Applications

S5 Scientific Thinking

S6 Scientific Tools and Technologies

S7 Scientific Communication

S8 Scientific Investigation

Work Sample & Commentary: *Buffer Lab*

The task

Students in a high school environmental science class were asked to compare an unbuffered solution with a buffered solution by using the technique of titration. This assignment was one of the lab activities in a unit on acid rain.

For related work on Acids and Bases, see "Acid/Base", page 40, and "Acid Rain", page 89.

Physical
Sciences
Concepts **S1**

Life
Sciences
Concepts

Earth and
Space Sciences
Concepts

Scientific
Connections and **S4**
Applications

Scientific **S5**
Thinking

Scientific Tools
and **S6**
Technologies

Scientific **S7**
Communication

Scientific
Investigation

The quotations from the Science performance descriptions in this commentary are excerpted. The complete performance descriptions are shown on pages 122-143.

Circumstances of performance

This sample of student work was produced under the following conditions:

alone	√ in a group
√ in class	√ as homework
with teacher feedback	with peer feedback
timed	opportunity for revision

What the work shows

S1c Physical Sciences Concepts: The student produces evidence that demonstrates understanding of chemical reactions, such as everyday examples of chemical reactions.

A B The student expresses understanding of the nature of chemical reactions in the concise explanations of the effects of buffers on [hydrogen] ion concentration.

C The student's explanation of why calcium carbonate is not a good buffer demonstrates an understanding of the role of ionic dissociation in a subsequent chemical reaction.

This work sample illustrates a standard-setting performance for the following parts of the standards:

S1b **Physical Sciences Concepts: Chemical reactions.**

S4a **Scientific Connections and Applications: Big ideas and unifying concepts.**

S4b **Scientific Connections and Applications: The designed world.**

S5a **Scientific Thinking: Frame questions to distinguish cause and effect; identify or control variables in experimental or non-experimental research settings.**

S5b **Scientific Thinking: Use concepts from Science Standards 1–4.**

S6a **Scientific Tools and Technologies: Use technologies and tools.**

S7a **Scientific Communication: Represent data and results in multiple ways.**

S7b **Scientific Communication: Use facts to support conclusions.**

L Buffer Lab

Data
pH titration with .02M Na_2HPO_4:

.1M HCl drops	pH
0	9.87
1	9.51
5	8.52
10	7.74
15	7.46
20	7.28
30	6.99
40	6.67
50	6.34
60	5.83
70	3.40
75	2.97
80	2.73
85	2.56
95	2.41
105	2.32
115	2.17
125	2.06

Formation of Phosphoric Acid

$$3H^+ + PO_4^{3-} \rightarrow H_3PO_4$$

pH titration with water (H_2O):

drops	pH
0	6.25
1	5.01
9	2.62
14	2.41
19	2.22
24	2.15
29	2.09
34	2.02

S4a Scientific Connections and Applications: The student produces evidence that demonstrates understanding of big ideas and unifying concepts, such as...cause and effect.

B The student explicitly states that increasing the proportion of Na_2HPO_4 (sodium hydrogen phosphate) in relation to the acid will result in the release of more ions.

Throughout the answer to question 1 and especially at **D**, the student expresses the results of the investigation as causal relationships.

E In the answer to question 2, the student clearly states the chemical cause behind the sudden change in the pH data.

Buffer Lab

S4 b Scientific Connections and Applications: The student produces evidence that demonstrates understanding of the designed world, such as the reasonableness of technological designs.

F Throughout the answer to question 6, the student logically and correctly identifies scientific limitations to the use of lime in neutralizing an acidic lake. The student's statements are actually conclusions based on the outcome of the investigation.

G At the end of the answer to question 6, the student describes a fundamental societal limitation—economic—on large-scale use of lime to neutralize an acidic lake.

S5 a Scientific Thinking: The student…identifies variables in experimental and non-experimental research settings.

B The student correctly identifies the proportion of Na_2HPO_4 as the variable that determines its capacity to absorb acid.

H The student correctly identifies the addition of lime as a variable that will increase pH, and states that the addition of other acids—another variable—will lower the pH.

I The student notes the simultaneous effects of two variables in this statement.

S5 b Scientific Thinking: The student uses concepts from Science Standards 1 to 4 to explain a variety of observations and phenomena.

J The student uses understanding of **S1** c, specifically ionization and buffering, to explain the phenomena observed.

K The student applies understanding of **S1** c to a new situation in the suggestion that biological ("organic") inhabitants of a lake may excrete basic substances, and that introduction of such species into a damaged lake might provide natural buffering.

S6 a Scientific Tools and Technologies: The student uses technology and tools…to observe and measure…with appropriate consideration of accuracy and precision.

L The student's collection of data demonstrates competence in using lab equipment (pH meter and equipment for titration) and the ability to observe and accurately measure phenomena. The student demonstrated appropriate consideration of accuracy and precision by recording consistent significant figures.

Lab Questions:

1. The graph for the titration of sodium phosphate has four areas made up of two key features. As labeled on the graph, section ① is decreasing. This shows that the buffer is working on the ions to buffer them. Section ② is level and is the optimum buffering range for this buffer. Section ③ is a steep decrease because the buffer can no longer support that amount of drops of acid. Finally, section ④ is level which shows that the buffer is working again.

② The reason that the curve drops off sharply below pH 6 is because the buffer is designed to keep the pH constant at a pH of @7. When the limit on the buffer (#of drops) is reached, it can no longer maintain the constant, and it plummets.

③ The curve for sodium phosphate and that for water are very different. The water appears to not be a decent buffer at all unless you want a pH of 1. The sodium phospate on the other hand has a gradual decent interspersed with areas of obvious buffering.

④ To increase the capacity of our sodium phosphate solution to absorb acid simply increase the proportion of Na_2HPO_4 to acid. This will make available more ions to be released to react with and bond with the acids.

Buffer Lab

5. Since the calcium carbonate doesn't dissolve in water, its ions cannot dissociate in order to bond with acids. Therefore it is a poor buffer that will probably have little to no effect on the solution.

6. There are several problems with using lime to neutralize an acid lake. First, the pH adjustment of a lake is a very delicate matter. The addition of lime will cause a large jump in the pH that will need to be lowered by the adding of other acids. Also, lime is a chalky, thick substance that will cloud the lake and possibly block out the sunlight. Finally, lime is very expensive to have to keep using to fix a lake.

7. With some investigation, one may find the existence of certain organic inhabitants of lake environments to live in the lake and excrete basic substances. It could be a bird who's droppings are basic, or a plant that will add basicity when it decomposes, or even a bacteria. If one could be found and introduced, the problem could be solved naturally.

8. The contents of commercial preparations used to increase the pH of fish tanks would have to consist of both bases and buffers. The bases would work on increasing pH, and the buffers would hold it at a constant level. If the pH changes too rapidly, all the fish in your tank will die.

Buffer Lab

S7 a Scientific Communication: The student represents data in multiple ways, such as tables and graphs…and selects the most effective way to convey the scientific information.

L M The student's data are expressed in both table and graph forms. The graph organizes data from the table so that a viewer can instantly compare the buffering abilities of sodium phosphate and water.

S7 b Scientific Tools and Technologies: The student uses technology and tools…to observe and measure…with appropriate consideration of accuracy and precision.

J The answer to question #3 indicates the student's ability to argue from evidence. The decision that water is not a good buffer is based on data produced through experimentation.

Spelling errors present in this work do not detract from the quality of the science.

Following are the lab questions answered by the student:

1. Examine your graph for the titration of sodium phosphate. Explain the shape of the three parts of the curve.

2. Explain why below pH 6 the curve drops off sharply.

3. Compare the titration curves obtained for water and for sodium phosphate. Explain the difference.

4. How could we increase the capacity of our sodium phosphate solution to absorb acid?

5. Calcium carbonate is not particularly soluble in water (very little of it will dissolve in water). What problem does this present.

6. "Lime" is actually calcium hydroxide [$Ca(OH)_2$]. Why is trying to neutralize an acidic lake using lime not a good idea?

7. Give a better strategy for neutralizing the waters of an acidic lake.

8. Predict the contents of commercial preparations used to increase the pH of fish tanks. Why is the method of increasing pH in the fish tank critical?

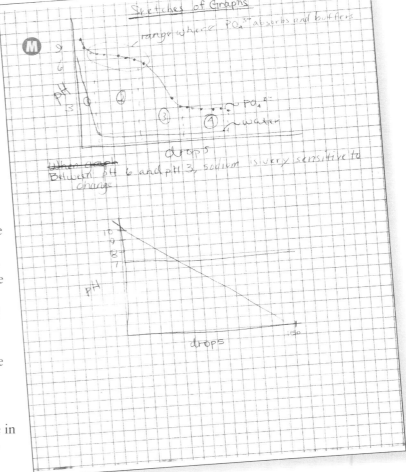

Work Sample & Commentary: *Heating Curve of a Substance*

The task

Students were asked to conduct a simple experiment in which they recorded temperature changes that accompany the melting and boiling of a pure substance. This assignment was given to students in a Science Research class.

Circumstances of performance

This sample of student work was produced under the following conditions:

√ alone

√ in class

   with teacher feedback

√ timed

√ in a group

√ as homework

   with peer feedback

   opportunity for revision

What the work shows

S1 b Physical Sciences Concepts: The student produces evidence that demonstrates understanding of structure and properties of matter, such as...characteristics of phase changes.

A The student describes the observed process in terms of phase change characteristics.

B C The student describes changes in temperature in terms of molecular interactions.

D The student's hypothesis clearly relates phase change and energy.

Sample 1

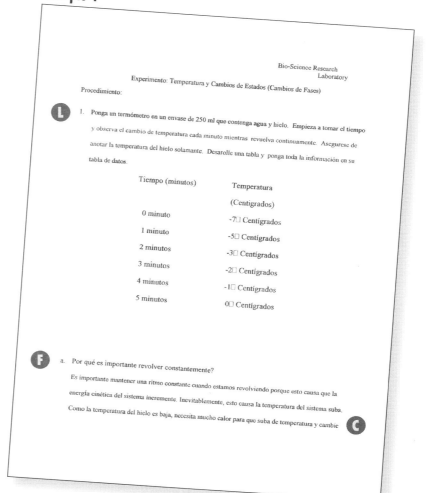

This work sample illustrates a standard-setting performance for the following parts of the standards:

S1 b **Physical Sciences Concepts: Structure and properties of matter.**

S1 e **Physical Sciences Concepts: Conservation of energy and increase in disorder.**

S4 a **Scientific Connections and Applications: Big ideas and unifying concepts.**

S5 b **Scientific Thinking: Use concepts from Science Standards 1–4.**

S6 a **Scientific Tools and Technologies: Use technologies and tools.**

S6 e **Scientific Tools and Technology: Recognize and limit sources of bias in data.**

S7 a **Scientific Communication: Represent data and results in multiple ways.**

S1 e Physical Sciences Concepts: The student produces evidence that demonstrates understanding of conservation of energy and increase in disorder, such as kinetic and potential energy...and effects of heat and pressure.

A F The student describes how a transfer of energy causes a phase change.

D The student describes the effects of heat in relative terms.

E The student demonstrates understanding of the relationship between kinetic energy, heat, and temperature.

S4 a Scientific Connections and Applications: The student produces evidence that demonstrates understanding of big ideas and unifying concepts, such as...cause and effect.

C G H The student demonstrates understanding of cause and effect relationships between change of temperature and change in state of matter.

The quotations from the Science performance descriptions in this commentary are excerpted. The complete performance descriptions are shown on pages 122-143.

S1 Physical Sciences Concepts

Life Sciences Concepts

Earth and Space Sciences Concepts

S4 Scientific Connections and Applications

S5 Scientific Thinking

S6 Scientific Tools and Technologies

S7 Scientific Communication

Scientific Investigation

Heating Curve of a Substance

Sample 1

S5 b Scientific Thinking: The student uses concepts from Science Standards 1 to 4 to explain a variety of observations and phenomena.

I The student uses the concept of phase change to explain constant temperature during the observation.

J The student compares the liquid and gaseous phases of water in terms of relative molecular organization and motion.

S6 a Scientific Tools and Technology: The student uses technology and tools (such as traditional laboratory equipment...) to observe and measure...phenomena, directly...with appropriate considerations of accuracy and precision.

K **L** **M** The student uses various pieces of laboratory equipment to observe and measure the effects of heat.

S6 e Scientific Tools and Technology: The student recognizes and limits sources of bias in data, such as observer and sample biases.

N The student indicates that calibration of the thermometer is needed in order to get an accurate temperature reading.

S7 a Scientific Communication: The student represents data and results in multiple ways, such as numbers, tables and graphs; [and] technical...writing; and selects the most effective way to convey the scientific information.

A **B** **D** **F** **G** **H** These items and others indicate the student's ability to convey information through technical writing. It should be noted that errors in Sample 1 should be corrected in a revision. In item 2a, for example "liquid to gas" should be corrected to "solid to liquid." In item 4a, the water molecules are most definitely in motion at 100 degrees Celsius. The student's logic is correct in 4a, but the statement regarding molecular motion indicates a misconception that needs to be corrected.

M **O** The student records data in tables.

P **Q** The student uses a graph to represent the data recorded in the tables.

I

...de estado. La temperatura de un hielo completamente sólido es de zero grados centígrados. Como las moléculas del hielo están tan juntas y sin casi moverse, se necesita más energía para que la temperatura cambie. La transferencia de energía a una temperatura constante de zero grados centígrados significa que el cubo de hielo esta pasando por un cambio de fase. Despues que el hielo se haya derretido completamente su temperatura comienza a subir.

2. Continua observando y anota la temperatura en intervalos de un minuto por cinco minutos.

Tiempo (minutos)	Temperatura (Centígrados)
0 minuto	0 Centígrados
1 minuto	0 Centígrados
2 minutos	1 Centígrados
3 minutos	3 Centígrados
4 minutos	5 Centígrados
5 minutos	6 Centígrados

a. Describe los cambios de estado (fases) que ocurrieron.

Durante la temperatura constante de zero grados centígrados el cubo de hielo pasó por cambio de fase. La substancia cambió de sólido a líquido. Despues que ha cambiado completamente de líquido a gas, la temperatura comenzó a subir a un grado centígrado. La energía cinética aumenta la temperatura haciendo que el hielo pasara por los cambios de fases.

M

3. Ponga un envase en una hornilla y continue observando y anotando cada minuto.

Tiempo (minutos)	Temperatura (Centígrados)
0 minuto	8 Centígrados
1 minuto	14 Centígrados
2 minutos	31 Centígrados
3 minutos	52 Centígrados
4 minutos	71 Centígrados
5 minutos	82 Centígrados
6 minutos	90 Centígrados
7 minutos	94 Centígrados
8 minutos	96 Centígrados

4. Continue midiendo la temperatura cada minuto hasta que comienze a hervir vigurosamente.

Tiempo (minutos)	Temperatura (Centígrados)
0 minuto	100 Centígrados
1 minuto	100 Centígrados
2 minutos	100 Centígrados
3 minutos	100 Centígrados
4 minutos	102 Centígrados
5 minutos	1 03 Centígrados

Heating Curve of a Substance

Sample 1

6 minutos   104□ Centigrados

a.   Describe los cambios de estado (fases) que ocurrieron.

Durante la temperatura constante de cien grados centigrados la substancia paso por un cambio de

fase. Esto es evidencia de energia potencial porque las moléculas no estan en movimiento. Despues

de haber cambiado completemente a liquido la temperatura commenzo a subir 101 grados

centigrados. Durante el incremento la energia es cinética.

5.   Haz una gráfica usando la información de las tablas.

a.   De acuerdo con la curva de calor, cual es el punto de fusion del hielo?

De acuerdo con la curva de calor que yo marqué, el punto de fusión del hielo es zero grados

centigrados.

b.   Que patrones observaste en la gr"afica?
El orden que yo observé en la curva de calor es que cuando el sólido está cambiando a
liquido la temperatura se conserva constante a cero grados centigrados.Despues de que el hielo
ha cambiado completamente a liquido la temperatura subió. Durante el cambio de fase la
temperatura permanese constante. Después que todo el liquido se ha convertido a gas la temperatura
subió.

c.   Como justificas la forma de la curva de calor?
La forma de la curva de calor es causada por el cambio de temperatura y fase.

d.   Como ha afectado el tiempo cada seccion de tu gráfica?
El tiempo ha afectado la curva de calor porque en algunas secciones tomo más tiempo
para cambiar de fase. En la curva de calor tomó más tiempo que la gráfica cambiará a de
liquido a gas que cambiará a sólido a líquido. Tomó más tiempo porque toma más cantidad
de energia de calor para cambiar de liquido a gas.

CONCLUSIONES.

1.   Si fueras a replicar este experimento con alcohol en vez de agua , que cambios sucederian?

Si este experimento se duplicara pero en vez de agua fuera hecho con alcohol el punto de
fusión y el punto de congelación seria diferente. El alcohol necesita menos energia de calor
para evaporarse y derritirse.

2.   Basandote en tus resulatdos de la curva de calor del agua, disena un experimento que justifique tu
hipotesis

Comience el experimento colocando el termómetro en un emvase de 250mL que debe contener
un cubo de alcohol. Observe y apunte cada cambio de temperatura al mismo tiempo que esta
revolviendo la substancia. Asegurase de mantener un ritmo constante cuando esta revolviendo el
alcohol. Revolviendo el alcohol incrementa la temperatura del sistema y hace que el sistema cambie
de fase más rápido. Acuerdese de apuntar la temperatura del cubo de alcohol solamente. Desarrolle
una tabla de información y apunte el tiempo y la temperatura del alcohol hasta que el alcohol liege el
punto de fusión que es-117 grados centigrados. Continue observando y apuntando la temperatura por
cinco minutos. Ponga el emvase en un plato caliente y continue observando y apuntando hasta que el
alcohol llege a su punto de ebullición, que es 79 grados centigrados. Despues continue a observar la
temperatura hasta que el sistema hierva vigorosamente. Cuando acaba el experimento, tome toda la
informacion y muestrela gráficamente.

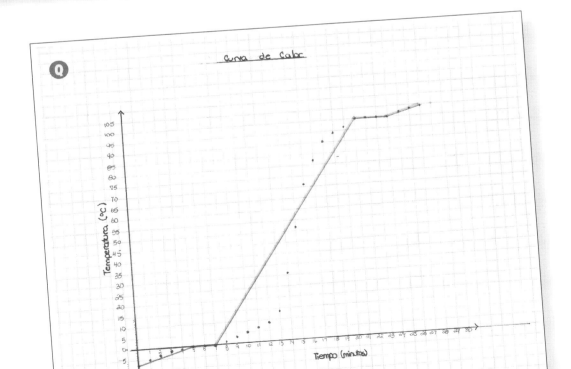

Heating Curve of a Substance

Sample 1 translation

Bio-Science Research
Laboratory

Experiment: Temperature and Change State (Phase Change)

Procedure: Answers

L   1.   Place a thermometer into a 250mL beaker containing ice and water. Start timing and observing temperature change each minute while stirring continuously. Be sure to record the temperature of the ICE only. Develop a chart, and then record the time and temperature on a data table.

Time (minutes)	Temperature (Celsius)
0 min.	-7° Celsius
1 min.	-5° Celsius
2 min.	-3° Celsius
3 min.	-2° Celsius
4 min.	-1° Celsius
5 min.	0° Celsius

F   a.   Why is it important to maintain a fairly constant rate of stirring?

It is important to keep a constant rate of stirring because this causes the Kinetic energy of the system to increase. Inevitability, this causes the temperature of the system to rise. Since the temperature of the ice is very low it needs a lot of heat and a rise in temperature to change in state. The temperature of a completely solid ice is always below zero degrees. Since the molecules of the ice are so tight   **C**

I   together more energy is needed to melt the ice. More kinetic energy is needed and that is why the temperature changes.   The transfer of energy and constant zero temperatures means that the block of ice is undergoing a phase change. After the entire ice has melted completely, its temperature begins to rise.

2.   Continue to observe and record the temperature at one-minute intervals for five minutes.

Time (min.)	Temperature (Celsius)
0 min.	0° Celsius
1 min.	0° Celsius
2 min.	1° Celsius
3 min.	3° Celsius
4 min.	5° Celsius
5 min.	6° Celsius

a.   Describe the changes of state (phase change) that occurs.

During the constant temperature of 0 degrees Celsius the solid underwent a phase change. The substance changed from a solid to a liquid.   After it had completely changed from liquid to gas, the temperature began to rise 1 degree Celsius.   The kinetic energy increases the temperature making the ice go through changes of phases.

M

3.   Place the beaker on a hot plate and continue to observe and record at one-minute intervals.

Time (min.)	Temperature (Celsius)
0 min.	8° Celsius
1 min.	14° Celsius
2 min.	31° Celsius
3 min.	52° Celsius
4 min.	71° Celsius
5 min.	82° Celsius
6 min.	90° Celsius
7 min.	94° Celsius
8 min.	96° Celsius

4.   Continue to measure the temperature each minute until vigorous boiling occurs.

Time (min.)	Temperature (Celsius)
0 min.	100° Celsius
1 min.	100° Celsius
2 min.	100° Celsius
3 min.	100° Celsius
4 min.	102° Celsius
5 min.	1 03° Celsius
6 min.	104° Celsius

Physical Sciences Concepts **S1**

Life Sciences Concepts

Earth and Space Sciences Concepts

Scientific Connections and Applications **S4**

Scientific Thinking **S5**

Scientific Tools and Technologies **S6**

Scientific Communication **S7**

Scientific Investigation

Heating Curve of a Substance

Sample 1 translation

a. Describe the changes of state (phase change) that occurs.

During the constant temperature of 100 degrees Celsius the liquid underwent a phase change. This is evidence of potential energy because the molecules are not in movement. After it had completely changed from liquid to gas, the temperature began to rise to 101 degrees Celsius. During the increase the energy is kinetic.

5. Graph the heating curve of water from the data table.

a. According to the heating curve you plotted, what is the melting point of the ice?

According to the heating curve I've plotted, the melting point of the ice is 0 degrees Celsius.

b. What patterns do you observe with your heating curve graph?

The pattern that I observe in my heating curve graph is that when the ice is changing into liquid the temperature of the liquid increased. During the phase change the temperature remains constant. After the liquid has converted to a gas the temperature begins to rise again.

c. How do you account for the shape of the heating curve?

The shape of the heating curve is accounted by the fact the there is a change in temperature and phase.

G d. How has time affected each section on your graph?

Time has affected each section of my heating curve graph because in some sections of the heating curve it took longer time to change phase. In the heating curve graph it took a longer time for the graph to change from liquid to gas than it took to change from solid to liquid. It took longer because it takes a greater amount of heat energy to change from liquid to gas.

CONCLUSIONS:

1 If you were to replicate this experiment with alcohol in place of water, what changes you happen?

HYPOTHESIS:

If this experiment were to be replicated but instead of water the experiment was done with alcohol the melting point and freezing point the experiment would be different. Also

D alcohol requires less heat energy to melt and evaporate than water..

2. Based on your data and results from Heating Curve of Water, design an experiment that will justify your hypothesis.

Place a thermometer into a 250ml beaker containing a solid block of alcohol. Start timing and observing temperature and speed up the phase changes. Be sure to record the temperature of the block of alcohol only. Develop a chart, and then record the temperature on a data table for the alcohol until the alcohol reaches it melting point of –117 degrees Celsius. Continue to observe and record the temperature at one-minute intervals for five minutes. Place the beaker on a hot plate and continue to observe and record at one- minute intervals until the alcohol reaches its boiling point of 79 degrees Celsius. Then continue to measure the temperature each minute until vigorous boiling occurs. After the experiment is completed graph the heating curve for alcohol.

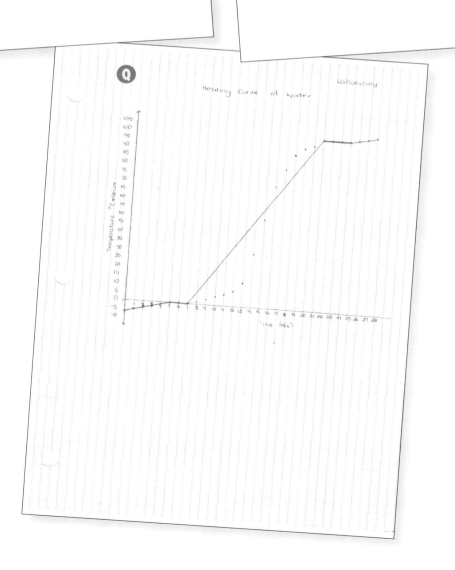

S1 Physical Sciences Concepts

Life Sciences Concepts

Earth and Space Sciences Concepts

S4 Scientific Connections and Applications

S5 Scientific Thinking

S6 Scientific Tools and Technologies

S7 Scientific Communication

Scientific Investigation

Heating Curve of a Substance

Sample 2

O

Температура в каждую минуту
1) 0°C
2) 1°C
3) 0°C   таяние
4) 1°C
5) 0°C
6) 0,5°C
7) 0°C

Температура на горячей поверхности
1) 8°C
2) 10,5°C
3) 18°C
4) 31°C
5) 46°C   жидкость
6) 56°C
7) 70°C
8) 80°C
9) 90°C
10) 101°C

Температура испарения
1) 102°C
2) 102°C   кипение
3) 102°C   жидкость и газ
4) 102°C

Вопрос: Почему температура остается постоянной?
Ответ: Потому что пока весь лёд не растает температура остается на уровне нуля.
Вопрос: Почему весь лёд одно-

H временно не превращается в воду во время таяния?
Ответ: Этого не происходит потому что требуется дополнительная энергия для завершения процесса.
Вопрос: Энергия поглощается или выделяется?
Ответ: Энергия поглощается льдом.
Вопрос: Это процесс экзо или эндотермический?
Ответ: Процесс этот эндотермический потому что происходит поглощение энергии.
Вопрос: Почему необходимо тепло для продолжения процесса?
Ответ: Тепло необходимо для продолжения процесса в целях полностью расстопить лёд и довести воду до кипения.

A Вопрос: Почему температура оставалась постоянной во время процесса таяния, но за тем повысилась когда весь лёд превратился в жидкость?

E Ответ: Это происходит потому что достигнув жидкой стадии лёд не находился более в точке замерзания. Он перешел в состояние жидкости. Повышая температуру мы увеличивали кинетическое движение что приводило

к повышению температуры жидкости.
Вопрос: Сравните молекулярные силы льда и воды.

B Ответ: Молекулы льда (замерзшей воды) плотно прилегают друг к другу и почти не двигаются. В молекулах "жидкой" воды больше расстояние между собой что приводит к большей возможности движения, т.е к увеличению кинетической энергии.

Вопрос: Сравните молекулярные силы в жидкости и газах.

J Ответ: В сравнении с водой в парах жидкости между молекулами большое расстояние, что позволяет им свободно двигаться в разных направлениях.

— Объяснение допущенной ошибки-
Причина того что темпе-
ратура кипения в данном
опыте зафиксирована °C, а замер-

N зание °C была в неточности

K показаний моего термометра. Я это обнаружила путем сравнения температур кипения воды в колбе моим термометром—102°C А моего соседа в той же колбе—100°C!

P

Точка кипения
стадия кипения
Увеличение потенциальной энергии

Температура в градусах °C

Точка таяния
Стадия замерзания
Увеличение потенциальной энергии

Время в минутах

Heating Curve of a Substance

Sample 2 translation

O

Temp every one minute
1) 0°C
2) 1°C
3) 0°C } melting
4) 1°C
5) .5°C
6) 0°C

Temp on hot plate
1) 8°C
2) 10.5°C
3) 18°C
4) 31°C
5) 46°C } Liquid
6) 56°C
7) 70°C
8) 80°C
9) 90°C
10) 101°C

Vapor Temp =
1) 102°C
2) 102°C } Boiling
3) 102°C } Liquid & Gas
4) 102°C

Q. Why does the temperature remain constant?
A: The temperature remains constant because until the ice completely melts it's al it's freezing point
Q: Why doesn't all of the ice change instantaneously during the melting process?
It doesn't change instantaneously because

H you have to keep adding energy in order for the ice to melt.
Q: Is energy absorbed or released?
A: Energy is absorbed by the ice.
Q: Is this an endothermic or exothermic process?
A: This process is endothermic because energy is absorbed.
Q: Why was heat needed for the continuation of the process.
A: Heat was needed to continue the process because in order for ice to completely melt and water to reach it's boiling point you needed more energy than just stirring the ice.
Q: Why did the temperature remain constant during melting, but increases when all ice has changed to liquid water?

A A: This occured because as all the ice melted it was no longer at the freezing point. It was at the liquid phase, thus trying to reach the boiling

E point. So an increase in heat = an increase in kenetic energy = increase in temperature.
Q: Compare intermolecular forces of solid and liquid water.

B A: The molecules in solid water are tightly packed, and barely moving. The molecules in a liquid are less tightly packed and have a rolling motion (increase in KE) liquid water and gaseous water
Q. ...

J A: Compared to liquid water gaseous water molecules are the least tightly packed and move in different direction.

- Explanation for error-
The reason that my boiling point is 102°C and my freezing point is

N

K 1°C is because the thermometer was off. The way I found this out is by placing my thermometer into by partner's beaker. While his thermometer read 100°C (boiling point) my thermometer still read 102°C!

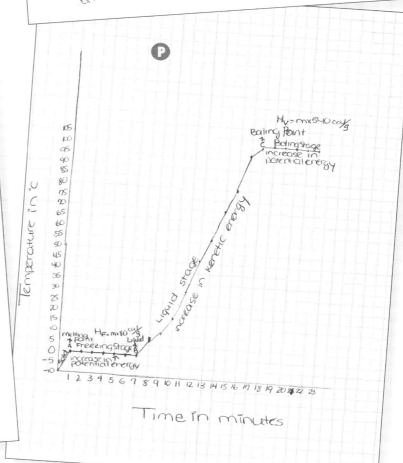

Hᵥ = m×540 cal/g
Boiling Point
Boiling Stage
increase in potential energy

Liquid stage
increase in kenetic energy

Melting Point   Hₑ = m×80 cal/g
Freezing Stage   Liquid
increase in potential energy

Temperature in °C

Time in minutes

Work Sample & Commentary: *Exothermic/Endothermic Reactions*

The task

This experiment was a modification of an experiment in the text *Chemistry: Visualizing Matter* (Holt, Rhinehart & Winston). In this activity, students were asked to design an experiment to prove whether a worker's claim that he was burned by a mixture two cleaning fluids was true. This assignment was given to a Regents chemistry class.

The quotations from the Science performance descriptions in this commentary are excerpted. The complete performance descriptions are shown on pages 122-143.

Circumstances of performance

This sample of student work was produced under the following conditions:

√ alone √ in a group

√ in class √ as homework

√ with teacher feedback with peer feedback

√ timed √ opportunity for revision

What the work shows

S1c Physical Sciences Concepts: The student produces evidence that demonstrates an understanding of chemical reactions such as every day examples of chemical reactions….

A In the statement of purpose the student states that the reaction between sodium hydroxide(NaOH) and hydrochloric acid(HCl) involved heat change.

B This understanding is also expressed in the hypothesis, which states that the mixture will produce sufficient heat to cause a burn.

Chemistry
1/20/99

The purpose of this experiment is to determine the heat of the reaction between Hydrochloric Acid, and Sodium Hydroxide.

A I will also determine the maximum temperature attained by mixing the two substances, and use the information to answer the main question: Does the mixture produce a sufficient amount of heat to cause a burn?

B Hypothesis:
The mixture will produce sufficient heat to cause a burn. When some chemicals are mixed they are more dangerous because, they release large amounts of heat.

C Related Background Information:
- All chemical changes involve energy. The energy change that takes place during a chemical change, generally are more noticeable than those taking place during a physical change.
- In some chemical reactions the products have less potential energy than the reactants. This occurs because, as the reactions proceeds the potential energy of the reaction decreases. This decrease occurs because some of the potential energy is converted (changed) to heat energy. This release of heat energy causes the substances to become hot.
- Chemical reactions that release heat energy are called exothermic. The reverse of this process would be an endothermic reaction.

Page 1

This work sample illustrates a standard-setting performance for the following parts of the standards:

S1c **Physical Sciences Concepts: Chemical reactions.**

S4a **Scientific Connections and Applications: Big ideas and unifying concepts.**

S5a **Scientific Thinking: Frame questions to distinguish cause and effect; identify and control variables.**

S5b **Scientific Thinking: Use concepts from Science Standards 1 to 4.**

S6a **Scientific Tools and Technologies: Use technology and tools.**

S7a **Scientific Communication: Represent data and results in multiple ways.**

S4a Scientific Connections and Applications: The student produces evidence that demonstrates understanding of big ideas and unifying concepts, such as…cause and effect.

C The question clearly indicates that the student is looking for a cause and effect relationship.

D The student determined that the mixture could cause a burn because of the heat generated during the reaction.

E The student states that the concentration of sodium hydroxide remaining unreacted was too small to cause a chemical burn.

Exothermic/Endothermic Reactions

S5a Scientific Thinking: The student frames questions to distinguish cause and effect; and identifies and controls variables in experimental and non-experimental research settings.

C The student frames the question appropriately.

F A review of the formulae in the "Analysis and Interpretation of Results" makes it very clear that the student identified and controlled variables, both in the experiment itself and in the follow-up analysis.

S5b Scientific Thinking: The student uses concepts from Science Standards 1 to 4 to explain a variety of observations and phenomena.

F Throughout the "Analysis and Interpretation of Results" the student uses physical science concepts from **S1c** expressed as formulae.

G The student expresses concepts from **S1c** in the "Related Background Information" section, and used them to develop the hypothesis.

S6a Scientific Tools and Technologies: The student uses technology and tools (such as traditional laboratory equipment…) to observe and measure objects…and phenomena, directly, indirectly, and remotely, with appropriate consideration of accuracy and precision.

H **I** The materials list and the "Experimental Procedure" section make it clear that the student used a graduated cylinder, a calorimeter, and a Celsius thermometer.

S7a Scientific Communication: The student represents data and results in multiple ways, such as numbers [and] tables…and selects the most effective way to convey scientific information.

F Throughout the "Analysis and Interpretation of Results" section, the student conveys scientific information through the use of formulae.

J **K** The student records data in a table format.

Methods & Data Procedure

H Materials:
2 grams of sodium hydroxide pellets
0.50 M of hydrochloric acid (100mL)
graduated cylinder
calorimeter
Celsius thermometer
stirring rod
gloves
goggles
spatula
watch glass

I Experimental Procedure:

Step 1 - I measured 100 mL or 0.50 M of HCl in a graduated cylinder. I poured the HCl in a Styrofoam cup in the calorimeter. Next, I recorded the temperature of the HCl solution to the nearest 0.1 °C

Step 2 - I measured the mass of a small dry beaker, and recorded it in my data table. Then I placed the pellets of sodium hydroxide in the beaker, and measured the mass of the sodium hydroxide (this was done quickly to prevent the absorption of moisture by the pellets).

Step 3 - I added the sodium hydroxide to the hydrochloric acid in the Styrofoam cup. I stirred the mixture and covered the lid of the calorimeter. Next, I measured, and recorded the highest temperature in the data table.

J Results:

Data Table 1

Initial temperature of HCl	Final Temperature of HCl	Temperature Change
20 °C	32°C	12°C

Page 2

K

Data Table 2

Mass of empty beaker	22.5 grams
Mass of beaker & NaOH	24.5 grams
Mass of NaOH	2.0 grams

F Analysis and Interpretation of Results:

1- Equation in the reaction:

$$HCl_{(aq)} + NaOH_{(s)} --- NaCl_{(aq)} + H_2O_{(l)}$$

2- Calculations:

Objective 1- To determine the heat released by the reaction, by using the Formula.

$$Heat = m \times \Delta t \times C_{p,H2O}$$

m = mass of water
Δt = temperature change
$C_{P,H2O}$ = specific heat capacity of H_2O

Δt = 12 °C
$C_{P,H2O}$ = 4.180 J/g °C
m = 100 grams

$$Heat = 100g \times 12°C \times 4.180 \frac{J}{g.°C}$$

= 5021 Joules
= 5.021 K. Joules

Objective 2 - To calculate the number of moles of NaOH in the solution used in the reaction.

Page 3

S1 Physical Sciences Concepts

Life Sciences Concepts

Earth and Space Sciences Concepts

S4 Scientific Connections and Applications

S5 Scientific Thinking

S6 Scientific Tools and Technologies

S7 Scientific Communication

Scientific Investigation

Exothermic/Endothermic Reactions

Page 4:

$$40 \text{ grams of NaOH} = 1 \text{ mole of NaOH}$$

$$2.0 \text{ grams of NaOH} = 1 \text{ mole of NaOH} \times \frac{2 \text{ grams of NaOH}}{40 \text{ grams of NaOH}}$$

$$= 0.05 \text{ mole of NaOH}$$
$$= 5 \times 10^{-2} \text{ mole NaOH}$$

Objective 3- To determine the amount of heat produced by the 1 mole of NaOH:

Since 5.0×10^{-2} moles of NaOH produced 5.02 KJ

$$1 \text{ mole Of NaOH produced } \frac{-5.02 \text{ KJ}}{5.0 \times 10^{-2} \text{ mole of NaOH}} \times 1 \text{ mole of NaOH}$$

$$= -101 \text{ KJ/mole}$$

* Since the reaction is exothermic, the change in energy has a negative sign.

1- <u>What I know about the drain cleaner</u>.

(A) The labeled drain cleaner was estimated to contain 55 grams of NaOH in the drain cleaner, and 450 mL of solution containing a total of 1.35 moles of HCl.

<u>What I know about burns</u>.

(A) Third degree burns can occur if the skin comes in contact for more than 4 seconds with water that is hotter than 60 °C (140 °F).

Page 4

Page 5:

3- <u>What I want to know</u>.

C (A) Could the mixture of NaOH and HCl produce enough heat to cause burns?

To answer this question, I need to find out how much heat was released when 55 grams of NaOH react with HCl.

Number of moles of NaOH in the cleaner
$$= 55 \text{ grams} \times \frac{1 \text{ mole of NaOH}}{40 \text{ grams of NaOH}}$$
$$= 1.375 \text{ moles of NaOH in the mixture.}$$

Amount of heat produced when 1.375 moles react with HCl:
$$\Delta H = 1.375 \text{ moles} \times \frac{101 \text{ KJ}}{1 \text{ mole of NaOH}}$$
$$= 139 \text{ KJ.}$$

Next I need to find out the temperature change resulting from the reaction. By using the formula:

$$\text{Heat} = \text{mass of water} \times \Delta t_{H2O} \times C_{P, H2O}$$

$$\Delta t_{H2O} = \frac{139\,000 \text{ Joules}}{450 \text{ grams of } H_2O} \times \frac{1 \text{ g} °C}{4.184 \text{ Joules}}$$

$$\Delta t_{H2O} = 73.8 °C$$

Final temperature of the mixture $= 25 °C + 74 °C$
$$= 99 °C$$

Page 5

Page 6:

3- <u>What I learned</u>.

D (A) The mixture was likely to cause a burn because 99 °C is much higher than 60 °C, which is the temperature at which a third degree burn is likely to occur.

E (B) The burn was not likely to be caused by direct contact with the chemical, since 1.35 moles of the HCl solution was neutralized by the 1.35 moles of the NaOH solution. Only 0.025 moles of NaOH remained unreacted, an amount too small in concentration to cause a chemical burn.

(C) Chemicals can be harmful if their special storage needs are ignored.

(D) Glass is heat sensitive, and will shatter if there is a sudden change in temperature, due to a chemical reaction.

<u>Discussion</u>:

Sources of Error:

(A) The metal stirring rod could have caused an increase in the heat of the reaction. A glass stirring rod would have been better.

(B) Some of the NaOH pellets started to absorb moisture before I added them to the HCl.

(C) Heat could have been lost during the time of adding the $NaOH_{(s)}$ to the $HCl_{(aq)}$.

(D) The drain cleaner was in liquid form but in our last experiment we used the actual NaOH pellets.

Page 6

Work Sample & Commentary: *Density of Sand*

The task

Sample 1 was an entry in a Golden State Examination Science Portfolio for the category "problem solving investigation." Students were required to submit a piece of work and the "Self-Reflection Sheet." In this case, the student designed and conducted an investigation to determine the density of sand. Sample 2 was done in class as a regular lab.

Circumstances of performance

This sample of student work was produced under the following conditions:

alone	√ in a group
√ in class	as homework
√ with teacher feedback	√ with peer feedback
timed	√ opportunity for revision

The work was done with a partner and written up individually.

What the work shows

S1 b Physical Sciences Concepts: The student produces evidence that demonstrates understanding of the structure and properties of matter....

A B C Throughout the work, the student explained the relationship between mass, volume, and density, often with a level of detail revealing excellent conceptual understanding. There is also ample evidence that the student appreciated the relevance of density in everyday situations.

This work sample illustrates a standard-setting performance for the following parts of the standards:

S1 b Physical Sciences Concepts: Structure and properties of matter.

S5 a Scientific Thinking: Frame questions to distinguish cause and effect; and identify or control variables.

S5 e Scientific Thinking: Evaluate the accuracy, design, and outcomes of investigations.

S5 f Scientific Thinking: Work individually and in teams.

S6 a Scientific Tools and Technologies: Use technology and tools.

S7 e Scientific Communication: Write instructions that others can follow.

Sample 1

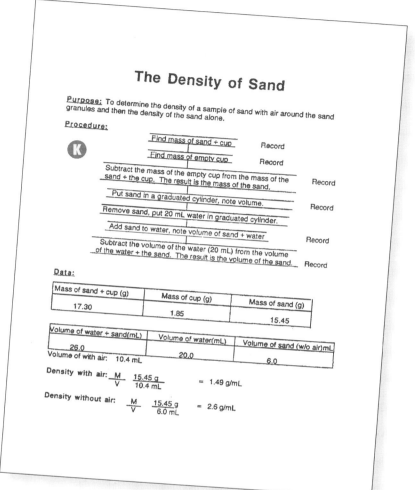

The Density of Sand

Purpose: To determine the density of a sample of sand with air around the sand granules and then the density of the sand alone.

Procedure:

K

Find mass of sand + cup	Record
Find mass of empty cup	Record
Subtract the mass of the empty cup from the mass of the sand + the cup. The result is the mass of the sand.	Record
Put sand in a graduated cylinder, note volume.	Record
Remove sand, put 20 mL water in graduated cylinder.	
Add sand to water, note volume of sand + water	Record
Subtract the volume of the water (20 mL) from the volume of the water + the sand. The result is the volume of the sand.	Record

Data:

Mass of sand + cup (g)	Mass of cup (g)	Mass of sand (g)
17.30	1.85	15.45

Volume of water + sand(mL)	Volume of water(mL)	Volume of sand (w/o air)mL
26.0	20.0	6.0

Volume of with air: 10.4 mL

Density with air: $\frac{M}{V}$ $\frac{15.45\ g}{10.4\ mL}$ = 1.49 g/mL

Density without air: $\frac{M}{V}$ $\frac{15.45\ g}{6.0\ mL}$ = 2.6 g/mL

S5 a Scientific Thinking: The student frames questions to distinguish cause and effect; and identifies or controls variables in experimental and non-experimental research settings.

D Here and throughout, the work displays evidence of appropriate scientific thinking and use of experimental data to reach conclusions.

S5 e Scientific Thinking: The student identifies problems; proposes and implements solutions; and evaluates the accuracy, design, and outcomes of investigations.

E F G The student continually evaluated and critiqued the appropriateness of the experimental design and the accuracy of the measuring process, and described the situations in which the techniques employed would be most effective.

For related work on Density, see "Flinkers", page 42, "Discovering Density", page 93, and "Density", page 173.

The quotations from the Science performance descriptions in this commentary are excerpted. The complete performance descriptions are shown on pages 122-143.

S1 Physical Sciences Concepts

Life Sciences Concepts

Earth and Space Sciences Concepts

Scientific Connections and Applications

S5 Scientific Thinking

S6 Scientific Tools and Technologies

S7 Scientific Communication

Scientific Investigation

Density of Sand

S5f Scientific Thinking: The student works individually and in teams to collect and share information.

E Comparison of results among groups provided partial confirmation of results.

H The student has acknowledged the benefits of collaboration.

S6a Scientific Tools and Technologies: The student uses technology and tools (such as traditional laboratory equipment...) to...measure objects directly, indirectly..., and with appropriate consideration of accuracy and precision.

I J The student used traditional methods.

E Comparison of results among groups was an effective method for judging accuracy.

S7e Scientific Communication: The student communicates in a form suited to the purpose and the audience, such as by writing instructions that others can follow....

Sample 1

Calculations and Analysis:

1. This lab was conducted using sand sample A. The mass of the sand was found by finding the mass of the sand in the cup, and then subtracting the mass of the cup. The mass of the sand was 15.45 g. The sand's volume with air, which was found by placing the sand in a graduated cylinder, was 10.4 mL. The sand's volume without air, which was found using the water displacement method, was 6.0 mL.

2. The density of the sand with air was found to be 1.49 g/mL, and the density of the sand alone was 2.6 g/mL. The sand with the air had a lower density than the sand alone. The equation for density is mass divided by volume. For both density calculations, the mass of the sand was the same. However, the volume of the sand with the air was larger than the volume of the sand alone. This is because the grains of sand were separated by air, which made the volume larger than it would be if air was not present. Since the volume of the sand with air was larger, it had a lower density.

3. Our answers were compared with those of four other groups.

   group #1: density with air   1.4 g/mL
              density without air 2.5 g/mL

   group #2   density with air   0.65 g/mL
              density without air 1.02 g/mL

   group #3   density with air   3.0 g/mL
              density without air 1.5 g/mL

   group #4   density with air   1.49 g/mL
              density without air 2.73 g/mL

4. Three out of the four groups we compared results with had answers very similar to our own. One group, #2, had results that were very different. Since density is an intensive property, the difference in sample sizes among the other groups should not have affected the results. Other groups also may have made errors in their measurements or in their procedures. By double-checking each group's measurements and calculations, it would be possible to determine which group had the most accurate results.

5. The procedure utilized in this lab would work well for small, irregular solids such as sand. Many objects, however, would be far too large to place in a graduated cylinder and use the water displacement method. In their instance larger containers could be used. It also would also be much easier to determine the density of regular solids using calculations of length, width, and other dimensions in conjunction mathematical formulas. This method was extremely successful in this example.

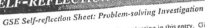

GSE Self-reflection Sheet

GSE Self-reflection Sheet: Problem-solving Investigation

1. *Thoroughly* explain the scientific concept you are investigating in this entry. Give specific examples that show how this concept relates to your Problem-solving Investigation.

   The purpose of this experiment was to determine the density of sand with air around it and the density of sand alone. The main concept in this lab is how the density of a substance is affected by its mass and volume, namely through the presence or the absence of air around the sand when determining the volume of the sample. This investigation introduces the idea that density is an intensive property, a concept that is reinforced by providing for different groups to use varied amounts of sand when performing these calculations. Density of a given substance remains constant regardless of the size of the sample used. /

2. Describe, *in detail*, the part or parts of this investigation YOU personally designed.

   This lab contained only a purpose, not a procedure. It was up to the students to design the entire method of determining the density of the sand both with and without air. I designed the plan to use the water displacement method for the volume of the sand without air, and to simply place the sand in a graduated cylinder in order to find it's volume with air. Please see the procedure section on page 1.

3. Describe how the scientific concept you investigated in this component is related to a real-world issue or personal experience (you may include issues that affect society or the environment).

   The difference in density of objects around us is an integral part of our world. It would be rather difficult to float in the bathtub if water's density were as low as that of air, and just as difficult if water had a density similar to that of a solid. In the same way, it is crucial to our way of thinking and living that density be an intensive property. If the density of a given substance varied with the size of the sample measured, the results could be catastrophic. Imagine buying a 4"x4"x4" block of wood with which to build your home, and finding it to be of a much different consistency and stability than a 50"x50"x50" block of the same type of wood! Everyday we rely on the properties of density for our most basic functions and activities. This experiment simply made us aware of them.

GSE Self-reflection Sheet: Problem-solving Investigation (cont'd)

4. Describe how working with others on this investigation helped to increase your understanding of science.

   Although a hypothesis was not necessary in this investigation, my group worked together to develop a procedure in order to fulfill the purpose of this investigation. My partner and I brainstormed for a great length of time, debating the most efficient set-up and procedures to achieve the most accurate results. This involved many ideas being rejected as inefficient or inaccurate. For example, our first instinct was to simply spill the sand out onto the triple beam balance when determining its mass. Careful thought and discussion, however, caused us to realize that this would result in lost sand and therefore inaccurate results. We then devised a more accurate plan of weighing the sand within the cup, and then removing the sand from the cup and weighing the cup alone. We then subtracted the mass of the empty cup from the mass of the cup and the sand, and indirectly determined the mass of the sand. The entire procedure for this investigation was the result of a collaborative effort between my partner and I.

5. What did you conclude from the investigation? Was the conclusion the same as or different from what you expected? Describe how your observations and data support your conclusions.

   From this investigation, we concluded that a sample of sand has a lower density when it is surrounded by air than when air is not present. My partner and I found sand surrounded by air to have a density of 1.49 g/mL, whereas sand that was not surrounded by air had a density of 2.6 g/mL. My partner and I found it interesting to discover that the presence or absence of air affects the density of a substance. This discovery was shown by the difference in our calculations of the density of the sand with air and without air. By comparing our results with those of other lab teams, we concluded that density is an intensive property. Although all of the teams used different amounts of sand in their calculations, their results were very similar, and in some cases identical to our own. This means that the density of a given substance does not change with the size of the sample measured.

   H In chemistry, as in most areas in life, collaborative efforts achieve the most accurate results in the most efficient manner. Working with a partner or a with a group enables individuals to master concepts and ideas that would be difficult or impossible for them to understand on their own. While brainstorming ideas for the procedure, my partner and I were able to "bounce" ideas off of one another and receive feedback and new ideas in return. In the same manner, if one partner had overlooked a small detail that might impede the obtaining of accurate results, the second partner was quick to see that potential problem and propose a solution. Through exchanging ideas, critique, questions, and information, my partner and I were able to understand the concepts presented in this investigation.

Sample 2

Density of Sand

03-12-99

Mas Volimik Sab:

1. Objektif:

Nan esperyans saa, Objektif mwen se pou mwen jwenn yon jan pou mwen Kalkile mas volimik sab ak lè ak mas volimik sab san lè.

2. Materyèl:

Pou mwen te fè esperyans saa, mwen te itilize: Beche, tib gradye, antonnwa, sab, dlo, espatil avèk yon balans.

3. Machaswiv:

Premye bagay mwen te fè, se te Pran yon Kantite sab. Mwen mete sab la nan yon beche, mwen pran pwa beche a anvan epi mwen pran pwa tou de ansanm. Apres sa, mwen vide menm sab la nan tib gradye a, epi mwen mezire volim sab la. Mwen anrejistre rezilta mwen yo, epi mwen divize pwa sab la ak volim sab la pou mwen jwenn mas volimik sab la ak lè.

Dezyèm bagay mwen te fè, se vide enpe dlo nan tib gradye a, epi mwen mezire volim dlo a. Lè fini, mwen

vide menm Kantite sab mwen te itilize nan premye pati esperyans lan nan tib gradye ki gen dlo a mwen bwase yo ansanm pou mwen ka retire lè ki nan sab la. Mwen mezire volim dlo a ansanm ak sab la epi mwen fè soustraksyon pou mwen Kpab jwenn volim sab la poukont li. Rezilta mwen jwenn nan se volim sab la san lè.

Pou mwen fini, mwen divize pwa sab la ak volim sab la san lè pou mwen jwenn mas volimik sab la san lè.

4. Rezilta:

1. Pwa tib gradye a ⇒ 49.4g
2. Volim. sab la ⇒ 2ml
3. Pwa sab la avèk tiba ⇒ 52.6g
4. Pwn sab la ⇒ 3.2g
5. Mas volimik sab la ak lè ⇒ 3.2g ÷ 2ml = 1.6g/ml
6. Volim dlo a ⇒ 5ml
7. Volim sab la ak dlo ⇒ 6.2ml
8. Volim sab ⇒ 6.2ml - 5ml = 1.2ml
9. Mas volimik sab la san lè ⇒ 3.2g ÷ 1.2ml = 2.7 g/ml

5. Konklizyon:

Lè mwen fin fè esperyans sa, mwen vin wè ke mas volimik sab san lè plis ke mas volimik sab ak lè. Konklizyon mwen tire sèke si ou ta pran menm volim sab ak lè ak sab san lè, sab ki pa gen lè ladan l' nan ap peze plis pase sab ki gen lè landvil' nan.

MAS VOLIMIK* SAB

Travay an gwoup pou w planifye yon esperyans ki pou pèmèt ou chèche mas volimik sab ak lè ki antoure chak grenn sab yo ak mas volimik sab ki pa gen lè ladan l. Fè esperyans lan an gwoup oubyen poukont ou. Ekri yon rapò sou esperyans lan.

ANN REFLECHI SOU ESPERYANS LAN

Lè ou fin ekri rapò sou esperyans lan, reponn kesyon sa yo:

1. Esplike konsèp syantifik ou te envestige nan esperyans lan.

konsèp syantifik mwen envestige nan esperyans lan se mas volimik. Mwen te vle konnen si sab san lè pi lou ke sab ak lè lè yo gen menm volim.

2. Ki rapò ki genyen ant konsèp syantifik sa a ak lavi toulejou?

Rapò ki genyen ant konsèp syantifik saa ak lavi toulejou sèke ou konn bezwen materyèl ki genyen diferan mas volimik selon travay ou vle fè a. Pa egzanp, si ou vle fè yon avyon oubyen yon bato, ou bezwen yon materyèl ki solid men ki pa twò lou.

3. Esplike kouman travay an gwoup ede w nan rechèch sa a e kouman li ede w konprann konsèp syantifik lan pi byen.

Travay nan gwoup ede mwen paske nenpòt erè mwen te fè, yon lòt moun nan gwoup la wè erè a, epi nou korije li ansanm.

4. Ki konklizyon ou tire nan rechèch la? Èske se sa ou te panse k ap rive? Esplike kouman konklizyon w lan baze sou done ou te ranmase yo.

Konklizyon mwen tire de esperyans mwen an sèke lè ou genyen 2 Kalite sab ki gen menm volim, sab ki san lè a ap toujou pi lou ke sab ki ak lè a.
Lè mwen di de Kalite sab, mwen vle di:
1. Sab ak lè.
2. sab san lè.

* Mas volimik - density

Density of Sand

Sample 2 translation

Chemistry Report

Density of Sand

1. <u>Objective:</u>
   In this experiment, my objective is to find the density of sand in the presence of air and without the presence of air.

2. <u>Materials:</u>
   To do this experiment, I used: beaker, graduated cylinder, funnel, sand, scale, water.

3. <u>Procedure:</u>
   The first thing I did was to take a certain quantity of sand. I poured the sand into a beaker. I weighed the empty beaker before weighing it together with the sand. Then, I poured the same amount of sand (from the beaker) into a graduate cylinder and I measured the volume of the sand.
   I recorded the results. Then I divided the weight of the sand into its volume to find its density in the presence of air.
   The second thing I did was to pour some water into the graduate cylinder, then I measured the volume of the water. When I finished, I poured the same quantity of sand I had used in the first part of the experiment into the graduate cylinder that contains the water. I stirred them (water and sand) up so that I could get rid of the air in the sand. I measured the volume of the water together with the sand, then I did a subtraction to find the volume of the sand by itself. The result I found was the volume of the sand without the presence of air.
   To finish, I divided the weight of the sand by the volume of the sand to find the density of the sand without the air being present.

4. <u>Results:</u>

1) Weight of the graduate cylinder	49.4g	
2) Volume of the sand	2ml	
3) Weight of the sand	3.2g	
4) Weight of the sand and the cylinder	52.6g	
5) Density of the sand with air	3.2g/2ml=1.6g/ml	
6) Volume of water	5ml	
7) Volume of the sand and water	6.2ml	
8) Volume of sand	6.2ml–5ml=1.2ml	
9) Density of the sand without air	3.2g/1.2ml=2.7g/ml	

   J

5. <u>Conclusion:</u>
   When I finished with the experiment, I realized that the density of the sand without air is more than the density of the sand with the air. The conclusion I drew is that if you consider the volume of the sand with air and the volume of the sand without air, the sand without air weighs more than the sand with air.

DENSITY OF SAND

Work in a group to design an experiment to determine the density of sand with air around the sand granules and then the density of the sand alone. Write a report based on the experiment.

LET US REFLECT ON THE EXPERIMENT

Answer the following questions after completing your report:

1. Describe the scientific concept you have investigated in the experiment.

The scientific concept I investigated was density. I wanted to know if sand without air is heavier than sand with air when they have the same volume.

2. Describe how the scientific concept you have investigated is related to everyday life.

The relationship between this scientific concept and everyday life is that you sometimes need materials that have different densities depending on the type of work you want to do. For example, if you want to make an airplane or a boat, you need a material that is strong but not too heavy.

3. Describe how working in a group helped to increase your understanding of the scientific concept.

Working in a group helped me because whatever mistake I made, another member of the group was able to see it, and together we were able to correct it.

4. What did you conclude from the investigation? Was the conclusion the same as or different from what you expected? Describe how your observations and data support your conclusion.

The conclusion that I drew from this experiment is that when you have 2 types of sand with the same volume, the sand without air will always be heavier than the sand with air. When I say two types of sand, I mean:
   1) sand with air
   2) sand without air

Physical Sciences Concepts **S1**

Life Sciences Concepts

Earth and Space Sciences Concepts

Scientific Connections and Applications

Scientific Thinking **S5**

Scientific Tools and Technologies **S6**

Scientific Communication **S7**

Scientific Investigation

Work Sample & Commentary: *Density*

The task

The students were asked to describe how to find the density of different substances.

Circumstances of performance

This sample of student work was produced under the following conditions:

alone	√ in a group
in class	√ as homework
with teacher feedback	with peer feedback
timed	opportunity for revision

What the work shows

S1b Physical Sciences Concepts: The student produces evidence that demonstrates understanding of the structure and properties of matter....

A Here, and throughout the work, the students show their understanding of density.

S5e Scientific Thinking: The student identifies problems, proposes...solutions....

B The students point out that customary technique for finding the volume of an irregular solid, water displacement, which they used for the rock, will not work for solids with densities less than water. They propose a reasonable solution to that problem by suggesting that the less dense solid be attached to a very dense solid, such as iron, so that the combined density would be greater than water. Thus, the combined solid would sink.

This work sample illustrates a standard-setting performance for the following parts of the standards:

S1b Physical Sciences Concepts: Structure and properties of matter.

S5e Scientific Thinking: Evaluate the accuracy, design, and outcomes of investigations.

S6a Scientific Tools and Technologies: Use technologies and tools.

S7a Scientific Communication: Represent data and results in multiple ways.

S7e Scientific Communication: Communicate in a form suited to the purpose and the audience.

For related work on Density, see "Flinkers", page 42, "Discovering Density", page 93, and "Density of Sand", page 169.

The quotations from the Science performance descriptions in this commentary are excerpted. The complete performance descriptions are shown on pages 122-143.

Student work (handwritten, in Chinese)

如何测量物质的密度.

我们生活在由物质构成的客观世界中，不同的物质具有不同的特性，因而构成了各种各样的物体。

物质的特性是多种多样的，如气味、颜色、光泽、软硬程度等，它们都可以做为鉴别物质的依据。密度也是物质的一种重要特性，不同物质的密度一般不同。鉴别物质时，也可以先测定出该物质的密度，用测量值与密度表进行对照，往往可以确定它是什么物质。例如，宇航员从月球上采集到的物质样本，地质勘探队员找到的矿石为常常需要通过测定它们的密度，作为鉴别它们是由什么物质构成的一个依据。在生活中，我们可以利用测量密度，鉴定金首饰的含金量。

A 单位体积的某种物质的质量叫做物质的密度。根据密度的定义，密度的公式可表示为：

$$密度 = \frac{质量}{体积}$$

字母 d 表示密度，m 表示质量，V 表示体积，则：

$$d = \frac{m}{V}$$

密度的单位常用克/厘米³ 或 克/毫升表示。

物质有固、液、气三态。测量不同状态物质的密度，需用不同的方法。

二. 测量固体的密度. (器材：天平、刻度尺、量筒、水、长方体金属块、石块)

1. 测量形状规则物体的密度. (长方体金属块)

i) 用天平称出它的质量 m.

ii) 用刻度尺量出它的长、宽、高，用公式 $V = L \cdot W \cdot H$ 算出体积 V，最后用公式 $d = \frac{m}{V}$ 则可得出密度.

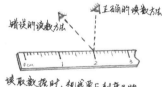

错误的读数方法 / 正确的读数方法

D 刻度尺要尽量贴近被测的物体，刻度尺不要歪斜，要与被测物体平行.

读取数据时，视线要与刻度尺的尺面垂直.

2. 测量形状不规则但密度大于水的物体 (石块)

i) 用天平称出它的质量 m.

ii) 在量筒中盛水，读出量筒中水的体积 V_1，将物体浸没在水中，读出底面水的数 V_2，物体的体积为 $V = V_2 - V_1$.

iii) 用公式 $d = \frac{m}{V}$，得出物体的密度.

在读取数据时，读出凹月面最低正的刻度.

Density

二. 测量液体的密度（器材：天平、量筒、待测液体）

(1). 先用天平称出量筒的质量 m_1.

(2). 将待测液体倒入量筒，称出待测液体与量筒的总质量 m_2，待测液体的质量为 $m = m_2 - m_1$.

(3). 读出液体的体积

(4). 利用公式 $d = \frac{m}{V}$ 算出该液体的密度.

三. 测量空气的密度（器材：球胆（或皮囊）连着一根带夹子的肢管、天平、水槽、量筒、水、打气筒）

(1). 取一个球胆（或皮囊）接一根带夹子的肢管，空气打入在，用天平称出它们的质量 m_1.

(2). 用下列装置（如图），用力挤压球胆，用排水集气法，在量筒中收集气体，装气完毕后，将紧夹子，上下移动量筒，使其内外水平面一样高，以保证气体压强与外面大气压相同，整后由量筒刻度读出气体的体积 V.

(3). 称出余下气体后球胆的质量 m_2，则收集在量筒内气体的质量为 $m = m_1 - m_2$.

(4). 利用公式 $d = \frac{m}{V}$ 算出空气的密度.

（4.）

C

数据记录如下：

物体	质量 (g)	体积 (cm³)				密度 (g/cm³)
		长 (cm)	宽 (cm)	高 (cm)	体积	
金属块	180.01	7.4	5.4	1.6	63.94	2.83
石块	41.81	水筒 400	水面刻块 417.5	石块 17.5		2.39
液体	量筒 266.90 量筒加液体 564.61 液体 297.71			300.0		0.99
空气	球胆加 空气 81.86 球胆 81.60 甲气 0.26			260.0		0.001

把测出的结果与密度表相对照，可以得出：

结论：金属块是铝，石块是花岗岩，液体是水

实验中的误差是不可避免的，但我们应该尽量减小。上述物体的密度表示如下图：

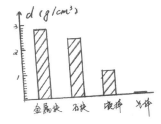

由上述测量结果可知，气体的密度最小，其次是液体，固体的密度最大。所以，大多数固体在液体中下沉。实际上，也有些固体的密度小于液体，比如木块和冰的密度就小于水的密度，将它们放入水中会上浮。那么，如何测量这些固体的体积呢？比如，测量形状不规则的木块体积时，我们可先用细线将木块与铁块系在一起，这样有木块就能够全部浸入水中，用浸水法测量即可。

你能想出如何测量冰的密度的方法吗？

（5.）

B

S6a Scientific Tools and Technologies: The student uses technology and tools…to observe and measure objects…directly and indirectly…with appropriate consideration of accuracy and precision.

C Attention to accuracy is evident in the care taken with significant digits.

D **E** Attention to precision is evident in the comments about holding and reading a ruler and reading the level of the graduate cylinder.

S7a Scientific Communication: The student represents data and results in multiple ways, such as…tables, and graphs;…diagrams….

C The table is well designed to show which values were measured and which were calculated.

S7e Scientific Communication: The student communicates in a form suited to the purpose, such as by writing instructions that others can follow….

Throughout the work, especially at **D** and **E**, the instructions are very straightforward and easy to follow.

Density

HOW DO WE FIND THE DENSITY OF THE DIFFERENT MATTER?

We live in an objective world consisted of numerous matter. The different matter is characterized by different properties, thus it results in the formation of a variety of objects which are, in turn, formed by matter.

Matter has certain pertinent characteristics, such as smell, color, luster, and hardness, etc. According to these characteristics, the matter could be identified. Density is also an important characteristic of the matter. Usually the density varies with the different matter. An unknown matter could be identified by finding its density and then comparing the densities of substances. For instance, the specimen collected by astronauts from the moon and the rocks collected by geologists are always identified based on their densities. We also can determine the gold content in a specific gold jewelry by its density.

A Density is the mass per unit volume of an object. According to the definition, the formula of the density is expressed as:

$$\text{Density} = \frac{\text{Mass}}{\text{Volume}} \quad \text{or} \quad D = M / V$$

The density is expressed in grams per cubic centimeter (g / cm³) of grams per milliliter (g / ml).

Matter exists in one of three phases — solid, liquid, or gas. We can measure the density of matter in any phase by using the certain method. Let's do the following experiments to find the densities of different objects in different phases.

Materials: balance, ruler, graduated cylinder, metal rectangular prism , rock, and water.

A. To Find the Density of a Solid
1. Metal Prism, a Regular Shape Solid

-1-

Procedure:
(1) Use the balance to measure the mass of the metal prism.
(2) Use the ruler measure the length, width and the height of the metal prism.
(3) Calculate the volume of the metal prism by the formula V = l • w • h.
(4) Find its density by the formula D = M / V.

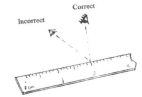

Correct

Incorrect

D The scale mark should be as close to the object as possible. Keep the ruler to be parallel to the edge being measured.

The view of vision should be perpendicular to the scale.

2. Rock, an Irregular Shape Solid

Procedure:
(1) Use the balance to measure the mass of the rock.
(2) Pour some water into the graduated cylinder and read the volume of the water, V_1. Submerge the rock into the water completely and read the total volume, V_2. Then the volume of the rock is $V = V_1 - V_2$
(3) Calculate the density of the rock by D = M / V

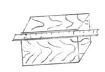

Read the level of the meniscus

E

-2-

B. To Find the Density of a Liquid
Materials: balance, graduated cylinder, and unknown liquid
Procedure:
(1) Use the balance to measure the mass of the empty graduated cylinder, M_1.
(2) Pour the liquid into the graduated cylinder and then measure the total mass M_2. The mass of the liquid is $M = M_1 - M_2$.
(3) Read the volume of the liquid in the graduated cylinder.
(4) Calculate the density of the liquid by D = M / V

C. To Find the Density of a Gas
Materials: balance, balloon, rubber tube with a clip, water trough, graduated cylinder, water, and air pump
Procedure:
(1) Connect the balloon with the rubber tube and pump the air into the balloon. Then use the balance to measure the mass of this balloon set, M_1.
(2) Set up the equipment as the diagram shown below. Collect some air in the graduated cylinder by squeezing the balloon and then clip the tube. Move the graduated cylinder until the level of water inside as the same as outside so that the air pressure inside is equal to outside. Read the volume of the collected air, V.
(3) Measure the mass the balloon set again, designated as M_2. The mass of the air in the graduated cylinder is $M = M_1 - M_2$.
(4) Calculate the density of the air by D= M / V.

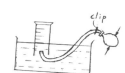
clip

-3-

C Records:

Object	Mass (g)			Volume (cm³)				Density (g / cm³)
Metal Prism	180.01		length	width	height	volume		2.83
			7.4	5.4	1.6	63.94		
Rock	41.81		Water	water & rock	rock			2.39
			400	417.5	17.5			
Liquid	grad.cyl	g.c.&liquid	liquid	300.0				0.99
	266.90	564.61	297.91					
Air	bal.&air	balloon	air	260.0				0.001
	81.86	81.60	0.26					

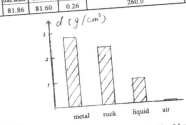

d (g/cm³)

metal   rock   liquid   air

Conclusions:
Comparing the data from the experiment with the table of densities, we conclude that the metal is aluminum, the rock is granite, and the liquid is water.
A certain degree of aberration is inevitable in any measuring. However, we should minimize errors.

B The densities of the four objects is expressed by a bar graph below. We can see through the graph that the order of the densities from least to most is gas, liquid, and solid. That's why most of the solids would sink in the water, but not all solids do. There are some solids whose density could be smaller than that of water, such as wood and ice. They would, instead, float on the water surface. How do we measure the volume of that kind of solids? To measure the volume of wood, for instance, we could rap the wood with a piece of iron together first , so that the wood could be sunk completely after being placed into the water.
Can you state the method to find the density of ice now?

-4-

Work Sample & Commentary: *DNA Models*

For related work on Reproduction, see "Butterflies", page 47, and "It's All in the Genes", page 106.

Physical
Sciences
Concepts

Life
Sciences
Concepts **S2**

Earth and
Space Sciences
Concepts

Scientific
Connections and **S4**
Applications

Scientific
Thinking

Scientific Tools
and
Technologies

Scientific
Communication

Scientific **S8**
Investigation

The quotations from the Science performance descriptions in this commentary are excerpted. The complete performance descriptions are shown on pages 122-143.

The task

Student groups were asked to design and build models representing DNA molecules. The models were to include details such as base pairs and nucleotide components, and to illustrate the overall double-stranded and helical nature of DNA.

Circumstances of performance

This sample of student work was produced under the following conditions:

alone   √ in a group

in class   as homework

√ with teacher feedback   with peer feedback

timed   √ opportunity for revision

What the work shows

S2 b Life Sciences Concepts: The student produces evidence that demonstrates the molecular basis of heredity, such as DNA….

A The students illustrate complementary base pairs; alternate sugar-phosphate side chains, and appropriate placement of the nucleotide components. The model also shows the double stranded and helical nature of DNA. It includes an illustrated key [not shown]. The students attempted to illustrate the dynamic nature of the molecule with a crank handle that turns the model that is not visible in the photo.

B The students had an opportunity to revise their initial submission **A**. They more accurately depict the sugars and they added the phosphates. An attempt was made to illustrate more clearly the spatial relationship between these nucleotide components. In further revising the model, the hydrogen bonds between the nucleotide base pairs could be illustrated along with a more accurate depiction of accurate base pair size.

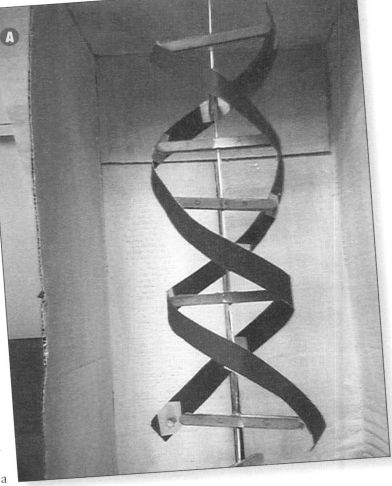

A

C The students illustrate complementary base pairs, hydrogen bonding, alternate sugar phosphate side chains, and appropriate placement of the nucleotide components. The model also shows the double stranded nature of DNA and the process of the unzipping and formation of replicated strands. However, this model does not illustrate the helical nature of DNA, an omission that should be corrected in a revision.

This work sample illustrates a standard-setting performance for the following parts of the standards:

S2 b Life Sciences Concepts: Molecular basis of heredity.

S4 a Scientific Connections and Applications: Big ideas and unifying concepts.

S8 c Scientific Investigation: Design.

DNA Models

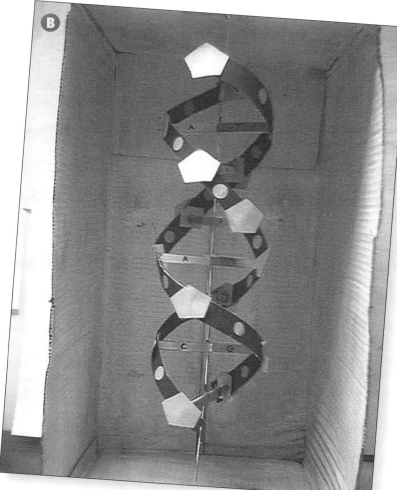

S4a Scientific Connections and Applications: The student produces evidence that demonstrates understanding of big ideas and unifying concepts, such as order and organization....

A B C The students demonstrated in model form the organization of the DNA molecule.

S8c Scientific Investigation: The student demonstrates scientific competence by completing [a] design.

A B C The students developed and executed designs that, while requiring revision, were creative and largely accurate.

Physical
Sciences
Concepts

S2 Life
Sciences
Concepts

Earth and
Space Sciences
Concepts

S4 Scientific
Connections and
Applications

Scientific
Thinking

Scientific Tools
and
Technologies

Scientific
Communication

S8 Scientific
Investigation

Work Sample & Commentary: *DNA Reflection*

The quotations from the Science performance descriptions in this commentary are excerpted. The complete performance descriptions are shown on pages 122-143.

Physical Sciences Concepts

Life Sciences Concepts

Earth and Space Sciences Concepts

Scientific Connections and Applications **S4**

Scientific Thinking

Scientific Tools and Technologies **S6**

Scientific Communication **S7**

Scientific Investigation

The task

One component of the task entitled "The Double Helix, Let's Unwind" was a bio-ethics position paper which was supported by documentation from the Internet and other sources. This sample of student work was a piece of reflective writing excerpted from an internet research paper. The excerpt discusses the students' experience using the Internet as a source of information. The work was part of a multi-task project, which was done by a team of students.

Circumstances of performance

This sample of student work was produced under the following conditions:

alone	√ in a group
in class	√ as homework
√ with teacher feedback	√ with peer feedback
timed	√ opportunity for revision

What the work shows

S4 d Scientific Connections and Applications: The student produces evidence that demonstrates understanding of impact of technology, such as constraints and trade-offs…and problems and benefits.

A The student clearly states expectations.

B C D E The student lists problems encountered, such as minimal information, in-operative servers, the amount of time required to bring up information, and students' limited access to technology.

F

The Perils of Surfing

A For the BioResearch DNA Project, our class was instructed to conduct our research via the internet. This instruction did not strike us as unreasonable. Actually, we though the internet would make our research efforts much easier. We were inclined to believe that the internet abounded with information for our respective searches. However, all our inclinations were dashed in the face of reality.

According to a colleague involved with the project, "…I found that the internet wasn't all it was cracked up to be." One complaint borne against the internet is that information about genetic engineering is very minimal. One could put out a **B** search for, let's say protein synthesis, but all one would find would be a fleeting mention of it in a DNA article.

C Another problem presented by the internet was the very inconvenient service. When one puts in a request for a web site one expects an affirmative answer however many servers were down. Too many web servers were either down or no longer in service. The most exasperating aspect to this prob- **D** lem was that the computer would take two to three minutes to bring up this information.

Although the internet is very useful, it still has many 'bugs' to be worked out. The fact remains that with the students busy schedule trying to use the internet is not very time efficient. Using the internet for science/medical searches takes valuable time that could be spent studying. When I went to the library to use the internet stayed there almost three hours and was rewarded with six web addresses, four of which had down servers.

E While the internet may be good for online shopping and downloading games and music, the fact remains that most high school students do not have access to science and medical data online.

S6 a Scientific Tools and Technologies: The student uses technology and tools (such as…computer aids) to observe and measure objects, organisms, and phenomena, directly, indirectly, and remotely, with appropriate consideration of accuracy and precision.

F The entire work shows that students used computers and the Internet to collect data.

S7 c Scientific Communication: The student critiques published materials, such as popular magazines and academic journals.

B C The student noted both the minimal nature of the internet references and the lack of accessibility.

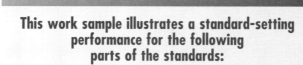

This work sample illustrates a standard-setting performance for the following parts of the standards:

S4 d Scientific Connections and Applications: Impact of technology.

S6 a Scientific Tools and Technologies: Use technology and tools.

S7 c Scientific Communication: Critique published materials.

Work Sample & Commentary: *DNA Concept Map*

The task

Students in a high school biology class were asked to create a concept map to show the relationship between DNA, its components and those of RNA. Students had to present their map and defend its structure to the class.

Circumstances of performance

This sample of student work was produced under the following conditions:

alone	√ in a group
√ in class	as homework
√ with teacher feedback	with peer feedback
timed	√ opportunity for revision

The work was done in teams of three students.

What the work shows

S2b Life Sciences Concepts: The student produces evidence that demonstrates understanding of molecular basis for heredity, such as DNA….

A B C The concept map shows the components of DNA, and the bonds that hold them together. The work shows the role of hydrogen bonds but does not distinguish them as weak, nor does it show location of the bonds. However, the overall organization of the concept map is logical and reasonably accurate.

D E F The concept map also includes key concepts such as formation of a complementary strand, transcription, and RNA.

F G The organizations of DNA and RNA are shown in terms of double versus single strand; note substitution of uracil for thymine.

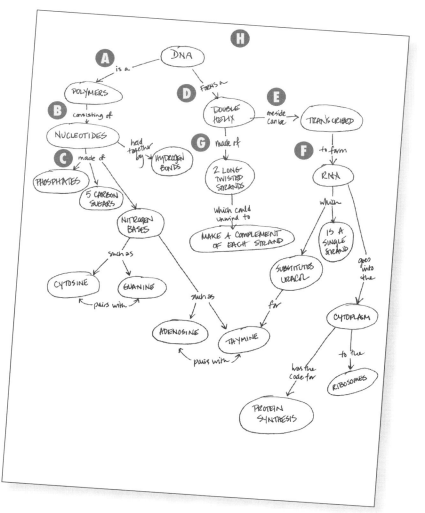

S4a Scientific Connections and Applications: The student produces evidence that demonstrates understanding of big ideas and unifying concepts, such as order and organization [and] models….

D E F The relationship between DNA and RNA production is clearly shown.

S7e Scientific Communication: The student communicates in a form suited to the purpose and the audience….

H The concept map is readable by students at differing levels of reading skill and is useful for a variety of learning styles.

For related work on Reproduction, see "Butterflies", page 47, and "It's All in the Genes", page 106.

The quotations from the Science performance descriptions in this commentary are excerpted. The complete performance descriptions are shown on pages 122-143.

This work sample illustrates a standard-setting performance for the following parts of the standards:

S2b Life Sciences Concepts: Molecular basis for heredity.

S4a Scientific Connections and Applications: Big ideas and unifying concepts.

S7e Scientific Communication: Communicate in a form suited to the purpose and the audience.

Physical Sciences Concepts

S2 Life Sciences Concepts

Earth and Space Sciences Concepts

S4 Scientific Connections and Applications

Scientific Thinking

Scientific Tools and Technologies

S7 Scientific Communication

Scientific Investigation

Work Sample & Commentary: *DNA Model*

For related work on Reproduction, see "Butterflies", page 47, and "It's All in the Genes", page 106.

Physical
Sciences
Concepts

Life
Sciences
Concepts **S2**

Earth and
Space Sciences
Concepts

Scientific
Connections and **S4**
Applications

Scientific
Thinking

Scientific Tools
and
Technologies

Scientific **S7**
Communication

Scientific
Investigation

The quotations from the Science performance descriptions in this commentary are excerpted. The complete performance descriptions are shown on pages 122-143.

The task

Students were asked to build working models to show how the instructions for specifying an organism's characteristics are carried in DNA and its subunits. Students were required to give an oral presentation of their models.

Circumstances of performance

This sample of student work was produced under the following conditions:

alone	in a group
in class	√ as homework
with teacher feedback	√ with peer feedback
timed	√ opportunity for revision

What the work shows

S2a Life Sciences Concepts: The student produces evidence that demonstrates understanding of the cell, such as cell structure and function relationships....

A B C The student clearly and succinctly demonstrates an understanding of the structural context of DNA within the cell.

D E The entire "Discussion" section clearly explains some basic biochemical structures and functions within the DNA molecule. The section concludes with an accurate application of these functions.

F The student's model is an accurate representation of the structure of the DNA molecule.

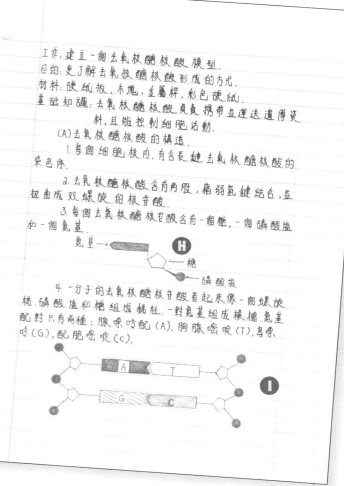

This work sample illustrates a standard-setting performance for the following parts of the standards:

S2a Life Sciences Concepts: The cell

S4a Scientific Connections and Applications: Big ideas and unifying concepts.

S4b Scientific Connections and Applications: The designed world

S7a Scientific Communication: Represent data and results in multiple ways

S7d Scientific Communication: Explain a scientific concept or procedure to other students.

S4a Scientific Connections and Applications: The student produces evidence that demonstrates understanding of big ideas and unifying concepts, such as...models, form and function....

G The entire work is evidence that the student knows how to plan and build a model, and how to use a model to explain difficult concepts, such as the form and function of the DNA molecule and its subunits.

DNA Model

S4 b Scientific Connections and Applications: The student produces evidence that demonstrates understanding of the designed world, such as the...development of agricultural techniques....

E The student briefly describes how humans have applied knowledge of the structures and functions of the DNA molecule to agriculture.

S7 a Scientific Communication: The student represents data and results in multiple ways, such as...diagrams, and...technical...writing; and selects the most effective way to convey the scientific information.

G The entire report is concisely and accurately written.

H **I** **J** The student illustrates the written report with carefully and accurately drawn diagrams.

S7 d Scientific Communication: The student explains a scientific concept to other students.

A **B** The student interprets the model.

D The student reports clearly and succinctly about the structures and functions represented by the model.

K The student provides easily replicated instructions for building a similar model.

Physical
Sciences
Concepts

S2 Life
Sciences
Concepts

Earth and
Space Sciences
Concepts

S4 Scientific
Connections and
Applications

Scientific
Thinking

Scientific Tools
and
Technologies

S7 Scientific
Communication

Scientific
Investigation

(B)去氧核醣核酸的複製.
　1.細胞分裂前,去氧核醣核酸必須複製.
　2.去氧核醣核酸梯子在橫檔的氮基對間裂開,就像拉開拉鍊一樣.
　3.其他氮基依照 A-T. C-G 的方式黏附在每個露出的另一半梯子上.
　4.每股和它互補的核苷酸,形成兩個一模一樣的新的去氧核醣核酸分子.

J

步驟:1.鋸成十個一樣大小的薄木條做橫檔.
　2.取部分木條,每個半用墨綠色紙,半用淡黃色紙包起來,代表C-G配對,但是兩頭不包.
　3.其餘的木條,每個半用淺綠色紙,半用橘色紙包起來,代表 A-T 配對,也是兩頭不包.
　4.在每個木條中央鑽個洞,好讓金屬桿可以把他們貫穿起來,並排列成螺旋形的梯子.
　5.在兩個硬紙板帶子上,各切割十個跟木條寬度一樣大小的長方形洞.使木條的兩端剛好可以塞進洞裏.

討論:
1.一個核苷酸有那些成分?我用什麼顏色代表它們?
一每個核苷酸有一個糖,一個磷酸鹽和一個氮基.白色代表磷酸鹽.棕色木端代表糖.淺綠色代表腺嘌呤 (A),淡黃色代表鳥嘌呤 (G),橘色代表胸腺嘧啶 (T),墨綠色代表胞嘧啶 (c).
2.去氧核醣核酸中的氮基如何配對?它們的化學成分一樣嗎?
一胞嘧啶 (c) 總是匹配鳥嘌呤 (G),胸腺嘧啶 (T) 總是匹配腺嘌呤 (A).它們的化學成分不同,嘌呤比嘧啶長,嘌呤與其互補之嘧啶結合,才能使梯的橫檔保持一定的長度.
3.去氧核醣核酸分子的兩半如何結合在一起?
一它們依腺嘌呤配胸腺嘧啶 (A-T),胞嘧啶配鳥嘌呤 (c-G) 的方式,靠微弱的氫鍵聯合.
4.什么控制細胞酶的產生?
一細胞去氧核醣核酸上氮基順序的遺傳密碼決定酶的產生.
5.遺傳資料怎樣在去氧核醣核酸上設定密碼?
一遺傳資料藉蓋去氧核醣核酸上的核苷酸順序,來設定密碼.
6.去氧核醣核酸的梯形構造如何適應複製?
一梯子每個橫檔的核苷酸裂開,露出來的核苷酸接納互補的核苷酸,完成梯形構造.
7.人類如何從去氧核醣核酸的知識獲益?
一透過紀錄,人類已用選擇配種和其他方法去

去製造他們所屆好的特性的生物,我們目前對去氧核醣核酸的了解容許我們操控基因,並發展新種生物及特性的新個組合.

F

DNA Model

Translation

TASK: to build a DNA model

PURPOSE: to better understand the way in which the DNA ladder is constructed

MATERIALS: cardboard, block, metal rod, color construction paper

INTRODUCTION: DNA is responsible for carrying and transmitting hereditary information as well as controlling the life activities of a cell.

A) the Structure of DNA:

1. Inside the nucleus of each living cell are chromosomes which contain long strands of DNA.
2. DNA consists of two strands of nucleotides, joined by weak hydrogen bonds and twisted into double helix.
3. Every DNA nucleotide contains a sugar, a phosphate group, and a nitrogenous base.
4. A molecule of DNA looks like a twisted ladder, the phosphates and sugar make up its uprights.
   The base pairs: A-T, and C-G make up its rungs.

B) The Replication of DNA

1. DNA replication must occur before cell division.
2. The DNA ladder breaks between the nitrogen bases in the steps like unzipping a zipper.
3. The other nitrogen bases attach to each exposed half of the ladder.
4. Each strand and its complementary partner then form two new identical DNA molecules.

PROCEDURE:

1. to saw 10 thin wooden plates of equal size to make steps of the ladder
2. to wrap some plates half with dark green and half with light yellow paper to represent C-G base pairs, while leaving both ends unwrapped
3. to wrap the other plates half with light green and half with orange paper to represent A-T base pairs, also leaving both ends unwrapped
4. to drill a hole in the middle of each plate so that a metal rod can penetrate through them, while being arranged like a twisted ladder
5. On each of two cardboard strips, cut 10 slots of the same size as wooden plate width so that the ends of the wooden plates can be stuck into the slots

1

DISCUSSION:

1. What are the basic components of a nucleotide?
   --a sugar, a phosphate and nitrogen base
   Which color did I use to represent these nucleotide components?
   --white color for phosphate, brown wooden end for sugar, dark green for cytosine, orange for thymine, light green for adenine, light yellow for guanine

2. How are the nitrogenous bases in DNA paired?
   -- Cytosine is always paired with guanine,. Adenine is always paired with thymine. Purines(Adenine and guanine) are longer than pyramidines(thymine and cytosine).

3. Explain how the two halves of the DNA molecule are held together
   --They are held by weak hydrogen bonds.

4. What controls the production of enzymes by the cells?
   --The genetic code in the sequence of bases in a cell's DNA controls the synthesis of its enzymes.

5. How is hereditary information encoded in DNA ?
   --Hereditary information is encoded by means of the sequence of nucleotides in DNA.

6. How is DNA's ladder structure adapted for replication?
   --An unzipping takes place between the nucleotides at each rung

7. How do humans benefit from the knowledge of DNA ?
   --Throughout recorded history, humans have used selective breeding and other methods to produce organisms with desirable traits. Our current understanding of DNA allows for the manipulation of genes and the development of new combination of traits and new varieties of organisms.

2

Work Sample & Commentary: *Endocrine Feedback Exercise*

The task

Students were given a data table showing a high school student's blood glucose levels as measured hourly over a 24-hour period. They were asked to graph the data; to draw conclusions about regulatory response from the data; and to use their conclusions to make inferences about the effects of injected insulin on diabetes.

Circumstances of performance

This sample of student work was produced under the following conditions:

√ alone   in a group

  in class   √ as homework

√ with teacher feedback   with peer feedback

√ timed   opportunity for revision

What the work shows

S2 a Life Sciences Concepts: The student produces evidence that demonstrates understanding of the cell, such as…regulation and biochemistry.

A The student understands that substances within the blood last for a finite time, and used this information to explain why regular injections of insulin are required to regulate diabetes.

B This answer accurately explains what happens to sugar in the blood after a meal. It also points out that insulin is involved in the entry of glucose into various cells.

Endocrine Feedback Exercise

Introduction:
The Endocrine System consists of a group of glands located all around the body that produce and secrete chemical messengers. These messengers, or **hormones**, travel through the blood stream causing effects in specific **target** tissues. The endocrine system serves as a fine tuner for maintaining homeostasis in the body. This system, combined with the nervous system, serves to control all body reactions and behaviors.

Hormone secretion by the various endocrine glands is controlled by delicate series of actions known as **feedback**. In this process the production and/or secretion of hormones is regulated by the presence or absence of a second blood chemical. For instance, the secretion of both glucagon and insulin, by the pancreas, is regulated by the presence or absence of glucose in the blood.

In this exercise you will examine the body's response to the normal change in blood glucose during a typical day.

Directions
Use the information on the chart below to construct a line graph of the % blood glucose over the course of a high school student's day. This student generally eats 3 meals a day, and is a member of the school's football team.

Time of Day	% Blood Glucose	Time of Day	% Blood Glucose
7AM	45	7PM	45
8AM	30	8PM	43
9AM	28	9PM	30
10AM	30	10PM	28
11AM	30	11PM	30
12 NOON	48	12 MIDNIGHT	29
1PM	43	1AM	29
2PM	30	2AM	28
3PM	30	3AM	30
4PM	24	4AM	28
5PM	28	5AM	30
6PM	30	6AM	30

Breakfast is at 6:30AM
Lunch is at 11:30AM
Dinner is at 6PM

Football Practice is from
3:30PM – 6:30PM

Analysis Questions
1. In your own words, describe what is happening to the blood glucose levels throughout the day.
The glucose levels increase shortly after each meal is eaten. During practice, the level of glucose decreases.
2. What effect did eating have on the blood glucose level?
Eating increases the blood glucose levels

3. Why do you think there is a slight delay in the change of blood glucose levels after eating?
The delay is due to the fact that the food must be digested so that it can break down into glucose.

This work sample illustrates a standard-setting performance for the following parts of the standards:

S2 a Life Sciences Concepts: The cell.

S4 a Scientific Connections and Applications: Big ideas and unifying concepts.

S4 c Scientific Connections and Applications: Health.

S5 b Scientific Thinking: Use concepts from Science Standards 1–4.

S6 c Scientific Tools and Technologies: Analyze data.

S7 b Scientific Communication: Argue from evidence.

S4 a Scientific Connections and Applications: The student produces evidence that demonstrates understanding of big ideas and unifying concepts, such as…change and constancy; and cause and effect.

C D The answers demonstrate an understanding that eating as well as normal and strenuous metabolic demands cause changes in blood sugar levels, and that the effects of those changes are regulatory responses to maintain homeostasis.

S4 c Scientific Connections and Applications: The student produces evidence that demonstrates understanding of health, such as nutrition and exercise, [and] disease….

A E In the discussion of diabetes, the connection between the presence of insulin and the ability of the body to absorb glucose into cells is clearly stated.

B The student accurately correlates the regulatory effect of injected insulin with the production of glycogen.

For related work on Response to Environment, see "Bean Farmers", page 44, "Water Tolerance", page 50, "Toasted Bread", page 54, and "Snails", page 104.

The quotations from the Science performance descriptions in this commentary are excerpted. The complete performance descriptions are shown on pages 122-143.

Endocrine Feedback Exercise

S5 b Scientific Thinking: The student uses concepts from Science Standards 1–4 to explain a variety of observations and phenomena.

B E Concepts related to **S2 a** are accurately applied in making inferences about the regulatory effects of injected insulin.

F G H I J K Concepts related to **S2 a** are accurately applied in making inferences about the data in the table.

S6 c Scientific Tools and Technologies: The student analyzes data using concepts and techniques in Mathematics Standard 4, such as...appropriate data displays.

L The points on the graph are correctly plotted. The student chose appropriate scales and intervals for the graph, and the axes are correctly labeled. The use of a ruler or straight edge for drawing the axes and connecting lines would be recommended in a revision.

S7 b Scientific Communication: The student argues from evidence, such as data produced...by others.

A B E The students correctly interpret the data presented in the table, and use their conclusions to make inferences about the effects of injected insulin.

G 4. What happens to the amount of glucose in the blood between:

lunch and football practice: The amount of glucose gradually decreases

during football practice: The amount slowly increases

H 5. Which hormone is responsible for the change in blood glucose levels between:

7:00AM and 11:00AM Insulin

3:00PM and 5:00PM Glucagon

A 6. Diabetes is a condition where the pancreas no longer produces any (or enough) insulin. If this student was a diabetic and did not know it, how would his blood sugar graph be different? The glucose levels in the blood would be higher than that of a person without diabetes.

What problems should this create for the student? The cells would not absorb enough glucose & would lack the energy to properly function. The person could pass out or even die

E 7. Hormones do not last in the blood stream indefinitely. For this reason your glands must constantly produce new hormones when needed. Using this information – why would a diabetic person require injections of insulin two or even three times a day? Insulin injections would need to be given 2 or 3 times a day because when the insulin is injected into the bloodstream, it will only last for a period of time. Since the body cannot elevate the insulin levels sufficiently on its own, more insulin must be injected

Use the following information to complete the concept map below

Insulin works to decrease the blood glucose levels by:
- allowing glucose to diffuse into cells
- stimulating cell respiration to occur
- stimulating the formation of storage glycogen in the liver and fat cells around the body

Glucagon works to increase the blood glucose levels by:
- increasing the conversion of stored fats and glycogen into glucose which is placed into the blood

[concept map: secretion of Insulin → causes → excess glucose in the blood to dissolve into the cell. glucose increases → normal blood glucose ← glucose decreases ← secretion of Glucagon → causes → the conversion of stored fats & glycogen which enters the bloodstream.]

Endocrine Feedback Exercise

Introduction:
The Endocrine System consists of a group of glands located all around the body that produce and secrete chemical messengers. These messengers, or **hormones**, travel through the blood stream causing effects in specific **target tissues**. The endocrine system serves as a fine tuner for maintaining homeostasis in the body. This system, combined with the nervous system, serves to control all body reactions and behaviors.
Hormone secretion by the various endocrine glands is controlled by delicate series of actions known as **feedback**. In this process the production and/or secretion of hormones is regulated by the presence or absence of a second blood chemical. For instance, the secretion of both glucagon and insulin, by the pancreas, is regulated by the presence or absence of glucose in the blood.
In this exercise you will examine the body's response to the normal change in blood glucose during a typical day.

Directions
Use the information on the chart below to construct a line graph of the % blood glucose over the course of a high school student's day. This student generally eats 3 meals a day, and is a member of the school's football team.

Time of Day	% Blood Glucose	Time of Day	% Blood Glucose
7AM	45	7PM	45
8AM	30	8PM	43
9AM	28	9PM	30
10AM	30	10PM	28
11AM	30	11PM	30
12 NOON	48	12 MIDNIGHT	29
1PM	43	1AM	29
2PM	30	2AM	28
3PM	30	3AM	30
4PM	24	4AM	28
5PM	28	5AM	30
6PM	30	6AM	30

Breakfast is at 6:30AM
Lunch is at 11:30AM
Dinner is at 6PM

Football Practice is from 3:30PM – 6:30PM

Analysis Questions
D 1. In your own words, describe what is happening to the blood glucose levels throughout the day. Throughout the day, blood glucose levels fluctuate. During physical exercise, the glucose levels are at their lowest. And during lunch, glucose levels in the blood are at their highest

2. What effect did eating have on the blood glucose level? It raised it significantly

I 3. Why do you think there is a slight delay in the change of blood glucose levels after eating? There is a slight delay in the change of blood glucose levels after eating because the food needs to be digested and the sugar must be circulated throughout the bloodstream.

Endocrine Feedback Exercise

J 4. What happens to the amount of glucose in the blood between:

lunch and football practice: During lunch, glucose is at its highest and
during football practice glucose levels drop to their lowest

during football practice: The glucose levels drop significantly

K 5. Which hormone is responsible for the change in blood glucose levels between:

7:00AM and 11:00AM   Insulin

3:00PM and 5:00PM   Glucagon

6. Diabetes is a condition where the pancreas no longer produces any (or enough) insulin. If this student
was a diabetic and did not know it, how would his blood sugar graph be different?

His blood sugar would be high and off the charts.

What problems should this create for the student?

He would probably pass out, dehydrate or maybe these would be a
possible death.

B 7. Hormones do not last in the blood stream indefinitely. For this reason your glands must constantly
produce new hormones when needed. Using this information – why would a diabetic person require
injections of insulin two or even three times a day? A diabetic person who would
require injections of insulin two or even three times a
day because since insulin works to decrease the
blood glucose levels by allowing glucose to diffuse into
cells, stimulating cell respiration to occur and stimulating
the formation of
storage glycogen in
the liver and fat
cells around the body.
since a diabetic
person does
not produce
enough
insulin,
they
would
need to
receive
two to three
shots
a
day to
prevent
their
glucose levels
from rising
to
high.

Use the following information to complete the concept map below

Insulin works to decrease the blood glucose levels by:
- allowing glucose to diffuse into cells
- stimulating cell respiration to occur
- stimulating the formation of storage glycogen in the liver and fat cells around the body

Glucagon works to increase the blood glucose levels by:
- increasing the conversion of stored fats and glycogen into glucose which is placed into the
blood

secretion of **Insulin** → causes → Glucose to diffuse into the cell

glucose increases

normal blood glucose

glucose decreases

secretion of **Glucagon** → causes → Glucose to increase in the blood stream

L

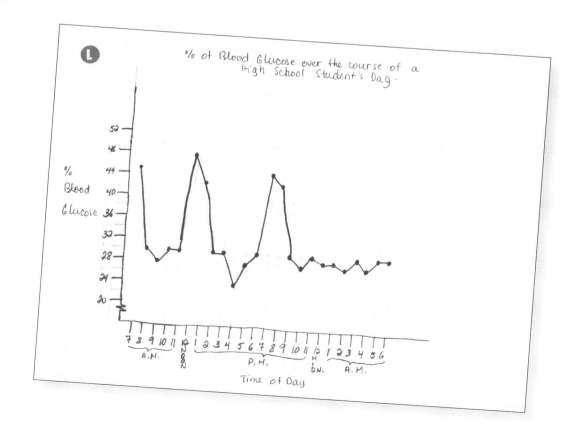

% of Blood Glucose over the course of a High School Student's Day.

% Blood Glucose

Time of Day

Work Sample & Commentary: *Eagles*

The task

Small groups of students performed simulations that modeled the effects of predators and other environmental stresses, both natural and human-caused, on a prey population. Students were required to graph their data, and to draw a series of conclusions based on comparisons of their data.

For related work on Interdependence, see "Biomes", page 52, "Bio Box", page 98, "Owl Pellets", page 101, and "The Invincible Cockroach", page 188.

Circumstances of performance

This sample of student work was produced under the following conditions:

alone	√ in a group
√ in class	as homework
√ with teacher feedback	with peer feedback
timed	√ opportunity for revision

What the work shows

S2d Life Sciences Concepts: The student produces evidence that demonstrates understanding of interdependence of organisms, such as...competition among organisms in ecosystems; and human effects on the environment.

A The student states that, by itself, natural competition among predator species doesn't significantly impact any one species. This conclusion was drawn directly from the data collected during the simulation.

B The student draws a correct conclusion about the indirect impact of pollution on a predator species.

The quotations from the Science performance descriptions in this commentary are excerpted. The complete performance descriptions are shown on pages 122-143.

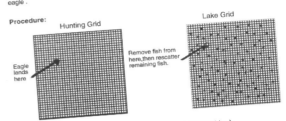

Ecology Unit- Predator-Prey Relationships

Background: Eagles mate for life. Each pair of eagles occupies, defends, and hunts a well defined territory. Each eagle hunts twice a day and will share the fish it catches with its mate, but it will feed itself first. If an eagle does not eat a total of nine fish in any three day period, it grows too weak to hunt and dies. Be sure to examine the data for each three-day period as you continue. If one eagle dies, continue hunting with the remaining eagle.

Procedure:

Hunting Grid

Lake Grid

Eagle lands here

Remove fish from here, then rescatter remaining fish.

1. You have two 400 cm grids that represent 4 km lakes (10 cm = 1 km). This is where the eagles hunt for food. This will be their only source of food.
2. The 2 small heavy paper squares represent your eagles. The M paper represents the male eagle. The F paper represents the female eagle.
3. Lay the two grids near each other on the lab table. Scatter 250 grains of white rice over one of the grids. Each grain represents a large fish in the lake. Assume that eagles eat only large fish.
4. The other grid is the hunting grid. Hold the M square (male eagle) about 30 cm above the hunting grid and drop it onto the grid. Remove the rice grains below the eagle. These represent " prey " that has been captured and eaten.
5. Each adult eagle hunts twice a day. Re-scatter the remaining rice and repeat steps 4 and 5. Total the number of fish caught by the eagles on Day 1, and record the data for Day 1 on Table 1 of the Observation Chart.
6. Repeat steps 4 through 6 nine more times. Complete Table 1.
7. Ospreys and eagles compete for food. What would happen if 2 osprey also hunted in the lake, each averaging a take of 3 fish per day? Repeat the simulation, removing 6 fish per day for the ospreys' catch, and record your results in Table 2.
8. A drought occurs that causes the water level of the lake to fall. This causes one quarter of the fish to die. Repeat the simulation under this condition and record your results in Table 3.
9. Phosphate pollution causes the algae in the lake to grow out of control. The algae growth reduces the amount of dissolved oxygen in the lake water and causes three quarters of the fish to die. Repeat the simulation under this condition and record your results in Table 4.
10. Graph your data and answer the questions that follow.

This work sample illustrates a standard-setting performance for the following parts of the standards:

S2d Life Sciences Concepts: Interdependence of organisms.

S2e Life Sciences Concepts: Matter, energy, and organization in living systems

S4c Scientific Connections and Applications: Health.

Physical Sciences Concepts

Life Sciences Concepts **S2**

Earth and Space Sciences Concepts

Scientific Connections and Applications **S4**

Scientific Thinking

Scientific Tools and Technologies

Scientific Communication

Scientific Investigation

Eagles

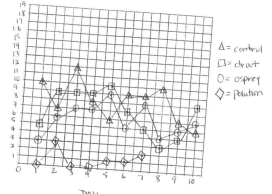

Table 1. Control

Day	1	2	3	4	5	6	7	8	9	10
No. of fish	10	7	12	8	6	9	9	10	6	5

Table 2. Osprey

Day	1	2	3	4	5	6	7	8	9	10
No. of fish	3	6	7	7	9	5	8	4	5	6

Table 3. trout

Day	1	2	3	4	5	6	7	8	9	10
No. of fish	5	9	9	9	10	7	5	3	4	8

Table 4. Polution

Day	1	2	3	4	5	6	7	8	9	10
No. of fish	0	3	0	0	1	1	2			

Δ = control
□ = drout
O = osprey
◇ = polution

DAY

F Conclusion – Small changes in the environment do not affect the eagle but large changes, such as pollution, does. Pollution killed a major part of the population in the lake.

S2 e Life Sciences Concepts: The student produces evidence that demonstrates understanding of matter, energy, and organization in living systems, such as…environmental constraints.

C D The student demonstrates understanding of seasonal and climate constraints on a food chain.

E The student recognizes the effect on the carrying capacity of an increase in a predator population. It should be noted, however, that the student's statement directly conflicts the conclusion drawn in item **A**. While both conclusions are logical and each one is correct within specific environmental conditions, the student should be challenged to describe in a revision the conditions that would support each statement.

S4 c Scientific Connections and Applications: The student produces evidence that demonstrates understanding of health, such as…resources, environmental stress, and population growth.

B F The student's conclusions are drawn directly from data collected during the simulation.

Analysis

1. How might eagle predation affect the fish population over time? I think that if the eagles get too many fish the fish population will not survive.

2. What effect, if any, might a small scale decrease in the fish population have on the eagle population? none. only large changes can have an effect on the eagles.

A 3. Ospreys and eagles compete for food. What effect, if any, might the competition have on the eagle population? none There was no change in the population.

C 4. Explain how a climate change might or might not indirectly affect the eagle population? Because there are fewer fish available for the eagles their population will decrease

D 5. How can a seasonal change affect the eagle population? Cold weather can freeze the lake and make it hard to catch fish so the eagles would go hungry.

B 6. Explain how pollution can indirectly affect the eagle population. Pollution kills the fish and eagles need the fish to live, so it will decrease the eagle population.

Discussion Questions:

1. What is the carrying capacity of an ecosystem? The carrying capacity of an ecosystem is how many organisms can survive successfully.

2. How would an increase in the eagle population affect the fish population? How is this similar to the competition from the ospreys?

E An increase in the eagle population is the same as competition from the ospreys because it reduces the number of fish and some eagles will go hungry and die

Work Sample & Commentary: *The Invincible Cockroach*

The task

Students were instructed to choose a species that most people would say is gross, frightening, or a pest (such as a slug, snake, mosquito, or cockroach). The species could be from any environment, including the student's own. Students were asked to prepare a written and pictorial research project of the species that was selected. The student's report needed to respond to these questions:

- How does the species function in its ecosystem?
- Why is it considered a pest?
- How do humans deal with this pest in their environment?
- If this species suddenly disappeared how might humans be affected?

The student's research needed to include collection of a specimen (if possible); a field journal with observations /drawings of the behavior; location, occupation, and morphology of the specimen; visits to museums or nature centers; and use of the Internet or other technologies (magnifiers, microscopes, etc.)

Circumstances of performance

This sample of student work was produced under the following conditions:

√ alone	in a group
√ in class	as homework
√ with teacher feedback	with peer feedback
√ timed	√ opportunity for revision

The work was submitted as a national competition entry.

This work sample illustrates a standard-setting performance for the following parts of the standards:

S2 f   Life Sciences Concepts: Behavior of organisms.

S4 a   Scientific Connections and Applications: Big ideas and unifying concepts.

S4 c   Scientific Connections and Applications: Health.

S6 d   Scientific Tools and Technologies: Acquire information from multiple sources.

S7 a   Scientific Communication: Represent data and results in multiple ways.

S7 b   Scientific Communication: Argue from evidence.

Sidebar

For related work on Interdependence, see "Biomes", page 52, "Bio Box", page 98, "Owl Pellets", page 101, and "Eagles", page 186.

Physical Sciences Concepts

Life Sciences Concepts **S2**

Earth and Space Sciences Concepts

Scientific Connections and Applications **S4**

Scientific Thinking

Scientific Tools and Technologies **S6**

Scientific Communication **S7**

Scientific Investigation

The quotations from the Science performance descriptions in this commentary are excerpted. The complete performance descriptions are shown on pages 122-143.

THE INVINCIBLE COCKROACH
by: _____
Staten Island, New York

A recent survey indicated that the cockroach was the most despised creature, beating out snakes, rats, bats, and spiders. I was able to observe this insect in its own environment when my father made an arrangement whereby I accompanied a health inspector on a tour of a roach-infested house.

The house I visited was old and not very clean. There was lots of clutter in the corners and the stove was very greasy. The inspector opened the food closet and I came face to face with the dreaded cockroach. In fact, I came face to face with several roaches. When the inspector moved a can, there seemed like hundreds. I was ready to run away.

The inspector explained to the people what they had to do in order to eliminate the problem. They needed to clean everything, remove the clutter, and throw out the old infested food. I never expected I would ever have to do research on the cockroach, but I became curious and wanted to find out what this bug was all about.

The cockroach that I saw is called the German cockroach or Blatella germanica. Humans consider it to be a pest because it invades where we live, eat and sleep. There are between 4,000 to 7,500 different species of roaches. Of this amount, only one percent are considered to be a pest. Some of the other more common species are:

  1) Oriental Cockroach-*Blatta orientalis*
  2) American Cockroach-*Periplaneta americana*
  3) Brownbanded Cockroach-*Supella longipalpa*

They have pathogens or bacteria on their bodies, but none have been known to be transmitted to humans. Their mouths are used for chewing, not biting. Most roaches are nocturnal, that is, they prefer the night and are sensitive to all forms of light except for the red spectrum. They are most active right after dusk and right before dawn. They are **A** according to a biological clock. This activity may be a response to a genetic defense because light may indicate the presence of humans, their most dangerous predator. They prefer to live in warm, moist places and

---

What the work shows

S2 f   Life Sciences Concepts: The student produces evidence that demonstrates understanding of behavior of organisms, such as the nervous system regulation [and] behavioral responses....

Ⓐ Ⓑ Ⓒ The student describes behaviors such as nocturnal activity, thigmotaxis, and reproductive specialization.

S4 a   Scientific Connections and Applications: The student produces evidence that demonstrates understanding of big ideas and unifying concepts, such as...form and function...and cause and effect.

Ⓓ Ⓔ Ⓕ The student provides detailed information about structures and functions.

Ⓖ Ⓗ The student makes logical and sophisticated inferences that suggest a causal relationship between increased pesticide use and three diverse factors: the cockroach's resistance to pesticides, climate conditions, and product marketing.

The Invincible Cockroach

are more abundant in tropical areas. However, they can live in almost any environment and they have been found in the North and South Poles.

Cockroaches are thought to be about 350 million years old, making them one of the oldest surviving creatures. They have been able to survive because of their rapid reproductive cycles and adaptability to poisons, environments, and even nuclear bombs. One of the largest is the Madagascar hissing cockroach, which has become a popular pet. Another large roach is Megaloblatta blaberoides, a resident of Central and South America. It has been measured at about 100mm long. Some roaches can fly and one has been measured to have a wing span of about one foot.

D Their ability to withstand radiation is very interesting. They have a very hard outer shell or exoskeleton, which is less prone to absorb radiation. Their skin molts, which means shedding, and this removes the radiation. In addition, they have an unusual different chromosome structure, which is difficult for radiation to shatter. The butterfly is similar to the cockroach in this respect.

B Although they live in proximity to each other in crevices or harbingers, they are not social insects such as the bee, termite, or the ant. This need to keep in touch with their surroundings is called thigmotaxis. Their immunity extends to poisons, and they are known to survive decapitation. I later read that this is possible because they have two nerve centers-one in the head, the other in the tail. The only way it would eventually die would be from dehydration. They can do without food for over one month, but they need water at least once a week. They will feed on all foods, grease, paint, wallpaper paste, and even bookbinding.

C The female will have up to forty babies at one time. Some species will mate only once and they will remain pregnant for the rest of their lives. Adults will live for an average of eight to fifteen months. Cockroaches reproduce on an average of four times per year. Females have a broader abdomen and are more rounded than the male. This constant reproduction adds to their ability to become immune to environment changes or pesticides. The basic structure of the cockroach has, however, remained the same since the middle of the Silurian period almost 365 million

S4 c Scientific Connections and Applications: The student produces evidence that demonstrates understanding of health, such as disease and epidemiology, personal and environmental safety; and resources, environmental stress and population growth.

G **H** The student makes logical inferences about the relationship between increased pesticide use and the cockroach's resistance to pesticides, climate conditions, and product marketing.

I The student names several diseases that roaches carry, such as Salmonella, staph and strep. The student discusses the relationship between cockroach skin molts and the increased incidence of allergic reactions and asthmatic conditions among children who live in poor urban areas.

S6 d Scientific Tools and Technologies: The student acquires information from multiple sources, such as print [and] the Internet....

J The bibliography shows that the student used print publications and downloaded information from the Internet.

Physical Sciences Concepts

S2 Life Sciences Concepts

Earth and Space Sciences Concepts

S4 Scientific Connections and Applications

Scientific Thinking

S6 Scientific Tools and Technologies

S7 Scientific Communication

Scientific Investigation

years ago. The life cycle of the cockroach is from egg-nymph-adult. This cycle is called simple metamorphosis. It means that the younger nymphs look very similar to the adult and will only differ in size.

E The basic anatomy of the cockroach is as follows:

1) eye - compound eyes made of 2,000 individual lenses. They see poorly in red light and well in green light.

2) antannae - provides sense of smell while the hairs on the legs give them a sense of touch.

3) cerci - two little hairs on the rear end act as a motion detector. It alerts the roach to run in the opposite direction.

4) mouth - moves side to side

5) reproduction - female gives off scent to lure male for reproduction purposes

Anatomy

6) esophagus -(throat) food travels down to stomach.

7) crop - section of esophagus used to store food. There is a second set of teeth in the digestive tract.

8) gastric caeca - provides enzymes to help in digestion.

9) malpighian tubules - cleans out wastes.

10) colon - produces excrement.

11) respiratory - breathes through spiracles on side of the body, supplies oxygen to rest of the body.

The cockroach that I observed is more important as a pest problem than as an important link in the food chain. Other species do provide nourishment for certain insects. In particular, spiders are its natural enemy. However, they are too sluggish to really inflict harm. Frogs, toads, and salamanders are more effective predators. Lizards are also very successful in catching the roach. In some parts of the world the lizard is kept as a pet just to keep the house clean of roaches. Humans have also used the cockroach as a source of nourishment and for its medicinal value.

The Invincible Cockroach

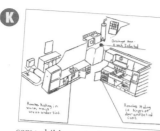

The roach, as a pest, is responsible for millions of dollars of spoiled food, pesticides, and damage to the environment from these pesticides. The non-deadly diseases they cause such as Salmonella, staph. and strep. have contributed to its being such a despised insect. Recent discoveries have suggested that the skin molts of the cockroach have caused allergic reactions and asthmatic conditions in some children who live in poor urban areas. If the roach were to disappear, humans would not have to spend millions of dollars trying to get rid of them. In addition, I feel that the chemicals that kill the roaches are doing more harm to people, animals, and plants than the roaches do themselves.

On one of the web sites, there was information from Rachel Carson's book, "Silent Spring," which was written over thirty years ago. It tells about the increasing and dangerous amounts of pesticides that are being used in America. It drew much attention and many laws were enacted to decrease the use of chemicals meant to control insects and keep them from contaminating food and invading our homes. I was very surprised to find out the following information:

**INCREASE IN PESTICIDE USE
UNITED STATES**

Pesticide Use in the USA

1964 Chemical Usage	1995 Chemical Usage
245 million kilograms	567 million kilograms

The reasons for this increase may be the pest's increasing resistance to pesticides, adverse climate factors and advertising, leading to greater user acceptance of pesticides. I think that we must find alternative means of controlling these insects. We cannot allow them to destroy our food supply, but we are only harming ourselves by using so many chemicals.

After studying this insect, I have become less afraid of it than when I went on the inspection tour. The more you learn about something, the less you fear it. I have seen how the insect's body works in many ways like ours: It chews and digests its food. It can reproduce. It will produce excrement to rid itself of waste. It is part of the world's ecosystem. Only a small portion of the thousands of species are considered pests with little value in the food chain. In a tropical rain forest, cockroaches live on the forest floor or high in trees where they are part of the food web. They also frequently inhabit caves where they are a source of food for bats. They are not as destructive as other insects, such as the termite. They don't spread deadly germs like the mosquito has been found to do. They are not as dangerous as the black widow spider or the killer bee. If the roach would disappear, the species I observed would not affect the ecosystem in a negative way because there are many other species which can be a source of food without being such a problem for humans. If people would study it some more, then maybe the cockroach will not rank as the number one hated creature in the next survey.

bibliography:

Biodiversity Forum. www.worldcorp.com/biodiversity

Environmental Protection Agency.www.epa.gov

Kids Web: Biology and Life Science. www.infomall.org/kidsweb/biology.html

Gaede, G. General and Comparative Endocrinology 75(2) 1989: 287-300.

Gordon, David. "The Complete Cockroach," excerpts from Website. Interview, 1997.

McKittrick, F.A. "A contribution to the understanding of cockroaches." Annals of the Entomological Society of America, 58 (1965): 18-22.

Morell, Matthew. Illustrations. January 1998.

National Geographic Society. www.nationalgeographic.com

New Jersey Online: Roach Anatomy. www.newjerseyonline.com

S7a Scientific Communication: The student represents data and results in multiple ways, such as numbers, tables, graphs, and drawings....

F H K In addition to the well-reasoned and well-written narrative, the student includes diagrams and a graph.

S7b Scientific Communication: The student argues from evidence, such as data produced through his or her own experimentation or data produced by others.

G H The student makes connections between different evidence to hypothesize that chemicals used to kill roaches might do more harm to people and other organisms.

K The student indicates how this report has influenced a personal attitude toward the species.

Work Sample & Commentary: *An Application of Eratosthenes's Method*

The task

During a laboratory lesson, students determined the circumference of a classroom globe using Eratosthenes's Method. After comparing their experimentally determined circumference with the accepted value for the circumference, students determined their percent error and identified possible sources of error. Finally, students were asked to apply this method to a novel situation—determining the size of the Unisphere in Flushing Meadows Park.

Circumstances of performance

This sample of student work was produced under the following conditions:

√ alone   √ in a group

√ in class   √ as homework

√ with teacher feedback   with peer feedback

    timed   √ opportunity for revision

What the work shows

S5 e Scientific Thinking: The student identifies problems; proposes and implements solutions; and evaluates the accuracy, design, and outcomes of investigations.

A In the procedure, the student describes a proposed solution to the problem of determining the Unisphere's size.

B In the answer to question 3 in the conclusion, the student evaluates the investigation and identifies possible sources of error.

This work sample illustrates a standard-setting performance for the following parts of the standards:

S5 e **Scientific Thinking: Identify problems; propose and implement solutions; and evaluate the accuracy, design, and outcomes of investigations.**

S6 a **Scientific Tools and Technologies: Use technologies and tools.**

S7 a **Scientific Communication: Represent data and results in multiple ways.**

S7 d **Scientific Communication: Explain a scientific concept or procedure.**

S7 e **Scientific Communication: Communicate in a form suited to the purpose and the audience.**

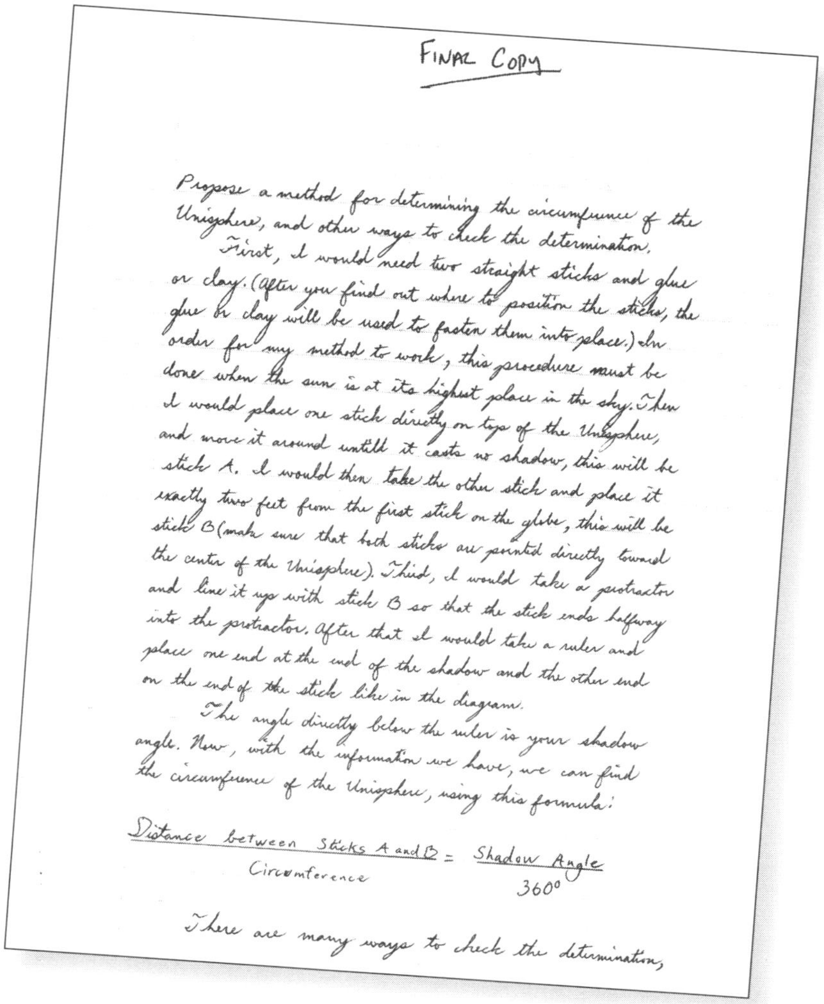

FINAL COPY

Propose a method for determining the circumference of the Unisphere, and other ways to check the determination.

First, I would need two straight sticks and glue or clay. (After you find out where to position the sticks, the glue or clay will be used to fasten them into place.) In order for my method to work, this procedure must be done when the sun is at its highest place in the sky. Then I would place one stick directly on top of the Unisphere, and move it around untill it casts no shadow, this will be stick A. I would then take the other stick and place it exactly two feet from the first stick on the globe, this will be stick B (make sure that both sticks are pointed directly toward the center of the Unisphere). Third, I would take a protractor and line it up with stick B so that the stick ends halfway into the protractor. After that I would take a ruler and place one end at the end of the shadow and the other end on the end of the stick like in the diagram.

The angle directly below the ruler is your shadow angle. Now, with the information we have, we can find the circumference of the Unisphere, using this formula:

$$\frac{\text{Distance between Sticks A and B}}{\text{Circumference}} = \frac{\text{Shadow Angle}}{360°}$$

There are many ways to check the determination.

S6 a Scientific Tools and Technologies: The student uses technologies and tools...to observe and measure objects...directly, indirectly and remotely, with appropriate consideration of accuracy and precision.

A C D In the diagrams, the student provides evidence of proper use of a ruler, a measuring tape, and a protractor.

E Data collected with the tools was subjected to appropriate consideration of accuracy by the calculation of the percent error for each experimental value.

The quotations from the Science performance descriptions in this commentary are excerpted. The complete performance descriptions are shown on pages 122-143.

Sidebar navigation:

Physical Sciences Concepts

Life Sciences Concepts

S3 Earth and Space Sciences Concepts

Scientific Connections and Applications

S5 Scientific Thinking

S6 Scientific Tools and Technologies

S7 Scientific Communication

Scientific Investigation

An Application of Eratosthenes's Method

S7 a Scientific Communication: The student represents data and results in multiple ways, such as numbers, tables, and…diagrams; technical and creative writing; and selects the most effective way to convey the scientific information.

A C D The student presented the procedure in writing and the data in two diagrams. Choosing to use diagrams to support the written procedure demonstrates selection of the most effective way to convey scientific information.

E In the data table, the student shows consideration of accuracy by calculating the percent error for each of the experimental values.

S7 d Scientific Communication: The student explains a scientific concept or procedure to other students.

A C D The procedure is explained and illustrated clearly.

F The answer to question 2 in the conclusion addresses variables that would affect the outcome of the investigation.

S7 e Scientific Communication: The student communicates in a form suited to the purpose and the audience, such as by writing instructions that others can follow….

A The clear, concise, and logically sequenced procedure, especially as supported by labeled diagrams, demonstrates understanding of Eratosthenes's Method and could be easily replicated by others.

Physical Sciences Concepts

Life Sciences Concepts

Earth and Space Sciences Concepts

Scientific Connections and Applications

Scientific Thinking **S5**

Scientific Tools and Technologies **S6**

Scientific Communication **S7**

Scientific Investigation

I will name three.

1.) You can make a model of the Unisphere, for example to a scale of 1/60, then you would repeat any procedure, (which only works with an over-head source of light) and whatever circumference you would come up with, you would multiply it by 60.

2.) You could do number 1.), except you would place stick B in a different place in the two hemispheres.

3.) You could simply measure the distance around the Unisphere with a tape measure.

Diagram:

C

Unisphere

Problem: How can you determine the circumference of the Unisphere?

Materials:

1.) 2 straight sticks
2.) Glue or clay (After you find out where to position the sticks, the glue or clay will be used to fasten them into place)
3.) protractor
4.) ruler

A **Procedure:**

First, I would place one stick on top of the Unisphere and move it around until it casts no shadow, this will be stick A. I would next take the other stick and place it some measured distance from stick A, this will be stick B. Make sure that both sticks are pointed directly toward the center of the Unisphere. Then, I would take the protractor and line it up with stick B so that the stick ends halfway into the protractor. After that, I would take a ruler and place one end at the end of the shadow and the other end on the end of the stick like in the diagram.

The angle directly below the ruler is your shadow angle. Now, with the information we have, we

An Application of Eratosthenes's Method

can find the circumference of the Unisphere, using this formula:

$$\underline{\text{Distance between Sticks A and B}} = \frac{\text{Shadow Angle}}{360°}$$
Circumference

Observations:

Diagram:

D

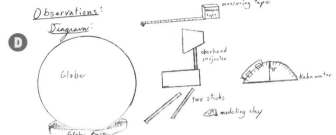

Globe

Globe Case

measuring tape

overhead projector

Kahn meter

two sticks

modeling clay

E Data Table:

Distance	Shadow ∡	Circumference		% Error
		Measured	Accepted	
7.6 cm.	58°	47.2 cm.	64.2 cm.	26.5%
9.2 cm.	49°	67.6 cm.	64.2 cm.	5.3%
7.0 cm.	30°	84.0 cm.	64.2 cm.	30.8%
11.7 cm.	60°	70.2 cm.	64.2 cm.	9.3%
6.0 cm.	20°	108.0 cm.	64.2 cm.	68.2%
12.5 cm.	50°	90.0 cm.	64.2 cm.	40.2%
9.3 cm.	37°	90.5 cm.	64.2 cm.	41.0%
Average Circumference		79.6 cm.	% Error for Average Circumference	23.9%

Conclusion:

You can determine the circumference of the Unisphere by using Eratosthenes' Principle and my procedure to solve the formula shown above. <u>How it applies to real life</u>: Scientists involved with space travel need circumference. They need it because if they wanted to launch a satelite to Mars, and the moon was in the way, they would need the circumference of the moon in order to avoid it properly and without collision.

1) Produce an explanation of how observations are used to determine circumference. Observations such as shadow angle and distance between the sticks are the keys to providing the solution to the formula:
$$\underline{\text{distance between two sticks}} = \frac{\text{shadow angle}}{360°},$$
circumference

which determines circumference.

F 2) How must this experiment have to be changed, if we were to conduct it at various seasons of the year? At various seasons of the year the sun is at different altitudes in the sky because of the earth's tilt on its axis and its revolution around the sun. Therefore at different seasons throughout the year the sun's rays hit the earth at different angles, causing the length of shadows to change. If the length of shadows changes then the stick which previously cast no shadow will now cast one, so this experiment must be changed by moving stick A again so it casts no shadow in order for the setup to work properly.

B 3) What are some sources of error? Some possible sources of error are that we measured the shadow angle or the distance between two sticks wrong, also, the stick that wasn't supposed to cast a shadow may have cast a slight one.

4) What are some alternate methods of determining the circumference of a large spherical object? You can determine the circumference of a large spherical object by using this procedure except with stick B in a different place on the sphere, also, you can simply use measuring tape to find the circumference.

Physical Sciences Concepts

Life Sciences Concepts

Earth and Space Sciences Concepts

Scientific Connections and Applications

S5 Scientific Thinking

S6 Scientific Tools and Technologies

S7 Scientific Communication

Scientific Investigation

Work Sample & Commentary: *Faulty Dough*

The task

Working in small groups, students constructed three-dimensional block diagrams of rock structures. They were then asked to discuss the rock structure and propose a possible sequence of geological events that could have produced that structure. After proposing a sequence of events, the students worked within their groups to model each event using modeling clay to represent rock. After the entire sequence of proposed events had been modeled in clay, the students were asked to compare and contrast their resulting clay structures with the original three-dimensional block diagrams. As a culminating activity, groups were asked to compare their proposed sequence of events and models with those of other groups.

The quotations from the Science performance descriptions in this commentary are excerpted. The complete performance descriptions are shown on pages 122-143.

Circumstances of performance

This sample of student work was produced under the following conditions:

alone	√ in a group
√ in class	as homework
√ with teacher feedback	with peer feedback
timed	√ opportunity for revision

The teacher facilitated the assignment and assisted the students with various aspects of the investigation. The student's work is a final revision.

Problem: How can we show the formation of geologic events using clay models?

Materials:
Plastic Knives
4 different colored clay (play-doh)
wax paper
rolling pin
tape
scissors

Vocabulary:
lithification
deposition
folding
erosion
faulting
emergence
submersion
Law of Superposition
Law of Cross-cutting relationships

Procedure:
1. First we take the 6 block diagrams, cut them out and assemble them with the tape.

2. The materials were given to us, and we did one of the diagrams together as a class. We followed the teacher's instructions on the construction of model #1.

K 3. The using the 4 colors of clay: red, white, yellow, and blue, we were assigned to construct 2 of the 6 block diagrams in our group of four. Red was sandstone. Blue was limestone, yellow was shale, and white was conglomerate. The unknown color used was green for our group (mixed blue and yellow). Depending on which block diagram you were assigned, you had to follow the pattern of which one came first.

L 4. We took some of the clay out and put it on the wax paper. One person rolled it flat with the rolling pin. (Be careful that the clay isn't rolled out too flat. Each layer should be around a quarter of an inch).

I 5. We constructed the model by putting one layer on top of another. At the end, we used the knife and cut it to make it more neat. If it was a certain geologic process involved (besides the deposition and lithification of a layer and erosion or submergence because you can't show submergence or erosion. Also, the deposition and lithification of a layer was just to put it on top of each other, we had to show it. For instance, if it was folded, we took the model and folded it. If some parts were eroded, we looked at the block diagram to see which part of it was eroded, and we peeled that layer off. If it showed faulting, we used the knife to cut it in half, and lifted one side up to show the foot wall.

This work sample illustrates a standard-setting performance for the following parts of the standards:

S3c **Earth and Space Sciences Concepts:** Origin and evolution of the Earth system.

S4a **Scientific Connections and Applications:** Big ideas and unifying concepts.

S5e **Scientific Thinking:** Identify problems; propose and implement solutions; and evaluate the accuracy, design, and outcomes of investigations.

S5f **Scientific Thinking:** Work individually and in teams.

S7a **Scientific Communication:** Represent data and results in multiple ways.

S7e **Scientific Communication:** Communicate in a form suited to the purpose and the audience.

What the work shows

S3c **Earth and Space Sciences Concepts:** The student produces evidence that demonstrates understanding of origin and evolution of the Earth system....

A B C D E F G H In modeling and describing the sequence of events which could result in a particular landform, the student demonstrates understanding that existing landforms are the product of an evolutionary process which occurs over time.

S4a **Scientific Connections and Applications:** The student produces evidence that demonstrates understanding of big ideas and unifying concepts, such as...models, form and function....

C D E F G H The six tables dramatically show the student's interpretation of each model. A review of each table shows that the student transferred learning from model to model as the investigation proceeded.

Faulty Dough

S5 e Scientific Thinking: The student identifies problems; proposes and implements solutions; and evaluates the accuracy, design, and outcomes of investigations.

I In step 5 of the procedural outline, the student evaluates the accuracy and design of the investigation and notes limitations of the models and the process by which the models were constructed.

J The student provides a troubleshooting list for subsequent investigators who might experience difficulty with the procedure.

S5 f Scientific Thinking: The student works individually and in teams to collect and share information and ideas.

K **L** Use of the word "we" indicates the collaborative nature of the investigation.

S7 e Scientific Communication: The student communicates in a form suited to the purpose and the audience, such as by writing instructions which demonstrates clarity of understanding so that other students can follow.

C **D** **E** **F** **G** **H** The student clearly communicates the way in which each geologic process was modeled. In correctly describing the geologic processes being modeled and the geologic principles involved, the student demonstrates clarity of understanding.

J The troubleshooting list provides for ease of replication of the investigation by other students.

S7 a Scientific Communication: The student represents data and results in multiple ways, such as tables,...diagrams, and...technical...writing; and selects the most effective way to convey the scientific information.

B The student used a diagram format effectively.

C **D** **E** **F** **G** **H** The student describes the steps for building each model in the six tables. Incorporating narrative descriptions of the model-building procedures into the tables is innovative and very effective. In choosing to organize the report in this way, the student relates each step of each procedure to a geological event and principle.

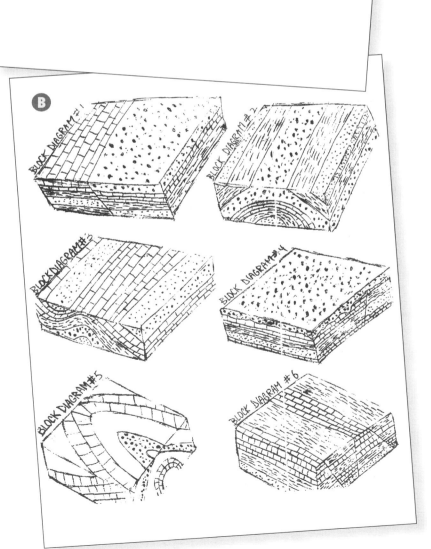

6. After the first model was done, we used the next period to make the second model. It was basically the same procedure, only now we had to follow a different block diagram.

7. When we were finished with everything, we went over the steps and the geologic principles involved.

J Things that might go wrong:
1. While constructing each layer, it might be too thin and fall apart once put together, so warn your students to make it a certain width.
2. Interpreting the block diagrams might be a little complicated. There are different sides to them, and it gets confusing for the students to try and figure out which one of the layers goes next. (I know that it was hard for me).
3. Students might get mixed up on the laws too. Most of them were the same, but some of them looked like it could be one thing, but it was really another, so it would be good to prepare them before starting.

Conclusion:
This project was actually fun, and we learned things too. We got to something hands on which made me visualize it better. We learned about the geologic processes and principles. We learned about the formation of **A** rocks, and what kinds of rocks there are, and what they've been through for all these years. I was proud that I understood that stuff, and made a geologic model. It was an interesting lab, and I hope that you're students learn as much as we did.

B BLOCK DIAGRAM #1 · BLOCK DIAGRAM #2 · BLOCK DIAGRAM #3 · BLOCK DIAGRAM #4 · BLOCK DIAGRAM #5 · BLOCK DIAGRAM #6

Physical Sciences Concepts

Life Sciences Concepts

S3 Earth and Space Sciences Concepts

S4 Scientific Connections and Applications

S5 Scientific Thinking

Scientific Tools and Technologies

S7 Scientific Communication

Scientific Investigation

Faulty Dough

C

BLOCK DIAGRAM NUMBER ___1___

step number	procedure	geologic process modeled	geologic principles involved
1	put down a layer of yellow clay	deposition and lithification of shale	superposition - in any series of sedimentary beds, the oldest beds are on the bottom and the youngest beds are at the top.
2	put down a layer of red clay	deposition and lithification of sandstone	superposition
3	put down a layer of yellow clay	deposition and lithification of shale	superposition
4	put down a layer of blue clay	deposition and lithification of limestone	superposition
5	put down a layer of white clay	deposition and lithification of conglomerate	superposition
6	cut through all layers of clay. Push one side slightly upward. Attach the layers.	normal faulting	law of cross-cutting relationships - faults are younger than the rocks in which they are found.
7	_____	emergence	_____
8	cut off part of the top layers, exposing the blue layer on one side, and the white layer on the other side.	erosion	_____

D

BLOCK DIAGRAM NUMBER ___2___

step number	procedure	geologic process modeled	geologic principles involved
1	put down a layer of red clay	deposition and lithification of sandstone	superposition - in any series of sedimentary beds, the oldest beds are on the bottom and the youngest beds are at the top.
2	put down a layer of yellow clay	deposition and lithification of shale	superposition
3	put down a layer of blue clay	deposition and lithification of limestone	superposition
4	put down a layer of white clay	deposition and lithification of conglomerate	superposition
5	put down a layer of yellow clay	deposition and lithification of shale	superposition
6	put down a layer of red clay	deposition and lithification of sandstone	superposition
7	fold the clay by applying pressure from the sides.	folding	law of cross-cutting relationships - folds are younger than the rocks in which they are found.
8	_____	emergence	
9	cut off part of the top layers, exposing the blue layer on one side, and the white layer on the other side.	erosion	

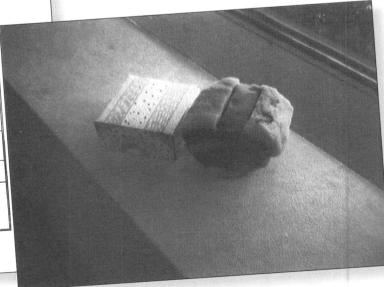

Physical Sciences Concepts

Life Sciences Concepts

Earth and Space Sciences Concepts • S3

Scientific Connections and Applications • S4

Scientific Thinking • S5

Scientific Tools and Technologies

Scientific Communication • S7

Scientific Investigation

Faulty Dough

(E)

BLOCK DIAGRAM NUMBER ___3___

step number	procedure	geologic process modeled	geologic principles involved
1	put down a layer of red clay	deposition and lithification of sandstone	superposition - in any series of sedimentary beds, the oldest beds are on the bottom and the youngest beds are at the top.
2	put down a layer of white	deposition and lithification of conglomerate	superposition
3	put down a layer of yellow	deposition and lithification of shale	superposition
4	put down a layer of blue clay	deposition and lithification of limestone	superposition
5	put down a layer of red clay	deposition and lithification of sandstone	superposition
6	fold the clay by applying pressure from the sides.	folding	law of cross-cutting relationships - folds are younger than the rocks in which they are found.
7	_____	emergence	_____
8	cut off part of the top layers, exposing the blue layer on one side, and the white layer on the other side.	erosion	_____

(F)

BLOCK DIAGRAM NUMBER ___4___

step number	procedure	geologic process modeled	geologic principles involved
1	put down a layer of blue clay	deposition and lithification of limestone	superposition - in any series of sedimentary beds, the oldest beds are on the bottom and the youngest beds are at the top.
2	put down a layer of red clay	deposition and lithification of sandstone	superposition
3	put down a layer of yellow clay	deposition and lithification of shale	superposition
4	put down a layer of blue clay	deposition and lithification of limestone	superposition
5	cut through all layers of clay. Push one side slightly upward. Attach the layers.	normal faulting	law of cross-cutting relationships - faults are younger than the rocks in which they are found.
6	_____	emergence	_____
7	cut across the top layer, in an irregular horizontal line, creating an unconformity	erosion	_____
8		submergence	
9	put down a layer of white clay	deposition and lithification of conglomerate	superposition
10	_____	emergence	_____
11		erosion	

Faulty Dough

G

BLOCK DIAGRAM NUMBER ___5___

step number	procedure	geologic process modeled	geologic principles involved
1	put down a layer of green clay	deposition and lithification of an unknown layer	superposition - in any series of sedimentary beds, the oldest beds are on the bottom and the youngest beds are at the top.
2	put down a layer of blue clay	deposition and lithification of limestone	superposition
3	put down a layer of green clay	deposition and lithification of an unknown layer	superposition
4	put down a layer of white clay	deposition and lithification of conglomerate	superposition
5	put down a layer of green clay	deposition and lithification of an unknown layer	superposition
6	put down a layer of blue clay	deposition and lithification of limestone	superposition
7	_____	emergence	_____
8	fold the clay by applying pressure from the sides. Tilt the model.	folding, with a plunging fold axis (anticline)	law of cross-cutting relationships - folds are younger than the rocks in which they are found.
9	cut off part of the top layers, exposing the layers below to conform to the diagram.	erosion	_____

H

BLOCK DIAGRAM NUMBER ___6___

step number	procedure	geologic process modeled	geologic principles involved
1	put down a layer of red clay	deposition and lithification of sandstone	superposition - in any series of sedimentary beds, the oldest beds are on the bottom and the youngest beds are at the top.
2	put down a layer of yellow clay	deposition and lithification of shale	superposition
3	put down a layer of blue clay	deposition and lithification of limestone	superposition
4	put down a layer of yellow clay	deposition and lithification of shale	superposition
5	put down a layer of blue clay	deposition and lithification of limestone	superposition
6	put down a layer of yellow clay	deposition and lithification of shale	superposition
7	cut through all layers of clay in two places. Push up two sides slightly. Attach the layers.	normal faulting (horst and graben)	law of cross-cutting relationships - faults are younger than the rocks in which they are found.
8	_____	emergence	_____
9	cut off part of the top layers, exposing the layers below to match the diagram.	erosion	_____

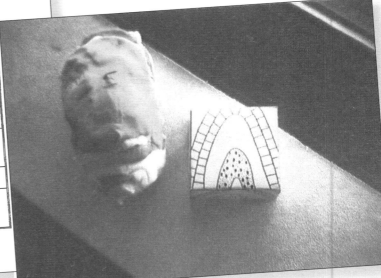

S1 Physical Sciences Concepts

APPENDIX

The elementary school standards are set at a level of performance approximately equivalent to the end of fourth grade. The middle school standards are set at a level of performance approximately equivalent to the end of eighth grade. The high school standards are set at a level of performance approximately equivalent to the end of tenth grade. It is expected that some students might achieve these levels earlier and others later than these grades.

The Science standards are founded upon both the National Research Council's National Science Education Standards and the American Association for the Advancement of Science's Project 2061 Benchmarks for Science Literacy. These documents, each of which runs to several hundred pages, contain detailed explication of the concepts identified here.

Elementary School

The student produces evidence that demonstrates understanding of:

S1a Properties of objects and materials, such as similarities and differences in the size, weight, and color of objects; the ability of materials to react with other substances; and different states of materials.

S1b Position and motion of objects, such as how the motion of an object can be described by tracing and measuring its position over time; and how sound is produced by vibrating objects.

S1c Light, heat, electricity, and magnetism, such as the variation of heat and temperature; how light travels in a straight line until it strikes an object or how electrical circuits work.

Middle School

The student produces evidence that demonstrates understanding of:

S1a Properties and changes of properties in matter, such as density and boiling point; chemical reactivity; and conservation of matter.

S1b Motions and forces, such as inertia and the net effects of balanced and unbalanced forces.

S1c Transfer of energy, such as transformation of energy as heat; light, mechanical motion, and sound; and the nature of a chemical reaction.

High School

The student produces evidence that demonstrates understanding of:

S1a Structure of atoms, such as atomic composition, nuclear forces, and radioactivity.

S1b Structure and properties of matter, such as elements and compounds; bonding and molecular interaction; and characteristics of phase changes.

S1c Chemical reactions, such as everyday examples of chemical reactions; electrons, protons, and energy transfer; and factors that affect reaction rates such as catalysts.

S1d Motions and forces, such as gravitational and electrical; net forces and magnetism.

S1e Conservation of energy and increase in disorder, such as kinetic and potential energy; energy conduction, convection, and radiation; random motion; and effects of heat and pressure.

S1f Interactions of energy and matter, such as waves, absorption and emission of light, and conductivity.

S2 Life Sciences Concepts

Elementary School

The student produces evidence that demonstrates understanding of:

S2 a Characteristics of organisms, such as survival and environmental support; the relationship between structure and function; and variations in behavior.

S2 b Life cycles of organisms, such as how inheritance and environment determine the characteristics of an organism; and that all plants and animals have life cycles.

S2 c Organisms and environments, such as the interdependence of animals and plants in an ecosystem; and populations and their effects on the environment.

S2 d Change over time, such as evolution and fossil evidence depicting the great diversity of organisms developed over geologic history.

Middle School

The student produces evidence that demonstrates understanding of:

S2 a Structure and function in living systems, such as the complementary nature of structure and function in cells, organs, tissues, organ systems, whole organisms, and ecosystems.

S2 b Reproduction and heredity, such as sexual and asexual reproduction; and the role of genes and environment on trait expression.

S2 c Regulation and behavior, such as senses and behavior; and response to environmental stimuli.

S2 d Populations and ecosystems, such as the roles of producers, consumers, and decomposers in a food web; and the effects of resources and energy transfer on populations.

S2 e Evolution, diversity, and adaptation of organisms, such as common ancestry, speciation, adaptation, variation, and extinction.

High School

The student produces evidence that demonstrates understanding of:

S2 a The cell, such as cell structure and function relationships; regulation and biochemistry; and energy and photosynthesis.

S2 b Molecular basis of heredity, such as DNA, genes, chromosomes, and mutations.

S2 c Biological evolution, such as speciation, biodiversity, natural selection, and biological classification.

S2 d Interdependence of organisms, such as conservation of matter; cooperation and competition among organisms in ecosystems; and human effects on the environment.

S2 e Matter, energy, and organization in living systems, such as matter and energy flow through different levels of organization; and environmental constraints.

S2 f Behavior of organisms, such as nervous system regulation; behavioral responses; and connections with anthropology, sociology, and psychology.

S3 Earth and Space Sciences Concepts

Elementary School

The student produces evidence that demonstrates understanding of:

S3 a Properties of Earth materials, such as water and gases; and the properties of rocks and soils, such as texture, color, and ability to retain water.

S3 b Objects in the sky, such as Sun, Moon, planets, and other objects that can be observed and described; and the importance of the Sun to provide the light and heat necessary for survival.

S3 c Changes in Earth and sky, such as changes caused by weathering, volcanism, and earthquakes; and the patterns of movement of objects in the sky.

Middle School

The student produces evidence that demonstrates understanding of:

S3 a Structure of the Earth system, such as crustal plates and land forms; water and rock cycles; oceans, weather, and climate.

S3 b Earth's history, such as Earth processes including erosion and movement of plates; change over time and fossil evidence.

S3 c Earth in the Solar System, such as the predictable motion of planets, moons, and other objects in the Solar System including days, years, moon phases, and eclipses; and the role of the Sun as the major source of energy for phenomena on the Earth's surface.

S3 d Natural resource management.

High School

The student produces evidence that demonstrates understanding of:

S3 a Energy in the Earth system, such as radioactive decay, gravity, the Sun's energy, convection, and changes in global climate.

S3 b Geochemical cycles, such as conservation of matter; chemical resources and movement of matter between chemical reservoirs.

S3 c Origin and evolution of the Earth system, such as geologic time and the age of life forms; origin of life; and evolution of the Solar System.

S3 d Origin and evolution of the universe, such as the "big bang" theory; formation of stars and elements; and nuclear reactions.

S3 e Natural resource management.

S4 **Scientific Connections and Applications**

Elementary School

The student produces evidence that demonstrates understanding of:

S4 a Big ideas and unifying concepts, such as order and organization; models, form and function; change and constancy; and cause and effect.

S4 b The designed world, such as development of agricultural techniques; and the viability of technological designs.

S4 c Personal health, such as nutrition, substance abuse, and exercise; germs and toxic substances; personal and environmental safety.

S4 d Science as a human endeavor, such as communication, cooperation, and diverse input in scientific research; and the importance of reason, intellectual honesty, and skepticism.

Middle School

The student produces evidence that demonstrates understanding of:

S4 a Big ideas and unifying concepts, such as order and organization; models, form, and function; change and constancy; and cause and effect.

S4 b The designed world, such as the reciprocal nature of science and technology; the development of agricultural techniques; and the viability of technological designs.

S4 c Health, such as nutrition, exercise, and disease; effects of drugs and toxic substances; personal and environmental safety; and resources and environmental stress.

S4 d Impact of technology, such as constraints and trade-offs; feedback; benefits and risks; and problems and solutions.

S4 e Impact of science, such as historical and contemporary contributions; and interactions between science and society.

High School

The student produces evidence that demonstrates understanding of:

S4 a Big ideas and unifying concepts, such as order and organization; models, form and function; change and constancy; and cause and effect.

S4 b The designed world, such as the reciprocal relationship between science and technology; the development of agricultural techniques; and the reasonableness of technological designs.

S4 c Health, such as nutrition and exercise; disease and epidemiology; personal and environmental safety; and resources, environmental stress, and population growth.

S4 d Impact of technology, such as constraints and trade-offs; feedback; benefits and risks; and problems and solutions.

S4 e Impact of science, such as historical and contemporary contributions; and interactions between science and society.

S5 Scientific Thinking

Elementary School

The student demonstrates scientific inquiry and problem solving by using thoughtful questioning and reasoning strategies, common sense and conceptual understanding from Science Standards 1 to 4, and appropriate methods to investigate the natural world; that is, the student:

S5 a Asks questions about natural phenomena; objects and organisms; and events and discoveries.

S5 b Uses concepts from Science Standards 1 to 4 to explain a variety of observations and phenomena.

S5 c Uses evidence from reliable sources to construct explanations.

S5 d Evaluates different points of view using relevant experiences, observations, and knowledge; and distinguishes between fact and opinion.

S5 e Identifies problems; proposes and implements solutions; and evaluates the accuracy, design, and outcomes of investigations.

S5 f Works individually and in teams to collect and share information and ideas.

Middle School

The student demonstrates scientific inquiry and problem solving by using thoughtful questioning and reasoning strategies, common sense and conceptual understanding from Science Standards 1 to 4, and appropriate methods to investigate the natural world; that is, the student:

S5 a Frames questions to distinguish cause and effect; and identifies or controls variables in experimental and non-experimental research settings.

S5 b Uses concepts from Science Standards 1 to 4 to explain a variety of observations and phenomena.

S5 c Uses evidence from reliable sources to develop descriptions, explanations, and models.

S5 d Proposes, recognizes, analyzes, considers, and critiques alternative explanations; and distinguishes between fact and opinion.

S5 e Identifies problems; proposes and implements solutions; and evaluates the accuracy, design, and outcomes of investigations.

S5 f Works individually and in teams to collect and share information and ideas.

High School

The student demonstrates skill in scientific inquiry and problem solving by using thoughtful questioning and reasoning strategies, common sense and diverse conceptual understanding, and appropriate ideas and methods to investigate science; that is, the student:

S5 a Frames questions to distinguish cause and effect; and identifies or controls variables in experimental and non-experimental research settings.

S5 b Uses concepts from Science Standards 1 to 4 to explain a variety of observations and phenomena.

S5 c Uses evidence from reliable sources to develop descriptions, explanations, and models; and makes appropriate adjustments and improvements based on additional data or logical arguments.

S5 d Proposes, recognizes, analyzes, considers, and critiques alternative explanations; and distinguishes between fact and opinion.

S5 e Identifies problems; proposes and implements solutions; and evaluates the accuracy, design, and outcomes of investigations.

S5 f Works individually and in teams to collect and share information and ideas.

S6 Scientific Tools and Technologies

S6 makes explicit reference to using telecommunications to acquire and share information. A recent National Center on Education Statistics survey recently reported that only 50% of schools and fewer than 9% of instructional rooms currently have access to the Internet. We know this is an equity issue—that far more than 9% of the homes in the United States have access to the Internet and that schools must make sure that students' access to information and ideas does not depend on what they get at home—so we have crafted performance standards that would use the Internet so that people will make sure that all students have access to it. New Standards partners have made a commitment to create the learning environments where students can develop the knowledge and skills delineated here.

Elementary School

The student demonstrates competence with the tools and technologies of science by using them to collect data, make observations, analyze results, and accomplish tasks effectively; that is, the student:

S6a Uses technology and tools (such as rulers, computers, balances, thermometers, watches, magnifiers, and microscopes) to gather data and extend the senses.

S6b Collects and analyzes data using concepts and techniques in Mathematics Standard 4, such as average, data displays, graphing, variability, and sampling.

S6c Acquires information from multiple sources, such as experimentation and print and non-print sources.

Middle School

The student demonstrates competence with the tools and technologies of science by using them to collect data, make observations, analyze results, and accomplish tasks effectively; that is, the student:

S6a Uses technology and tools (such as traditional laboratory equipment, video, and computer aids) to observe and measure objects, organisms, and phenomena, directly, indirectly, and remotely.

S6b Records and stores data using a variety of formats, such as data bases, audiotapes, and videotapes.

S6c Collects and analyzes data using concepts and techniques in Mathematics Standard 4, such as mean, median, and mode; outcome probability and reliability; and appropriate data displays.

S6d Acquires information from multiple sources, such as print, the Internet, computer data bases, and experimentation.

S6e Recognizes sources of bias in data, such as observer and sampling biases.

High School

The student demonstrates competence with the tools and technologies of science by using them to collect data, make observations, analyze results, and accomplish tasks effectively; that is, the student:

S6a Uses technology and tools (such as traditional laboratory equipment, video, and computer aids) to observe and measure objects, organisms, and phenomena, directly, indirectly, and remotely, with appropriate consideration of accuracy and precision.

S6b Records and stores data using a variety of formats, such as data bases, audiotapes, and videotapes.

S6c Collects and analyzes data using concepts and techniques in Mathematics Standard 4, such as mean, median, and mode; outcome probability and reliability; and appropriate data displays.

S6d Acquires information from multiple sources, such as print, the Internet, computer data bases, and experimentation.

S6e Recognizes and limits sources of bias in data, such as observer and sample biases.

S7 **Scientific Communication**

Elementary School

The student demonstrates effective scientific communication by clearly describing aspects of the natural world using accurate data, graphs, or other appropriate media to convey depth of conceptual understanding in science; that is, the student:

S7 a Represents data and results in multiple ways, such as numbers, tables, and graphs; drawings, diagrams, and artwork; and technical and creative writing.

S7 b Uses facts to support conclusions.

S7 c Communicates in a form suited to the purpose and the audience, such as writing instructions that others can follow.

S7 d Critiques written and oral explanations, and uses data to resolve disagreements.

Middle School

The student demonstrates effective scientific communication by clearly describing aspects of the natural world using accurate data, graphs, or other appropriate media to convey depth of conceptual understanding in science; that is, the student:

S7 a Represents data and results in multiple ways, such as numbers, tables, and graphs; drawings, diagrams, and artwork; and technical and creative writing.

S7 b Argues from evidence, such as data produced through his or her own experimentation or by others.

S7 c Critiques published materials.

S7 d Explains a scientific concept or procedure to other students.

S7 e Communicates in a form suited to the purpose and the audience, such as by writing instructions that others can follow; critiquing written and oral explanations; and using data to resolve disagreements.

High School

The student demonstrates effective scientific communication by clearly describing aspects of the natural world using accurate data, graphs, or other appropriate media to convey depth of conceptual understanding in science; that is, the student:

S7 a Represents data and results in multiple ways, such as numbers, tables, and graphs; drawings, diagrams, and artwork; technical and creative writing; and selects the most effective way to convey the scientific information.

S7 b Argues from evidence, such as data produced through his or her own experimentation or data produced by others.

S7 c Critiques published materials, such as popular magazines and academic journals.

S7 d Explains a scientific concept or procedure to other students.

S7 e Communicates in a form suited to the purpose and the audience, such as by writing instructions that others can follow; critiquing written and oral explanations; and using data to resolve disagreements.

S8 Scientific Investigation

Best practice in science has always included extensive inquiry and investigation, but these are frequently given less emphasis at the elementary level in the face of competing demands form English language arts and mathematics. There are many opportunities to learn science outside of school, including Scouts, Boys and Girls Clubs, 4-H, and Future Farmers of America. The work done in these venues can and should be used to provide evidence of meeting the standards.

Elementary School

The student demonstrates scientific competence by completing projects drawn from the following kinds of investigations, including at least one full investigation each year and, over the course of elementary school, investigations that integrate several aspects of Science Standards 1 to 7 and represent all four of the kinds of investigation:

S8 a An experiment, such as conducting a fair test.

S8 b A systematic observation, such as a field study.

S8 c A design, such as building a model or scientific apparatus.

S8 d Non-experimental research using print and electronic information, such as journals, video, or computers.

A single project may draw on more than one kind of investigation.

A full investigation includes:

- Questions that can be studied using the resources available.

- Procedures that are safe, humane, and ethical; and that respect privacy and property rights.

- Data that have been collected and recorded (see also Science Standard 6) in ways that others can verify and analyze using skills expected at this grade level (see also Mathematics Standard 4).

- Data and results that have been represented (see also Science Standard 7) in ways that fit the context.

- Recommendations, decisions, and conclusions based on evidence.

- Acknowledgment of references and contributions of others.

- Results that are communicated appropriately to audiences.

- Reflection and defense of conclusions and recommendations from other sources and peer review.

Middle School

The student demonstrates scientific competence by completing projects drawn from the following kinds of investigations, including at least one full investigation each year and, over the course of middle school, investigations that integrate several aspects of Science Standards 1 to 7 and represent all four of the kinds of investigation:

S8 a Controlled experiment.

S8 b Fieldwork.

S8 c Design.

S8 d Secondary research, such as use of others' data.

A single project may draw on more than one type of investigation.

A full investigation includes:

- Questions that can be studied using the resources available.

- Procedures that are safe, humane, and ethical; and that respect privacy and property rights.

- Data that have been collected and recorded (see also Science Standard 6) in ways that others can verify, and analyzed using skills expected at this grade level (see also Mathematics Standard 4).

- Data and results that have been represented (see also Science Standard 7) in ways that fit the context.

- Recommendations, decisions, and conclusions based on evidence.

- Acknowledgment of references and contributions of others.

- Results that are communicated appropriately to audiences.

- Reflection and defense of conclusions and recommendations from other sources and peer review.

High School

The student demonstrates scientific competence by completing projects drawn from the following kinds of investigation, including at least one full investigation each year and, over the course of high school, investigations that integrate several aspects of Science Standards 1 to 7 and represent all four of the kinds of investigation:

S8 a Controlled experiment.

S8 b Fieldwork.

S8 c Design.

S8 d Secondary research.

A single project may draw on more than one type of investigation.

A full investigation includes:

- Questions that can be studied using the resources available.

- Procedures that are safe, humane, and ethical; and that respect privacy and property rights.

- Data that have been collected and recorded (see also Science Standard 6) in ways that others can verify, and analyzed using skills expected at this grade level (see also Mathematics Standard 4).

- Data and results that have been represented (see also Science Standard 7) in ways that fit the context.

- Recommendations, decisions, and conclusions based on evidence.

- Acknowledgment of references and contributions of others.

- Results that are communicated appropriately to audiences.

- Reflection and defense of conclusions and recommendations from other sources and peer review.

CALIBRATION TASK FORCE

Board of Education of the City of New York

Roberto Benitez, Partnerships for Year Round-Learning, Office of School Programs and Support Services

Diana Canales, Science Specialist, Queens Multidisciplinary Resource Center

Ed Denecke, Staff Development Specialist, Queens Multidisciplinary Resource Center

Clifford Fee, Staff Development Specialist, Queens Multidisciplinary Resource Center

Gerald A. Haber, Assessment Specialist, Office of Performance Standards Division of Instructional Support

Regina McCarthy, Coordinator, Gateway Environmental Study Center

Carl M. Raab, Director of Academic Initiatives and Publications, Office of School Programs and Support Services

Laura Rodriguez, Assistant Administrative Superintendent

Office of Bilingual Education

Eliezer De Jesus, Mathematics/Science Resource Specialist

Archangelo Joseph, Mathematics/Science Resource Specialist

Annette Strubbe, Field Instructional Specialist

Michael C. Wang, Chinese Resource Specialist

Community School District 1

Merrilee Fiedler, Science Coordinator

John R. Grinins, Science Teacher, P.S. 34

Josie Suarez, Standards Coordinator

Community School District 2

Peter Kindfield, Ph.D., Science Staff Development Consultant

GinGee Moy, Science Staff Developer

Community School District 3

Howard Berger, Science Coordinator

David Getz, Staff Developer

Mary Anita Harvey, Teacher Consultant, CCNY/Students at the Center Program

Garo Tekeyan, Smart Process Coordinator

Community School District 4

Melissa Cancel, Science Teacher, Northview J.H.S

Carol Franken, Science Coordinator

Sandra Jenoure, Science Education Consultant

Liza Schneider, Science Teacher, P.S. 50

Community School District 5

Charles McWhales, Project Coordinator, Smart Process

Howard Nadler, Science Coordinator

Carmen W. Williamson, Science Facilitator, P.S. 30

Community School District 6

John Cafarella, former Science Director

Stacy Douglas, Science Facilitator

Marselle Heywood, Staff Developer

Mark Koesterich, Science Facilitator

Lillian Ramos, Science Staff Developer

Odille Santiago, Science Facilitator

Yvette Sy, Science Staff Developer

Community School District 7

Kenneth Harris, Science Teacher, I.S. 184

Anthony J. Viteritti, Director of Mathematics and Science

Community School District 8

Carol A. Rosario, Science Coordinator

Eugene K. Smith, Assistant Principal, P.S. 60X

Community School District 9

Deborah Disbrow, Science Staff Developer

Michael Kreindler, Science Staff Developer

Community School District 10

Judith Abel, Science Staff Developer

Jeffrey Felber, Director of Science

Wilfred Hemans, Assistant Principal, M.S. 143

Community School District 11

Katina Lotakis, Assistant Principal, M.S. 144

Rose Villani, Director of Science

Community School District 13

Maria Davis, Science Coordinator

David Lisbon, Science Resource Specialist

Community School District 14

Angel Brea, Science Teacher

Bruce Gamsey, Science Teacher/Co-Chair, District Science Committee

James R. Novara, Science Coordinator/Co-Chair District Science Committee

Community School District 15

Lisa Gioe-Cordi, Teacher, William Alexander Middle School #51

Judy Zaragoza Maher, Science Staff Developer

Christine Musmanno, Science Coordinator

Community School District 16

Sheila Dunston, District Science Coordinator

Community School District 17

Shellie Cohen, Science Coordinator

Dan Forbes, Science Teacher Trainer

Gueus Robert, Bilingual Science Teacher, M.S. 391

Community School District 18

Barbara Berg, Science Coordinator

Michael E. Checchi, Science Teacher, I.S. 211

Ingrid Thomas-Clark, Science Cluster Teacher, P.S. 235

Community School District 19

Lou Goldstein, Science Coordinator

Henry Smith, Science Teacher, P.S. 190K

Community School District 20

Trudy Adduci, Director of Mathematics and Science

Madeline P. Castañeda, Spanish Bilingual Teacher/Chair, Governance Committee, IMS, Ditmas Educational Complex, IS 62

Manette B. Gampel, Science Teacher, Dyker Heights Intermediate School #201

Community School District 21

Peter Chester, Science Coordinator

Community School District 22

Catherine Abbazia, Science Staff Developer

Joyce Genovesi, Science Coordinator, Principal of Environmental Study Center

Maxine Kovner, Science Staff Developer

Community School District 23

Cynthia Smith, Staff Developer

Michelle White, Science Teacher, JHS 275

Community School District 24

Frank M. Mifsud, Assistant Principal, William Cowper IS 73

Pamela Wasserman, Science Coordinator

Community School District 25

Ronnie Feder, Science Coordinator

Tatiana Gordon, Ed.D., ESL Teacher, P.S. 107Q

Pearl Philindas, Science Specialist, P.S. 184Q

Deborah Winiarski, Health Coordinator

Community School District 26

Joanne Halton, Science Teacher, P.S 186Q, Castlewood School

Judy Intraub, Science Coordinator

Community School District 27

Denise Brown, Science Teacher Trainer

Mohamed Khan, Mathematics Staff Developer

Phyllis Phillips, Coordinator of Mathematics and Science

Community School District 28

Barbara J. Bellafatto, Science Specialist

Anthony Galitsis, former Science Coordinator

Geraldine Goodstadt, Science Specialist

Audrey Saltsberg, Assistant Principal, JHS 157/Queens

Community School District 29

Harriett Diaz, Staff Developer

Diane Ehrlich, Director of Science

Community School District 30

Delrosa Marshall, Science Coordinator

Phyllis Mueses, Science Teacher, P.S. 152Q

Community School District 31

Luann Martin, Science Cluster Teacher, P.S. 45 John Tyler School

Mary Beth McCarthy, Science Coordinator

Michele Yennella, Science Teacher, Anning S. Prall IS 27

Community School District 32

Michelle G. Cambier, Science Coordinator

Barbara R. Convey, Director of Mathematics, Science & Technology

Alma Walton, Teacher

Community School District 75

Greg Borman, Staff Developer

Derek P. Ramdass, Staff Developer, Citywide Programs

Alternative High Schools and Programs

Melissa Cancel, Science Teacher, Northview Junior High

Juan Lantigeau, Science Teacher, Manhatten Comprehenisve Night & Day School

Shawn Reeves, Science Teacher, Coalition School for Social Change

Steve Zbaida, Science Staff Developer, Outreach Program

BASIS High Schools

Randy Barbarash, Assistant Principal, Science Department, Port Richmond High School

Derresa Davis, Science Instructional Specialist

Verona Moncrieffe, Assistant Principal Science, John Jay High School

Brooklyn High Schools

Nicholas Almonor, Bilingual Chemistry Teacher

Alan Ascher, Assistant Principal-Supervision Science, South Shore High School

Marianita Damari, Science Congruence Specialist, Brooklyn High Schools

Cynthia Edwards, Assistance Principal Science, George Wingate High School

Mara Ganeles, Assistant Principal Biology, Midwood High School

David Kiefer, Assistant Principal Physical Science, Midwood High School

Edmond Nurse, Physics Teacher, East New York Transit Tech

Veronica Peterson, Science Congruence Specialist

Yves Raymond, Bilingual Coordinator, Erasmus Hall Campus: High School for Science and Math

Bronx High Schools

Bart Bookman, Assistant Principal Science, A.E. Stevenson High School

Beatrice G. Werden, Science Congruence Specialist

Manhattan High Schools

Mingling Chang, Bilingual Teacher, Seward Park High School

Barbara Poseluzny, Assistant Principal Science, A. Philip Randolph Campus High School at City College

DeAnna Roberson, Science Congruence Specialist

Jinni Xu, Bilingual Teacher, Seward Park High School

Marion Gaita Zachowski, Science Congruence Specialist

Queens High Schools

Marc-Eddy Bellabe, Science Teacher, John Harvard School, P.S. 34

Yvette Bohlman, Chemistry Teacher, Forest Hills High School

Richard D. D'Auria, Director of Technology

Rick Hallman, Director of Instruction

Hedy Hoffman, Science Congruence Specialist

Svetlana I. Livdan, Bilingual Chemistry Teacher, Newcomers High School

Michael F. Renna, Assistant Principal Science, Hillcrest High School

Bank Street College

Don Cook, Project Director

Brooklyn College

Eleanor Miele, Assistant Professor, Science Education

City College of New York

Ellen Goldstein, Director, NASA TRC

Kingsborough Community College

Dr. Delores Lowe Friedman, Professor of Early Childhood Education

Lehman College

Dr. Fernando Espinoza, Assistant Professor, Program Advisor, Science Education

Marc Lazarus, Professor of Chemistry

Frederick T. Marin,PH.D., Teacher/Science Chair, W. Manhatten Outreach Center and Lehman College Leadership Group

Queens College

Dr. June Kasuga Miller, Professor of Science Education, Department of Secondary Education and YS

Rockefeller University

Dr. Bonnie Kaiser, Director, Precollege Science Education Programs

Council of Supervisors and Administrators

Arlene L. Shapiro, Supervisory Support Program

United Federation of Teachers/ Professional Development Program Teachers Centers

Rose Cavalluzzo, Teacher Center Staff, Campus Magnet High School

Robert Kleppel, Teacher Center Staff

Phyllis Walker, Teacher Center Staff, SESP

American Museum of Natural History

Dr. Maritza Macdonald, Director of Professional Development

Brooklyn Children's Museum

Karen Jarmon, Teacher Services Manager

City Parks Foundation

Dr. Mary J. Leou, Director of Education

Educational Equity Concepts, Inc.

Merle Froschl, Co-Director

Barbara Sprung, Co-Director

Maryann Stimmer, Science Program Associate

NASA

Frank Scalzo, Goddard Institute for Space Studies

New Visions for Public Schools

Elaine Morales-Thomason, Program Officer

New York Botanical Gardens

Donald C. Lisowy, Manager of Teacher Enhancement

New Standards/National Center on Education and the Economy

Ann Borthwick, Director, Standards Development and Applied Learning, LRDC

Gary Brockman, Consultant, New Standards, University of California, Office of the President

Gary Eggan, Senior Associate, Learning Research and Development Center

Georgia Makris, Science Program Assistant, New Standards, University of California, Office of the President

Annette Seitz, Research Associate, Learning Research and Development Center

Elizabeth Stage, Director of Science, New Standards, University of California, Office of the President

New York City Urban Systemic Initiative

Betty D. Burrell, Senior Associate Director, NYC Urban Systemic Initiative

Stephanie Caporale, Associate Director, NYC Urban Systemic Initiative

Elsie Chan, Director, NYC Urban Systemic Initiative

Dr. Robert J. Kane, Deputy Director, NYC Urban Systemic Initiative

Jonathan Molofsky, Associate Director, NYC Urban Systemic Initiative

Lawrence J. Pero, Senior Associate Director, NYC Urban Systemic Initiative

Myrna Rodriguez, Associate Director, NYC Urban Systemic Initiative

Judy Walsh, Associate Director, NYC Urban Systemic Initiative

ACKNOWLEDGMENTS

Phyllis Arnette, Director of Government Relations and Educational Field Markets, Texas Instruments Incorporated

Kathleen Bergin, Program Officer, National Science Foundation

Dr. James V. Bruni, Dean of Education, Lehman College

Michael Cascio, District 14, JHS 50K

Stephen DeMeo, York College

Jay Dubner, College of Physicians and Surgeons, Columbia University

Dr. Barbara C. Freeouf, Project Director, Streamline Certification, Brooklyn College

Dr. Alan Friedman, President, New York Hall of Science

Aminda Gentile, Director, United Federation of Teachers, Teachers Center Consortium

Janet Kaminsky, Director of Professional Development, Chancellor's District

Jeanette Kim, Program Coordinator, Education Department, New York Academy of Sciences

Dr. Noel Kriftcher, David Packard Center, Polytechnic University, Brooklyn

Linda Linton, Director of Public Affairs, Consolidated Edison of New York, Inc.

Lee Livney, Bronx Zoo/Wildlife Conservation Park

Dolores Mei, Deputy Executive Director, Division of Assessment and Accountability, NYC Board of Education

Frank Nappi, Council of Supervisors and Administrators

John W. Nassivera, Teacher Consultant, Institute For Literacy Studies, Lehman College

Rodney W. Nichols, President and CEO, New York Academy of Sciences

Ann Robinson, Director, Bronx Zoo/Wildlife Conservation Park

Elizabeth Schnee, Chancellor's Parent Advisory Council

John Schoener, John Schoener & Associates, Inc.

Frank Signorello, New York Hall of Science

Dr. Samuel Silverstein, College of Physicians and Surgeons, Columbia University

Dr. Morton Slater, Director of Gateway Schools, Mount Sinai Hospital

Marian Sloane, Staff Development Specialist, Brooklyn Multidisciplinary Resource Center

Louise Squitieri, Dean, Research & Grants, New York City Technical College

Dr. Rosamond Welchman, School of Education, Brooklyn College

Louisa Wuebbens, Director, Middle School Initiative, NYC Board of Education

Materials Used with Permission

American Association for the Advancement of Science. (1993). *Benchmarks for Science Literacy: Project 2061*. New York: Oxford University Press.

"The Density of Sand" task and the task's "Self-reflection Sheet." From the *Golden State Examination*. Copyright by California Department of Education, 721 Capital Mall, 4th Floor, Sacramento, CA 95814.

"Erosion" task. From *FOSS Landforms Module*, Activity 3, "Go with the Flow," 1992: The Regents of the University of California. Developed at the Lawrence Hall of Science, University of California at Berkeley, CA 94720-5200. Published and distributed by Delta Education, Inc., 80 Northwest Blvd., Nashua, NH 03060.

"The Invincible Cockroach" task, by Matthew Morrell. From *The Young Naturalist Awards, 1998*. The American Museum of Natural History, Central Park West at 79th Street, New York, NY 10024-5192.

"Light or Dark?" task. From SCIS3, Chapter 16, *Transferring Solar Energy to Water*. pp. 39-41. Delta Education, Inc., 80 Northwest Blvd., Nashua, NH 03060.

National Research Council. (1996). *National Science Education Standards*, Washington, D.C.: National Academy Press.

University of the State of New York and the State Education Department, *Learning Standards for Mathematics, Science, and Technology*, Albany, NY 12234.

"Water Tolerance" task. From FOSS *Environmental Module*, Activity 3, "Water Tolerance," 1992: The Regents of the University of California. Developed at the Lawrence Hall of Science, University of California at Berkeley, CA 94720-5200. Published and distributed by Delta Education, Inc., 80 Northwest Boulevard, Nashua, NH 03060.

References

American Association for the Advancement of Science. (1993). *Benchmarks for Scientific Literacy: Project 2061*. New York: Oxford University Press.

American Association for the Advancement of Science. (1997). *Resources for Science Literacy: Professional Development*. New York: Oxford University Press.

American Association for the Advancement of Science. (1990). *Benchmarks: Science for All Americans: Project 2061*. New York: Oxford University Press.

American Federation of Teachers. (1994). *Defining World Class Standards: A Publication Series*. Vol. 1-3. Washington, D.C.: Author.

American Federation of Teachers. (1995). *Making Standards Matter: A Fifty-State Progress Report on Efforts to Raise Academic Standards*. Washington, D.C.: Author.

Black, Paul, and Arkin, Myron. eds. (1996). *Changing the Subject: Innovations in Science, Mathematics, and Technology Education*. London and New York: Organisation for Economic Co-operation and Development.

The Business Task Force on Student Standards. (1995). *The Challenge of Change: Standards To Make Education Work For All Our Children*. Washington, D.C.: Business Coalition for Education Reform.

National Education Goals Panel, Technical Planning Group. (1993). *Promises to Keep: Creating High Standards for American Students*. Washington, D.C.: Author.

National Research Council. (1996). *National Science Education Standards*. Washington, D.C.: National Academy Press.

New Standards. (1997. *Performance Standards*. Washington, D.C. and Pittsburgh, PA: National Center on Education and the Economy and the University of Pittsburgh.

New Standards. (1995). *New Standards: Performance Standards—Consultation Draft*. Washington, D.C. and Pittsburgh, PA: National Center on Education and the Economy and the University of Pittsburgh.

Secretary's Commission on Achieving Necessary Skills. (1992). *Learning A Living: A Blueprint for High Performance- A SCANS Report For America 2000*. Washington, D.C.: U.S. Department of Labor.

Select Bibliography

Board of Education of the City of New York. (1995). *Curriculum Frameworks: Knowledge, Skills, and Abilities. Grades Pre-K - 12*. New York: Author.

Doran, Rodney et al. (1998). *Science Educator's Guide to Assessment*. Virginia: National Science Teachers Association.

Loucks-Horsley, Susan et al. The National Institute for Science Education (1998). *Designing Professional Development for Teachers of Science and Mathematics*. Thousand Oaks, CA: Corwin Press, Inc.

National Science Resources Center. (1998). *Resources for Teaching Middle School Science*. Washington, D.C.: National Academy Press.

National Science Resource Center. (1996). *Resources for Teaching Elementary School Science*. Washington, D.C.: National Academy Press.

International Association for the Evaluation of Educational Assessment. (1996). *Third International Mathematics and Science Study*. (TIMSS).

National Education Goals Panel. (1998). *National Education Goals Report*. Washington, D.C.: Author.

University of the State of New York and the State Education Department. (1996). *Learning Standards for Mathematics, Science, and Technology*. Albany, NY: Author.

University of the State of New York and the State Education Department. (1997). *Mathematics, Science, and Technology Resource Guide*. Albany, NY: Author.

Resources

As indicated in the introduction, the high expectations in these standards will require adequate resources for teachers and students, in some cases substantially more than currently in place. The kinds of resources and the rationale for having them are presented here, quoting the *National Science Education Standards* (National Research Council, 1996). A partial listing of science resources is provided to acquaint educators with some of the many organizations and programs that are available to support science education in New York City. Listed geographically and citywide, their services are offered to all teachers.

Program Standard D (National Research Council 1996, pp. 218-221)

The K-12 science program must give students access to appropriate and sufficient resources, including quality teachers, time, materials and equipment, adequate and safe space, and the community.

Learning science requires active inquiry into the phenomena of the natural world. Such inquiry requires rich and varied resources in an adequate and safe environment. The specific criteria for a science learning environment will depend on many factors such as the needs of the students and the characteristics of the science program. A student with rich experience in a topic might need access to additional resources within or outside the school; a student with a different language background might need supporting materials in that language; a student with a physical disability might need specially designed equipment; and a student with little experience using computer technology might need a tutor or a tutorial program. District policy makers and those in charge of budget allocations must provide the resources, and then school-level administrators and teachers must make sure that, once allocated, the resources are well used.

The most important resource is professional teachers. Needless to say, students must have access to skilled, professional teachers. Teachers must be prepared to teach students with diverse strengths, needs, experiences, and approaches to learning. Teachers must know the content they will teach, understand the nature of learning, and use a range of teaching strategies for science. Hiring practices must ensure that teachers are prepared to teach science and should include successful teachers of science in the selection of their new colleagues.

Districts should use professional development standards to provide teachers with opportunities to develop and enhance the needed capabilities for effective science teaching. Funding and professional time for such development is an essential part of district budgets.

The emphasis on the need for professional teachers of science does not diminish the need for other school personnel who enhance the science program. In addition to an administrative team and teaching colleagues, other support personnel might include the resource librarian, a laboratory technician, or maintenance staff.

Time is a major resource in a science program. Science must be allocated sufficient time in the school program every day, every week, and every year. The content standards define scientific literacy; the amount of time required to achieve scientific literacy for all students depends on the particular program. The time devoted to science education must be allocated to meet the needs of an inquiry-based science program. No matter what the scheduling model, a school schedule needs to provide sufficient and flexible use of time to accommodate the needs of the students and what is being learned. In addition to time with students and with colleagues, teachers of science also spend considerable time preparing materials, setting up activities, creating the learning environment, and organizing student experiences. This time must be build into the daily teaching schedule.

Conducting scientific inquiry requires that students have easy, equitable, and frequent opportunities to use a wide range of equipment, materials, supplies, and other resources for experimentation and direct investigation of phenomena. Some equipment is general purpose and should be part of every school's science inventory, such as magnifiers or microscopes of appropriate sophistication, measurement tools, tools for data analysis, and computers with software for supporting investigations. Other materials are topic specific, such as a water table for first graders or a reduced resistance air table for physics investigations. Many materials are consumable and need to be replenished regularly. Furthermore, policy makers need to bear in mind that equipment needs to be upgraded frequently and requires preventive maintenance.

Given that materials appropriate for inquiry-based science teaching are central to achieving the goals set forth in the

Standards, it is critical that an effective infrastructure for material support be a part of any science program. School systems need to develop mechanisms to identify exemplary materials, store and maintain them, and make them accessible to teachers in a timely fashion. Providing an infrastructure frees teachers' time for more appropriate tasks and ensures that the necessary materials are available when needed. Because science inquiry is broader than first-hand investigation, print, video, and technology sources of information and simulation are required. These are included in the materials-support infrastructure.

The teaching standards consistently make reference to the responsiveness and flexibility to student interests that must be evidenced in classrooms that reflect effective science teaching. The content standard on inquiry sets the expectation that students will develop the ability to perform a full inquiry. For such inquiry-based teaching to become a reality, in addition to what is regularly maintained in the school and district, every teacher of science needs an easily accessible budget for materials and equipment as well as for unanticipated expenses that arise as students and teachers pursue their work.

Collaborative inquiry requires adequate and safe space. There must be space for students to work together in groups, to engage safely in investigation with materials, and to display both work in progress and finished work. There also must be space for the safe and convenient storage of the materials needed for science. At the lower grade levels, schools do not need separate rooms for laboratories. In fact, it is an advantage in terms of long-term studies and making connections between school subject areas to have science as an integral part of the classroom environment. At the upper grade levels, laboratories become critical to provide the space, facilities, and equipment needed for inquiry and to ensure that the teacher and students can conduct investigations without risk. All spaces where students do inquiry must meet appropriate safety regulations.

Good science programs require access to the world beyond the classroom. District and school leaders must allocate financial support to provide opportunities for students to investigate the world outside the classroom. This may mean budgeting for trips to nearby points of interest, such as a river, archaeological site, or nature preserve; it could include contracting with local science centers, museums, zoos, and horticultural centers for visits and programs. Relationships should be developed with local businesses and industry to allow students and teachers access to people and the institutions, and students must be given access to scientists and other professionals in higher education and the medical establishment to gain access to their expertise and the laboratory settings in which they work. Communication technology has made it possible for anyone to access readily people throughout the world. This communication technology should be easily accessible to students.

Much of this standard is acknowledged as critical, even if unavailable, for students in secondary schools. It must be emphasized, however, that this standard applies to the entire science program and all students in all grades. In addition, this standard demands quality resources that often are lacking and seem unattainable in some schools or districts. Missing resources must not be an excuse for not teaching science. Many teachers and schools "make do" or improvise under difficult circumstances (e.g., crowded classrooms, time borrowed from other subjects, and materials purchased with personal funds). A science program based on the National Science Education Standards is a program constantly moving toward replacing such improvisation with necessary resources.

Citywide

New York City Board of Education: Division of Instructional Support, responsible for supporting instruction in all schools in all districts in New York City, (718) 746-4258; In-Service Courses (718) 935-5753; Multidisciplinary Resource Centers (MRC), provide professional development in science for New York City teachers; staff development specialists are familiar with many aspects of science instruction and have compiled many resources for teachers of science, 154-60 17th Avenue, Whitestone, NY 11357, (718) 746-3392; and 7102 Avenue T, Brooklyn, NY 11234, (718) 763-5492; Division of Management Information Services, (718) 488-3922; Office of School Programs and Support Services, (718) 935-5155; Science in the Seamless Day, (718) 574-2800 or (718) 927-5131; School Based Elementary Science Restructuring Program; (212) 795-8032 x421; SMART process, (212) 678-2918 or (212) 769-7553.

Alliance for Minority Participation (AMP), (212) 650-8854.

Chemistry Teachers Club of New York, c/o Al Delfiner, 207 Lincoln Place, Eastchester, NY 10707.

City University of New York: All CUNY colleges have specialized programs which address science education. For further information contact these colleges: Baruch College (212) 802-2000, Borough of Manhattan Community College (212) 346-8100, Bronx Community College (718) 289-5100, Brooklyn College (718) 951-5000, City College of New York (212) 650-7000, CUNY Law School (718) 575-4200, CUNY Medical School/Sophie Davis School of Biomedical Education (718) 650-5275, The Graduate School and University Center (212) 642-1600, Hostos Community College (718) 518-4444, Hunter College (212) 772-4000, Hunter College School of Social Work (212) 452-7000, John Jay College of Criminal Justice (212) 237-8000, Kingsborough Community College (718) 368-5000, LaGuardia Community College (718) 482-5000, Lehman College (718) 960-8000, Medgar Evers College (718) 270-4900, Mount Sinai School of Medicine (212) 241-6500, New York City Technical College (City Tech) (718) 260-5000, Queens College (718) 997-5000, Queensborough Community College (718) 631-6262, The College of Staten Island (718) 982-2000, York College (718) 262-2000.

Consolidated Edison, Inc., (212) 674-5470.

Council of Supervisors and Administrators (CSA), (718) 852-3000.

Educators for Gateway c/o Roberta Wallach, 1106 East 19th Street, Brooklyn, NY 11230.

EDUNET, (212) 838-0230

Elementary School Science Association (ESSA) c/o Dawn Adams, 1264 Sterling Place, Flushing, NY 11213.

Greenwall Foundation, (212) 679-7266.

National Action Council for Minorities in Engineering, Inc.: The TechForce Partnership for Scientific Learning (212) 279-2626.

New York Academy of Sciences, Education Department: New York City MaSTER Guide, published by the Academy is a comprehensive listing of professional development, curriculum materials, student and family programs mostly in and around the New York City metropolitan area. Their Internet site has much of the same information. 2 East 63rd Street, New York, NY 10021, (212) 838-0230, www.nyas.org.

New York Biology Teachers Association, Otto Burgdorf Student Science Conference and Competition (718) 846-7891. P.O. Box 192, Brooklyn, NY 11236, (718) 846-7891 www.nybta.org

New York City Department of Environmental Protection: Guided Facility Tours, Printed Resource Materials, Staff Development Workshops (718) 595-3506.

New York City Urban Systemic Initiative (NYC USI) (718) 260-4966.

New York Collaborative for Excellence in Teacher Preparation (718) 951-3113.

New York Urban League: New York City Project PRISM (Partners for Reform in Science and Math) (718) 756-3032.

Physics Teachers Club c/o John Augenstein, 269-15 79th Avenue, New Hyde Park, NY 11040

Science Council of New York City, Science Conference (212) 673-9030.

Teaching Matters, Inc., (212) 870-3505.

United Federation of Teachers (UFT), (212) 777-7500.

Bronx

Albert Einstein College of Medicine: YES To Science (718) 430-2093.

Bronx Zoo/Wildlife Conservation Park: Diversity of Lifestyles, Habitat Ecology Learning Program, Staff Development for Teachers, Grades K-12,(718) 220-6856; Wildlife Adventures for School Classes K-12 (718) 220-5131; Wildlife Inquiry through Zoo Education (WIZE) (718) 220-5114.

Herbert H. Lehman College: Dwight D. Eisenhower Professional Development Program (718) 960-8569.

Hostos Community College: Center for Pre-College Initiatives, TERRA Environmental Summer Science Camp (718) 518-4189.

Manhattan College: Dwight D. Eisenhower Professional Development Program (718) 862-7416.

New York Botanical Garden: School Programs (718) 817-8748, Teacher Enhancement Program (718) 817-8175.

Wave Hill: Environmental Science Camp for Girls, Forest Project Collaborative, School Program (718) 549-3200 x221

Brooklyn

Aquarium for Wildlife Conservation: School and Family Programs (718) 265-3453.

Brooklyn Botanic Garden: Junior Botanist Summer Program, Project GreenReach, School Workshops and Exploration Tours, Student Internships, Teacher Education Programs: What Did A Plant Ever Do For You? (718) 622-4433.

Brooklyn Center for the Urban Environment: Afterschool Programs and Afterschool Intern Program, Environmental Education Advisory Council, Environmental Science Summer Camp, Professional Development Workshops, School Programs (718) 788-8540.

Brooklyn Children's Museum: Animals Eat, EVI'DENTS, Plants and People (718) 735-4440.

Brooklyn College: Center for Educational Change (718) 951-5209, New Frontier Collaborative for Secondary Mathematics and Science Teachers (718) 951-5214, Science and Technology Entry Program (718) 951-5741.

Brooklyn Museum (718) 638-5000.

Brooklyn Union: Engineering Explorer Program; (718) 403-2808, Science in Industry Summer Academy (SISA) (718) 403-2511.

Catholic Science Council, Diocese of Brooklyn: Science Fair (718) 857-2700 x231.

Community School District #23: Summer Science Camp (718) 270-8663.

Environmental Quest: Questing Course (718) 941-9835.

Gateway Environmental Study Center: 718) 252-7307.

Long Island University, Brooklyn Campus (718) 488-1010.

Metropolitan New York Forest Ecosystem Council: (718) 965-6590.

National Space Society Education Chapter: NSS Student Competition (212) 724-5919, Space Science Technology Opportunities Education Conference (718) 531-8375.

New York City Technical College: Projects Room (718) 260-5206.

Polytechnic University: Center for Youth in Engineering and Science, Mathematics, Science, and Technology Fair (718) 260-3033.

State University of New York Health Science Center, Brooklyn: Genetics in Medicine (718) 745-0443.

Science Skills Center, Inc.: Summer Science Institute (718) 636-6213.

Wildlife Conservation Center. (718) 220-5131

Manhattan

American Committee for the Weizmann Institute of Science: Dr. Bessie F. Lawrence International Summer Science Institute (212) 779-2500.

American Museum of Natural History: Biodiversity Counts (212) 769-5938; College Courses for Teachers, Customized Professional Development, Summer Institutes (212) 769-5182; Teachers Workshops (212) 769-5141.

Bank Street College: Liberty Environmental Science Academy; (212) 875-4506, New Perspectives (212) 875-4656, Tiorati Workshop for Environmental Learning (914) 351-5354.

Central Park Conservancy: School Partnership Program, Student Field Programs, Teacher Resources, Teacher Workshops (212) 360-2720.

Central Park Wildlife Center/Wildlife Conservation Society: Children's Workshops, School Programs (212) 439-6517.

Children's Museum of Manhattan: High School Internships, In-School Programs, Museum Visits, Professional Development (212) 721-1223.

City College of New York: Environmental Studies; (212) 650-7953, Middle School Science Consortium (212) 650-6226, Teachers Restructuring Science Education (212) 650-7162, The Young Scholars Discovery Program (212) 650-6226, Young Scholars Program in Molecular Biology and Related Sciences (212) 650-6601, Workshop Center (212) 650-8436.

City Parks Foundation: Family Programs at the Urban Forest Ecology Center (212) 360-2746, Internships (212) 360-2740, Learning Garden Project (212) 360-2746, New York City Woodlands Teacher Training Institute (212) 360-2745, New Youth Conservationists (212) 360-2746, ParkLinks (212) 360-2745, School Programs at the Urban Forest Ecology Center (212) 360-2746, Teacher Resources (212) 360-2740, Teacher Training (212) 360-2745, Trees, Tales, and Woodland Trails (212) 360-2745.

City of New York/Parks and Recreation: Internship Program (212) 360-1349, Urban Park Rangers–Parks Conservation Corps (212) 360-8722.

City University of New York: Graduate School & University Center, Project STIR (212) 410-1100, Medical School, Bridge to Medicine (212) 650-8183 x 7740, Research Foundation, Summer Science Camp (212) 650-5471.

Classroom, Inc.: Model Site Program (212) 545-8814, System Initiative (212) 545-8814.

College Board: EQUITY 2000 (212) 713-8000.

Columbia University Double Discovery Center: Talent Search Program, Upward Bound Program (212) 854-3897.

Columbia University Teachers College: Colloquium Series on Advances in the Teaching of Math (212) 678-3381; Hollingworth Science Camp, Sunday Math and Science Enrichment Program (212) 678-3851; The New York Youth Network and The Center for Urban Youth and Technology (212) 678-3829.

Columbia University College of Physicians and Surgeons: State Pre-College Enrichment Program, Summer Minority High School Student/Teacher Initiative Program (212) 305-4157; Summer Research Program for Secondary School Science Teachers (212) 305-6899.

Cooper-Hewitt Museum: Summer Design Institute for Educators (212) 860-6977.

Council on the Environment of New York City: The Training Student Organizers Program (212) 788-7900.

Education Development Center/ Center for Children and Technology: Performance Assessment Videos for Teachers, Urban Mathematics, Science, and Technology Leadership Project, Young Scientist Club (212) 807-4200.

Educational Equity Concepts, Inc.: Playtime is Science (212) 725-1803.

Exxon Corporation: The Exxon Energy Cube (212) 685-9290.

Fordham University: Dwight D. Eisenhower Professional Development Program.

Gateway Program: The Mt. Sinai School of Medicine (212) 731-5990.

Girls Inc.: Operation SMART (Science, Math, and Relevant Technology) (212) 989-2438.

Horticultural Society of New York: Apple Seed, Library (212) 757-0915

Humane Education Committee: Humane Education in Our Schools, Humane Science Awards (212) 410-3095.

Hunter College: Biotechnology Workshops (212) 772-5297, In Service Program to Certify Out-of License Middle School/Junior High School Science Teachers (212) 642-2910, In Service Science Program for NYC Elementary School Teachers (212) 772-4287.

International Education and Resource Network (IEARN) (212) 870-2693.

Intrepid Sea-Air-Space Museum: Seaworthy Saturdays, Ships Ahoy! Science-Based Staff Development, Student Science Workshops, Teacher Familiarization Tour (212) 957-7050.

John Jay College of Criminal Justice: DDE II2 (212) 237-8923, John Jay Summer Computer Camp (212) 237-8926.

Marymount Manhattan College: Dwight D. Eisenhower Professional Development Program (212) 517-0522.

NAACP New York City ACT-SO (212) 783-0813.

NASA Regional Teacher Resource Center: Plane Talk Science Network (212) 650-6798, Resource Dissemination (212) 650-6993.

Nature Conservancy of New York: Student Internships (212) 997-1880.

New York Academy of Sciences: Junior Academy, Science Education Section, Science Research Training Program, Scientific Process, Practice, and Presentation: Applying Resources and Knowledge (SP3ARK) (212) 838-0230.

New York State Office of Parks, Recreation, and Historic Preservation: Operation Explore (212) 694-372.

New York University: Teacher Opportunity Corps and Dwight D. Eisenhower Professional Development Program (212) 998-5208.

Ninety Second Street YW-YMCA: Camp Tevah for Science and Nature (212) 415-5613, On the Brink: Breakthroughs In Science (212) 415-5615, Sunday Science Spectaculars (212) 415-5600.

Pace University: The Pace University DDE Integrated Math-Science-Technology Partnership Program (212) 346-1816.

Research Corporation: Partners in Science (212) 305-6899.

Rockefeller University: Science Outreach for Students (212) 327-7431.

Salomon Brothers Inc: Salomon-Robeson School Partnership (212) 783-7467.

Salvadori Educational Center on the Built Environment: Salvadori Educational Materials, Salvadori Middle School Program, Specialist-on-Site (212) 650-5497.

Settlement College Readiness Program: Science and Technology Entry Program; (212) 410-4444 x519, Big Sister Program (212) 509-9577.

Society of Women Engineers: Higher Education Outreach Program (212) 509-9577.

South Street Seaport Museum: Expeditionary Learning, Internships, Short-Format Courses, Teacher Training, Urban Archaeology: Digging Into History (212) 748-8590.

The River Project: Field Trips, Internships (212) 431-5787.

Urban Park Rangers: The Parklands Partnership, School Programs, Walks and Workshops (800) 201-7275.

Ventures in Education (212) 696-5717.

Queens

Alley Pond Environmental Center: Class Visits, Junior High and High School Programs, Outreach (718) 229-4000.

American Museum of the Moving Image: Science and the Moving Image (718) 784-4520.

Association of Computer Education: Computer Workshops (718) 898-7114.

City University of New York, Medical School: Dwight D. Eisenhower Professional Development Program, Queens Bridge to Medicine (718) 523-0960.

New York Hall of Science: After-School Science Club, Big Science Days, Family Programs, Junior High School Career Days, Outreach Lesson Modelling, Science Access Center, Science Career Ladder, Science Kid's Club and Young Explorer's Club, Student Workshops and Science Access Center Workshops, Teacher Training Workshops and Rental, (718) 699-0005.

Queens Botanical Garden: Adult Tours and Workshops, Children's Garden - Outdoor Learning Center, Children's Tours & Workshops, Student Work-Study Programs, Teacher Training/Consultation (718) 886-3800.

St. John's University: Metro New York Junior Science and Humanities Symposium (718) 969-8000 x6336.

York College: Math, Science, Technology Awards Program, Science Teachers Enhancement Program in the Physical Sciences, Summer Science Camp (718) 262-2716.

Staten Island

Clay Pit Ponds State Park Preserve: Gericke Farm Visit, Park Preserve Walk, Project Wild/Aquatic Wild, The Magic of Maple Sugaring (718) 967-1976.

College of Staten Island: Goals 2000, Net Tech, Project Discovery, Science and Technology Entry Program, Teaching Internship, Tech-Prep and Discovery Tech, Honors Research Internship, (718) 982-2325.

New York State Institute for Basic Research in Developmental Disabilities: Neuroscience Exploration Program and Science Apprentice Program (718) 494-5354.

Staten Island Children's Museum: Micro-Monsters, Science Help Line, Science Works, Setting the Stage for Science: In School Residency Program, Summer Mini-Camp (718) 273-2060 x156.

Staten Island Institute of Arts and Sciences: School Programs; (718) 727-1135.

Staten Island Science Teachers Association (SISTA) c/o Lenore Miller, 296 Arlene Street, Staten Island, NY 10314.

Staten Island Zoo: School at the Zoo, Teacher Workshops, Traveling Zoo Programs (718) 442-3174.

Long Island

Brookhaven National Laboratory: Science Museum School Programs (516) 344-4495.

Cold Spring Harbor Laboratory - DNA Learning Center: Advanced DNA Science, DNA Science, Field Trips, Fun with DNA, Introduction to Computer Design, World of Enzymes (516) 367-7240.

Dowling College: Adventures in Aviation and Transportation, Sky High Day Camp (516) 244-3320.

Goudreau Museum of Mathematics in Art and Science: Pi Day, Saturday Workshops: Enrichment Math For Students of Grades 5-8, Saturday Workshops: Graphing Calculator TI-82 for Beginners (516) 747-0777.

Hofstra University: Dwight D. Eisenhower Professional Development Program (516) 463-5561.

State University of New York, Old Westbury: Annual Long Island Mathematics Conference (LIMACON), Institute of Creative Problem-Solving for Gifted and Talented Students (516) 876-3261, Science Educators Enhancement and Development (SEED) Program; (516) 876-2733.

Upstate New York

Health, Safety and Research Alliance of New York State, Inc.: Speakers Bureau (914) 291-1944.

Hudson River Reserve: Educational Programs 914) 758-5193.

Hudson River Sloop Clearwater: Clearwater's Classroom of the Waves (914) 454-7673.

Mercy College (914) 693-7000.

Pace University: Urban Ecology Seminar (914) 773-3789.

Science Teachers Association of New York State–Westchester: Project Learning Tree Workshop (914) 639-6978.

State University of New York, Purchase: Elementary Science Leadership Institutes, Summer Earth Science Study for Classroom Teachers, Westchester Conference on Science, Math, and Technology Education, Woodrow Wilson Teacher Outreach Programs (914) 251-6675.

Taconic Outdoor Education Center: Environmental Education Programs, Skins and Skulls (914) 265-3773.

Statewide

New York State Education Department: Mathematice, Science, and Technology (518) 473-9471.

New York State Department of Environmental Conservation: DEC Summer Environmental Education Program (518) 457-3720.

New York State Marine Education Association (NYSMEA), Box 705, Mineola, NY 11501

New York State Science Leadership Association, 489 Echo Road, Vestal, NY 13850.

New York State Science Olympiad (914) 328-4209.

Science Teachers Association of New York State: Brooklyn, Queens, and Staten Island Section, Harry Kranpool, 31-31 138 St., Apt. 4-D Cheshire, Linden Hill, NY 11354-2625; Bronx, Manhattan, Westchester and Rockland Section, Marilyn Reiner, 9 Dalewood Drive, Suffern, NY 10901.

New Jersey

College Gifted Programs: Summer Institute For The Gifted (201) 334-6991.

Liberty Science Center: Birthday Parties, Camp In Program, Courses, Discovery Trails and Electronic Discovery, Teacher Sabbatical Program, Teacher Workshops (201) 451-0006.

New Jersey Institute of Technology: Summer Science Camp (201) 596-3550.

Rutgers University–Cook College: Camp Promise (908) 932-9164.

Woodrow Wilson National Fellowship Foundation: High School Biology Program (609) 452-7007.

National

American Association for the Advancement of Science (AAAS) 1200 New York Avenue, N.W., Washington, DC 20005, (202) 326-6400, www.aaas.org/

American Association of Physics Teachers: High School Photo and Physics Video Contests, Metrologic Physics Bowl Contest, Physics Teaching Resource Agents, The Physics Teacher, United States Physics Team (301) 209-3300.

American Chemical Society: Journal of Chemical Education, Say YES to a Youngster's Future (202) 986-1460, United States National Chemistry Olympiad (202) 872-6328, www.acs.org.

American Geological Institute: Geotimes, (703) 379-2480.

Association for Supervision and Curriculum Development (ASCD) (703) 578-9600.

Earthwatch: Teacher Fellowships for Worldwide Field Research (617) 926-8200 x118.

Johns Hopkins University Institute for the Academic Advancement of Youth: Distance Learning Project (410) 456-0277.

Museum of Science: Science-By-Mail (800) 729-3300.

National Academy of Sciences, www.nas.gov; National Research Council; Smithsonian Institute; National Science Resources Center.

National Aeronautics and Space Administration (NASA), Education Division: NASA provides many resources for aerospace education, including curriculum materials, information, resources, and links to many Internet sites. Code FE, NASA Headquarters, 300 E Street, S.W., Washington, DC 20546, (202) 358-1110, www.hq.nasa.gov/office/codef/education.

National Association of Biology Teachers, The American Biology Teacher, (800) 406-0775.

National Earth Science Teachers Association: The Earth Scientist, (800) 966-2481.

National Science Education Leadership Association: Perspectives on Science Education (703) 524-8646.

National Science Foundation, www.nsf.gov.

National Science Teachers Association (NSTA): NSTA is the largest national organization of science teachers. It publishes journals at each level of schooling: Science and Children, Science Scope, The Science Teacher, and Journal of College Science Teaching. It also publishes lists of science equipment and textbook suppliers, conducts competitions (e.g., Duracell Scholarship, Toshiba Explora Vision) and its website has information about science education, a comprehensive book store, and links to many other sites. 1840 Wilson Blvd., Arlington, VA 22201-3000 (703) 243-7100, www.nsta.org.

Science Service, Inc.: International Science and Engineering Fair, Westinghouse Science Talent Search (202) 785-2255.

Student Conservation Association: Resource Assistant Program (603) 543-1700.

United States Department of Education, Office of Educational Research and Improvement; Eisenhower National Clearinghouse for Mathematics and Science Education: ENC provides a comprehensive collection of curriculum resources in many formats (print, audio, multimedia, video, kits, and games. The Ohio State University, 1929 Kenny Rd, Columbus, OH 43210-1079, (800) 621-5785, www.enc.org.

Zero Population Growth, Inc.: Population Education Program (202) 332-2200.